Nordheim's Rules - Odd-Odd Nuclei p. 95

Magic Numbers   p. 87

Magnetic Moments - Schmitt Limit p. 70

γ-radiation multipole rule p. 109

α-Decay Barrier Height, Half-Lives, Energies p. 131

Hindrance factors for α-decay p 132

β-Spectrum   p 146

   log ft   pp 148-150

Selection Rules for β-decay p. 151

Condition for β^+-emission p 153

Kinetic Energy of Reaction "Q" p. 163

Reaction Cross-Sections p. 187

Range-Energy Curves pp 220 ff

Bremsstrahlung Radiation p. 226

Nuclear Spin Values   p. 356

Reactions p 281

Counters - Chapt 12

Introduction to

Nuclear

Physics and Chemistry

PRENTICE-HALL CHEMISTRY SERIES

BERNARD G. HARVEY

LAWRENCE RADIATION LABORATORY,
BERKELEY, CALIFORNIA

Introduction to

Nuclear

Physics and Chemistry

PRENTICE-HALL, INC.

ENGLEWOOD CLIFFS, N.J.

1962

Library of Congress Catalog Card Number 62-13510

Printed in the United States of America
C-49113

Preface

The purpose of the first part of this book is to describe the more important nuclear phenomena, and to present in a nearly nonmathematical way an outline of the relevant nuclear models and theories. The second part is devoted to a description of experimental equipment and methods. Even the most elementary account of the nucleus must unavoidably use some of the concepts of quantum mechanics. The first chapter therefore introduces this subject, but the treatment is necessarily a bare minimum.

The book is intended for students or research workers in any field of science who wish, or need, to study the atomic nucleus. I hope that it will introduce the subject in such a way that the continuing student can pass with the minimum of difficulty to more advanced treatments where a considerable knowledge of quantum mechanics is essential. The book is based on courses which I gave under the auspices of the University of California Engineering and Sciences Division. These in turn drew very heavily on the experience of Professors G. T. Seaborg and I. Perlman in teaching nuclear chemistry to upper division undergraduate and graduate students of chemistry in the University of California at Berkeley.

There will be found herein no discussion of the various applications of nuclear phenomena such as age determinations in archeology, tracer applications in biology, or the production of explosions. These applications are not essential to the study of the nucleus, in spite of their great importance, and in any case no single textbook of reasonable size and price can do justice to them all. By now, the applications are all well known within their own fields, and are better studied in that context. In any case, I can see no sense in grouping together a brief treatment of widely divergent topics merely because they have in common the occasional use of a counter of nuclear radiations.

That physics and chemistry are joined together in the title reflects my conviction that nuclear chemistry and nuclear physics are now indistinguishable. The importance of chemical techniques in nuclear research has diminished, but the importance of the nucleus as an object for study and research by chemists has not. Radiochemistry, for example—the study of the chemical properties of radioactive chemical elements—continues to exist as a branch of physical and inorganic chemistry. Radiation chemistry has, very properly, separated itself from nuclear chemistry and returned to physical chemistry.

I wish to extend my deep gratitude to the large number of my colleagues at the Lawrence Radiation Laboratory who contributed in so many ways. Elinor Potter made many drawings; Jean Rees provided many more. Dr. E. K. Hyde kindly permitted the use in Chapter 10 of several figures from an unpublished manuscript, and he and Drs. E. L. Kelly, F. Asaro, and P. Howe and Professor J. O. Rasmussen read parts of the manuscript. But above all, I wish to thank Professor I. Perlman of the University of California at Berkeley and Professor G. R. Choppin of the Florida State University for many helpful suggestions and criticisms. Professor Perlman's students used this text in a duplicated version, thus uncovering many errors and ambiguities. It is only owing to the wonderful hospitality of Dr. J. Thirion and his colleagues at the Centre d'Etudes Nucléaires de Saclay of the Commissariat à l'Energie Atomique de France, and to the generosity of the John Simon Guggenheim Foundation in providing a fellowship, that this book was ever finished. Finally, to my wife and family go my sincere thanks for their patience and tolerance.

Berkeley, California   BERNARD G. HARVEY
Saclay, France

Contents

Introduction to

Nuclear

Physics and Chemistry

CHAPTER 1

The Atom and Its Nucleus

A. The Discovery of the Nucleus

The idea that matter is composed of indivisible atoms originated very early in the history of science. For example, Democritus, writing in about 400 B.C., described an atomic theory that seems surprisingly modern. For example, atoms of different kinds were supposed to join together to form what we would now call molecules of various substances. However, the theory was not based firmly on experimental observations. In fact, its main support came only from the idea that, even with the sharpest imaginable knife, it would not be possible to continue indefinitely to subdivide matter. At some stage, one would come upon indivisible particles. For lack of evidence, the atomic theory failed to develop, and it was not until the early nineteenth century, when

1

experimental science began to assume something like its present form, that the evidence for the existence of atoms became compelling, mainly as a result of the work of Dalton and Avogadro. Even then, the evidence was indirect, since it was based upon the appearance of simple ratios in the laws of chemical combination. These ratios were most reasonably explained by assuming that compounds consisted of molecules, each containing small and fixed numbers of atoms. There was no direct observation of an atom or a molecule.

By the beginning of the twentieth century, the atomic theory was firmly established. The sizes and weights of atoms and molecules had been measured. The number of molecules in a gram molecular weight (Avogadro's number) was first obtained with reasonable accuracy by J. Perrin in 1911, by measuring the number of colloidal particles per unit volume at two different heights in a suspension of gamboge in water. Once Avogadro's number was known, it was possible to calculate the weight of a single molecule.

Rough values of the sizes of molecules were obtained from the study of gases, since the constant b of the van der Waals' equation is equal to four times the volume of all the molecules in one mole of the gas. In 1910, Rankine measured the viscosity of several gases, which enabled molecular diameters to be calculated from the kinetic theory. [For a gas of molecular weight M and density d, containing n molecules per cubic centimeter, the viscosity η at $T°$ A is related to the molecular diameter σ by the equation $\eta = (d/3)(\frac{3}{2}RTMn\sigma^2)^{1/2}$.]

As a result of these experiments, it appeared that the radius of atoms (in round numbers) was 10^{-8} cm, and that a weight of 1.6×10^{-24} gm corresponded to one atomic weight unit. (These approximate numbers are worth memorizing.) However, the experiments based on the kinetic theory of gases gave no information about the internal structure of atoms.

In 1897, J. J. Thomson discovered the electron in the rays emitted from the cathode of a discharge tube filled with gas at low pressure. It soon became clear that electrons entered in some way into the structure of all atoms, since they were obtained with any gas in the discharge tube. However, atoms were known to be electrically neutral, while the electrons were found to carry a charge of negative electricity. Obviously, atoms that contain electrons must also contain somewhere a positive electric charge which exactly neutralizes the charge of the electrons.

In 1910, Thomson suggested that atoms consist of a positively charged sphere of radius about 10^{-8} cm in which the electrons are embedded. The electrons were supposed to revolve within the sphere in shells which fitted together like the skins of an onion. The positive sphere was responsible for nearly all the mass of the atom, since electrons were known to be much lighter than atoms. For a short time, the Thomson theory was successful, but there were several phenomena for which it could give no convincing explanation.

The discovery of radioactivity by Becquerel in 1896 provided the experimental tools which eventually brought about the downfall of the Thomson atomic model. Among the rays emitted by radioactive substances, there appeared particles which were identified as atoms of helium bearing a positive electrical charge. These helium ions (for which the old name "α-particles" is still used), were employed by Geiger and Marsden in 1909 as projectiles with which to bombard thin metallic foils. According to the Thomson atomic model, the α-particles passing close to atoms in the foils would be deflected by virtue of the electrostatic repulsion between the positive charges contained in the atom and the α-particle. However, since the positive charge of the atom was neutralized by the close proximity of the electrons embedded in it, it was expected that the force of repulsion would not be very strong. Therefore it would be a rare event for an α-particle to suffer a very large deflection. The experiments of Geiger and Marsden showed that large deflections were many orders of magnitude more common than expected.

To explain this result, Rutherford in 1911 proposed a new atomic model in which the electrons were located at a much greater distance from the positive charge, so that the electric fields were not so completely neutralized. It was thus possible to account for the high frequency with which the α-particles were deflected through large angles. Rutherford proposed that all the positive charge, and nearly all the mass of the atom, was concentrated in an extremely small *nucleus*. The electrons were distributed around the nucleus in a sphere of atomic dimensions (i.e., about 10^{-8} cm diameter). A quantitative treatment of the problem of deflection of α-particles was then possible if two assumptions were made. The first assumption was that the diameters of both the nucleus and the α-particle were so small that both of them could be treated as geometrical points. The second assumption was that the electrostatic force of repulsion between the two electrically charged bodies was at all distances inversely proportional to the square of the distance between them (Coulomb's law). This law of force was known to be obeyed very accurately by objects much larger than electrons and nuclei, at much greater distances of separation, but it was not at all obvious that it would continue to be true on the atomic scale. Deflection of the α-particle by the electrons of the atom is negligible because of the great mass of the α-particle relative to the electrons. They are no more able to deflect it than collision with a small fly is able to deflect a bird in flight. With these assumptions, Rutherford arrived at the following equation to describe the scattering of the α-particles:

$$N = \frac{QntZ_1^2 Z_2^2}{16E^2 r^2} \csc^4 \frac{\phi}{2} \tag{1.1}$$

where N is the number of α-particles falling per second on a surface of unit area placed at a distance r from the scattering foil; ϕ is the angle between the original direction of the α-particles and their direction after scattering; Q is the number of α-particles per second incident on the scattering foil; E is the kinetic energy of the incident α-particles; Z_1 and Z_2 are the electrical charges (in electrostatic units) of the α-particle and the nucleus of the element of which the scattering foil is made; and n is the number of atoms per unit volume of the foil while t is the foil thickness.

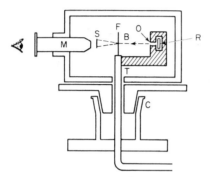

The validity of equation (1.1) was tested very carefully by Geiger and Marsden using the very simple apparatus which is shown in Figure 1.1. In their experiment, α-particles from the radioactive substance R passed through the orifice O to form a narrow beam B. After passing through the scattering foil F, they struck the screen S. This screen was coated with zinc sulfide, which has the very useful property of emitting a tiny flash of light when struck by an α-particle. These light flashes were observed and counted by means of the microscope M. The source R and the foil F were mounted on a conical groung joint C so that they could rotate with respect to the fixed screen and microscope. Thus the number of α-particles hitting the screen per minute could be observed as a function of the angle ϕ.

Fig. 1.1. Apparatus of Geiger and Marsden for the study of α-particle scattering

Some of the results obtained by Geiger and Marsden for the scattering of α-particles by a thin gold foil are shown in Table 1.1.

According to equation (1.1), the quantity shown in the right-hand column of Table 1.1 should remain constant as the angle ϕ is changed provided that all the other quantities remain unchanged. The experimental results are in reasonably good agreement with this expectation.

In further similar experiments, Geiger and Marsden were able, by the use of equation (1.1), to obtain approximate values for the magnitude of the positive charge of the atomic nucleus responsible for the scattering of the α-particles. They found that, for the elements heavier than aluminum, the charge (in units of the charge of the electron) was roughly equal to one half the atomic weight of the element. Van den Broek, in 1913, made the important suggestion that the nuclear charge (measured in these same units) is in fact exactly equal to *the atomic number of the element*, and this suggestion has since been amply confirmed.

As we have already seen, Rutherford made the simplifying assumptions that both the nucleus and the α-particle were point electrical charges, and that the repulsive force between them was given by Coulomb's inverse square law at all distances of separation. These assumptions should cease to be valid if the α-particles approach the nucleus to a distance so small as to be comparable with the diameter of the nucleus.

TABLE 1.1. Typical Results of Geiger and Marsden for the Scattering of α-Particles from Thin Gold Foils

Angle of deflection ϕ	Number of light flashes per unit time, N	$\dfrac{N}{\csc^4(\phi/2)}$
150°	33.1	28.8
135	43.0	31.2
120	51.9	29.0
105	69.5	27.5
75	211	29.1
60	477	29.8
45	1435	30.8
37.5	3300	35.3
30	7800	35.0

When this happens, we may think of the two particles as actually colliding, so that the force between them ceases to be of a purely electrostatic nature. The experimentally observed scattering should then diverge from equation (1.1). Rutherford and Chadwick, in 1925, were unable to detect any divergence from the Coulomb inverse square law of force between α-particles and copper nuclei at a distance as small as 1.2×10^{-12} cm, and they concluded that the radius of the copper nucleus must be less than this figure. Actually it is now known that the radius of this nucleus is about 6×10^{-13} cm. The α-particles available to Rutherford and Chadwick had insufficient energy to overcome the Coulomb repulsion exerted on them by the nucleus, and they were thus unable to approach close enough for deviations from the inverse square law to show up. If high energy particles from cyclotrons are used, the deviations show up very clearly.

From all these experiments, then, there emerged a picture of the internal structure of atoms. The existence of the nucleus was amply confirmed and approximate values were obtained for its size and electrical charge. However, it was not possible to say anything about the organization of the cloud of electrons that surrounds the nucleus.

B. The Bohr Model of the Atom

The Rutherford atomic model could not be reconciled with the principles of physics as they were understood at the end of the nineteenth century. There seemed to be no reason why the electron cloud should not be attracted closer and closer towards the nucleus by the electrostatic force between charges of opposite sign, until eventually the charges were neutralized. This difficulty could be countered by supposing that the electrons revolve in orbits around the nucleus at such a speed that the centrifugal force exactly balances the electrostatic force. However, this suggestion only raises a new difficulty. According to nineteenth century theories, electrons traveling in such orbits would continuously radiate energy in the form of electromagnetic waves, and they would therefore very rapidly slow down and then collapse into the nucleus.

In the early days of the twentieth century, there were other and equally severe difficulties in physics. Lummer and Pringsheim measured very carefully the intensity of light radiated from "black bodies" (i.e., objects which completely absorb light which falls on them, reflecting none and transmitting none). They found that the intensity of the light of various wavelengths emitted by bodies of various temperatures was not in agreement with calculations which were firmly based on fundamental theories of physics. The difficulty was finally resolved in 1900 by Planck, by means of a revolutionary suggestion. Planck proposed that the oscillating electrons, which are responsible for the emission of light from heated bodies, could only have *certain definite quantities of energy*. When an oscillating electron emitted energy in the form of light, it could only do so by reducing its energy from one of the definite energy levels to a second definite level of lower energy. Energies of the oscillating electron between the two levels were not permitted.

It was a consequence of this theory that when an oscillating electron changed its energy by an amount E, the frequency ν of the emitted light was given by the important equation

$$E = h\nu \qquad (1.2)$$

where h is a constant which is now universally known as Planck's constant. It has the value 6.6252×10^{-27} erg-seconds.

It was Einstein who first pointed out a further revolutionary deduction which could be made from Planck's theory. He suggested that, since the oscillating electrons could only change their energy in discrete "jumps" from one "allowed" energy value to another, the light emitted in these jumps must itself consist of separate particles. These light particles were given the name "light quanta," and later on, as their particle nature became clearer, the name photon began to be used. This conclusion, of course, appeared to be completely inconsistent with the very firmly established wave theory of light. However, the theory of light quanta was soon successful in explaining many phenomena such as fluorescence and the photoelectric effect (the emission of electrons from many substances under the influence of light). In addition, Planck's hypothesis of discrete energy jumps (which became known as the Quantum Theory), was able to explain why the heat capacities of solids decrease at low temperatures, whereas earlier theories predicted that there would be no such decrease.

In 1913, Bohr applied the quantum theory to the Rutherford atomic model. He suggested that there were certain special electron orbits which were stable, in the sense that they were exempt from the rule that electrons revolving in orbits should continuously radiate energy. In these special orbits, the electrons could retain the same energy for an indefinite period of time. Each such orbit corresponded to a definite energy of the atom. The electrons could be raised to an orbit of higher energy by the absorption of a light quantum by the atom; if the electron returned to its original orbit, a light quantum (photon) would be emitted. The frequency ν of the emitted light was given by the equation

$$\nu = \frac{E_2 - E_1}{h} \tag{1.3}$$

where E_2 and E_1 are the initial and final energies of the atom.

Since the electron orbits could correspond only to definite energy values, it follows from equation (1.3) that only certain definite frequencies of light could be emitted from atoms. Thus Bohr's assumptions were in agreement with the well-known observation that the spectra of light emitted by atoms consist of discrete lines at frequencies which are characteristic of the element concerned. Bohr was able to calculate the frequencies of the lines in the hydrogen spectrum. To do this, it was necessary to specify exactly in what way an allowed electron orbit differed from one that was not allowed. Bohr proposed that the allowed orbits were those in which the angular momentum of the electron was a whole multiple of $h/2\pi$. Since angular momentum is a very important quantity in the discussion of the properties of atoms and nuclei, it is worth a short digression at this point.

Angular momentum plays the same part in the theory of angular motion that ordinary (linear) momentum plays in the theory of linear motion. Figure 1.2 (a) shows a body of mass m and velocity v moving past the fixed point O in such a way that its distance of closest approach to O is r. Then the linear momentum of the body is mv, and its angular momentum about an axis perpendicular to the page and passing through O is defined as mvr. The axis is the one about which an observer would have to turn his head if he were standing at O and watching the body pass by.

Consider now that the rigid body shown in Figure 1.2 (b) is in rotation about an axis passing through O, with an angular velocity of ω radians per

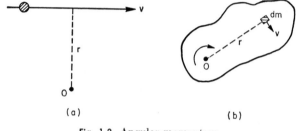

(a)   (b)

Fig. 1.2. Angular momentum

second.   The linear velocity v of an element situated at a distance r from the axis is

$$v = \omega r$$

If the mass of the element is dm, then by definition, its angular momentum about O is $vr\,dm = \omega r^2\,dm$.   The total angular momentum of the body is therefore $\int \omega r^2\,dm$, and since ω is the same for all parts of the body, it is equal to $\omega \int r^2\,dm$.   The quantity $\int r^2\,dm$ will be familiar as the moment of inertia I of the body for rotation about the axis through O.   Hence

$$\text{Angular momentum} = I\omega$$

In this equation, I and ω are analogous to m and v respectively in the equation

$$\text{Linear momentum} = mv$$

Just as the linear momentum of a body is changed by the application of a *force*, and remains constant in time if there is no external force, so is the angular momentum changed only by the application to the body of a *torque*.

Like linear momentum, angular momentum is a vector quantity. Linear momentum is represented by a vector whose length represents the magnitude of the momentum and whose direction is the same as the direction of motion.   Angular momentum is represented by a vector which lies in the same direction in space as the axis about which the rotation is taking place, and whose length represents the magnitude of the angular momentum.   We shall return to the discussion of the properties of angular momentum in Chapter 4.

Bohr's postulate about the distinguishing characteristic of the allowed electron orbits can then be written in the form

$$\text{Angular momentum} = m_e v r = \frac{lh}{2\pi} \qquad (1.4)$$

where m_e, v, and r are the mass, velocity, and orbit radius of the electron, and l is any whole number. With this assumption, Bohr found that the frequencies of the lines of the hydrogen spectrum were

$$\nu = \frac{2\pi^2 e^4}{h^3} \frac{m_e m_p}{m_e + m_p} \left(\frac{1}{n_1^2} - \frac{1}{n_2^2} \right) \qquad (1.5)$$

where e is the charge of the electron, m_p is the mass of the hydrogen nucleus, and n_1 and n_2 are whole numbers. If we set $n_1 = 2$ and then allow n_2 to have the values $3, 4, 5 \cdots$, then the calculated frequencies are found to agree very closely with the series of hydrogen lines known as the Balmer series. Setting n_1 equal to other small whole numbers gives rise to other series of calculated frequencies which again agree very exactly with experimental measurements.

The various numbers n_1 and n_2 which appear in equation (1.5) correspond to the various allowed orbits of the single electron in the hydrogen atom. $n = 1$ corresponds to the innermost orbit, $n = 2$ to the next, and so on. Equation (1.5) may thus be interpreted as follows. When the electron jumps from the n_2th to the n_1th orbit, the energy liberated appears as a quantum of light (a photon) whose frequency ν is given by equation (1.5). The energy of the photon, according to equation (1.2), is equal to $h\nu$. Observe that although we speak of light as though it consists of particles (photons), we also find it necessary to refer to its frequency, as though it were a wave phenomenon. We shall return to this point later.

Whole numbers, such as the l and the n which appeared in the equations above, appear very frequently in the quantum theory. They are called *quantum numbers*, and as we shall see, they may be used to distinguish the various allowed states in which a system such as a nucleus or a hydrogen atom may be found.

C. Quantum Mechanics

A certain familiarity with some of the qualitative concepts of quantum mechanics is essential for the understanding of nuclear phenomena. It is obviously not possible to do justice to the subject in a short section. The reader is urged to read and re-read this section as he proceeds through this book. A study of some of the general texts listed at the end of this chapter is also highly recommended.

Between 1913 and about 1923, Bohr's theory of atomic structure enjoyed many successes, but as time passed, serious difficulties also appeared. It became clear that new ideas were required. In 1924, de Broglie made the revolutionary suggestion that, just as light waves behaved in some ways as particles, so particles such as electrons should behave in some ways as though they were waves. To a particle of mass m and velocity v, he assigned a wave of frequency ν and wavelength λ given by

$$\lambda = \frac{h}{mv}, \qquad \nu = \frac{E}{h} \qquad (1.6)$$

These equations were soon confirmed by Davisson and Germer, who found that a beam of electrons gave rise to a diffraction pattern when reflected from a crystal of nickel, in just the same way that a beam of light is diffracted by reflection from a diffraction grating.

There is no way in which Newton's laws of motion can account for the behavior of particles which diffract like waves. The laws agree very accurately with experimental measurements made with objects of "ordinary" size, but there is great danger in trying to use a theory outside the region of conditions for which it has been experimentally confirmed. It was obvious that some new form of the laws of motion was required for objects of small size such as electrons, and clearly the new laws should take account of the diffraction of particles observed by Davisson and Germer.

In 1927, Schrödinger developed a new method for the solution of dynamical problems which was immediately found to give results in agreement with experimental observations even for very small objects. Furthermore, its results were in agreement with Newton's laws when applied to large objects. Schrödinger was guided to the discovery by analogies with vibrating systems such as violin strings, which, like waves, have the properties of wavelength and frequency.

Schrödinger's method involves the use of a famous equation which is known as the Schrödinger wave equation. It is not possible to "prove" this equation from more fundamental assumptions, any more than Newton's laws of motion could be proved. Nevertheless, the Schrödinger equation is justified by the agreement of its consequences with the results of experiments.

For simplicity, let us consider a one-dimensional system, for example a particle moving along the x axis of a coordinate system. If its mass is m and its linear momentum is p, then its kinetic energy is $p^2/2m$. Let the potential energy of the particle be $V(x)$, which is some function of x. (In other words, the potential energy of the particle depends in some way upon its distance from the origin along the x axis). The potential energy might be due to a gravitational field or (if the particle is charged) to an electric field.   Then the total energy E of the particle is

$$E = \frac{p^2}{2m} + V(x) \tag{1.7}$$

This simple equation can be converted into the Schrödinger equation by substituting certain mathematical expressions for p and E.   The particular choice of expressions is justified only by the fact that the resulting equation gives results in agreement with experiments.

The expressions for momentum and energy are called operators, since they are in fact instructions that a mathematical operation is to be performed.   For example, $\div b$ is an operator, which, when joined to an operand such as y, gives the expression $y \div b$, meaning that the operation to be performed upon y is a division by b.   The operators which represent momentum and energy are

$$p = \frac{\hbar}{i} \frac{\partial}{\partial x}$$
$$E = -\frac{\hbar}{i} \frac{\partial}{\partial t} \tag{1.8}$$

The p operator means that partial differentiation with respect to x must be performed upon some operand (as yet unspecified), and the result multiplied by $\hbar/i$.   (The symbol $\hbar$—pronounced h-bar—means $h/2\pi$, which is a combination of constants that occurs so often that a special symbol is justified.)   The symbol i is the imaginary quantity $\sqrt{-1}$.   In the E operator, the partial differentiation is to be performed with respect to the time, t.   In each case, the operand is a function which is given the symbol Ψ; its meaning will be discussed in more detail below.

The potential energy $V(x)$ must also be replaced by an operator, but in this case, the operator is simply $V(x) \times$, which merely multiplies the operand Ψ by $V(x)$.   Substituting the operators and their operands into equation (1.7) gives

$$-\frac{\hbar}{i} \frac{\partial \Psi}{\partial t} = \frac{1}{2m} \left(\frac{\hbar}{i} \right)^2 \frac{\partial^2 \Psi}{\partial x^2} + V(x)\Psi$$

or

$$-\frac{\hbar}{i} \frac{\partial \Psi}{\partial t} = -\frac{\hbar^2}{2m} \frac{\partial^2 \Psi}{\partial x^2} + V(x)\Psi \tag{1.9}$$

The function Ψ, which would be obtained by the solution of the differential equation (1.9), is a function of the two variables x and t.   However, equations of the type of (1.9) cannot usually be solved.

If $V(x)$ depends only on x and not on t, which is usually the case, then the function Ψ can be expressed as a product of the two functions $\psi(x)$ and $\varphi(t)$, each of which depends on only one of the variables x and t.   The wave equation (1.9) can then be separated into two equations, one of which has t as its only variable, while the other contains only x. The latter equation, which is called the time-independent Schrödinger equation, has the form

$$\frac{d^2\psi}{dx^2} + \frac{2m}{\hbar^2} [E - V(x)] \psi(x) = 0 \tag{1.10}$$

Solution of this equation for a particular dynamical system involves insertion of the proper form for the potential energy $V(x)$, and integration to obtain the function ψ which satisfies the differential equation. For example, if the problem involves the motion of an electron in the vicinity of an atomic nucleus of atomic number Z, then the potential energy of the system is $V = -Ze^2/r$, where e is the electronic charge and r is the distance between the electron and the nucleus.

The equation involving only time is

$$\frac{d\varphi}{dt} = -\frac{i}{\hbar} E\varphi(t) \tag{1.11}$$

It can easily be integrated to give

$$\varphi(t) = e^{-iEt/\hbar} \tag{1.12}$$

We must return to the meaning of the Ψ function (which is called a wave function), but first we must mention some additional properties which it is found necessary to attribute to it in order that it should be a physically meaningful solution of the wave equation. First, both Ψ and $\partial\Psi/\partial x$ must be finite, continuous, and single-valued at all points in space. A function which becomes infinite, has a discontinuity, or can assume more than one value at any point, is physically meaningless. Second, the product of Ψ and its complex conjugate Ψ^* when integrated over all space, must be equal to unity i.e.,

$$\int_{-\infty}^{+\infty} \Psi^*\Psi \, dx = 1$$

The complex conjugate is obtained from Ψ merely by replacing any and all i's ($\sqrt{-1}$) by $-i$'s.

A wave function which satisfies all these requirements can then be used to calculate the *average value* of any dynamical quantity (such as the energy, position, momentum, or angular momentum) of the system by means of the equation

$$\text{Average value} = \int_{-\infty}^{+\infty} \Psi^*(\text{operator})\Psi \, dx \tag{1.13}$$

In equation (1.13), we must insert the operator appropriate to the dynamical quantity whose average value we wish to calculate. These average values are usually called expectation values, written in parentheses $\langle\ \rangle$. Thus the expectation value of the momentum p is written $\langle p \rangle$.

The use of terms such as "average" and "expectation" implies that it is not always possible to calculate an actual value of a dynamical quantity, but only an average value. For example, it is not possible to calculate an exact distance between the electron and the nucleus of a hydrogen atom. We can, however, calculate the average distance between them, or, what amounts to the same thing, the probability that the electron will be found at any particular time at a given distance. These statements imply that the electron is not always at the same distance from the nucleus, and in fact, atoms do behave as though their electrons spend some of their time close to the nucleus and some of their time at large distances from it.

If we insert the energy operator into equation (1.13) in order to calculate the energy of a hydrogen atom, the result turns out to be a constant. In other words, every time that we measure the energy of a hydrogen atom, we will obtain the same result. All hydrogen atoms have the same energy, all the time. Which quantities turn out to be constants will depend on the system under consideration. For nuclei, the constant quantities of most interest to us are the energy and the angular momentum.

At about the time that Schrödinger first published the wave equation, an apparently quite different theory was proposed by Heisenberg. His approach made use of the mathematical calculus of matrices. (A matrix is an array of numbers obeying certain definite rules for addition and multiplication.) It was soon shown, however, that the Schrödinger and Heisenberg methods were actually mathematically identical. Since 1926, further work has given birth to a general theory which is known as *quantum mechanics*. It is important to realize that quantum mechanics is perfectly general, and applies to the mechanical properties of any system regardless of its size. Thus the motion of a plane in flight is governed by the laws of quantum mechanics just as much as is the motion of an electron around a nucleus. However, for large systems, the errors involved in the use of "ordinary" or "classical" mechanics are quite trivial, so that in practice it is not necessary for engineers to use quantum mechanics.

The difficulty in understanding some of the ideas presented above arises largely from their unfamiliarity. Instinct calls out for some "proof" of the Schrödinger equation. However, we can no more "prove" it than we can prove Newton's laws of motion. We must appeal to experiment, and when this is done, it is found that quantum mechanics yields results that are in agreement with the experiments, whereas classical mechanics often does not.

We now return to consider in more detail the application of the

Schrödinger equation to the hydrogen atom. We specify the position of the nucleus, whose mass is m_n, by the Cartesian coordinates x_1, y_1, and z_1. The position of the electron, whose mass is m_e, is given by the coordinates x_2, y_2, and z_2. The potential energy of the electron due to the electrostatic force between it and the nucleus is given by $V(r) = -e^2/r$, where r is the distance of the electron from the nucleus. r can be expressed in terms of the coordinates x_1, y_1, z_1, x_2, y_2, and z_2. The wave equation (1.10), takes the form

$$\frac{1}{m_n}\left(\frac{\partial^2 \psi}{\partial x_1^2} + \frac{\partial^2 \psi}{\partial y_1^2} + \frac{\partial^2 \psi}{\partial z_1^2}\right) + \frac{1}{m_e}\left(\frac{\partial^2 \psi}{\partial x_2^2} + \frac{\partial^2 \psi}{\partial y_2^2} + \frac{\partial^2 \psi}{\partial z_2^2}\right) + \frac{2}{\hbar^2}[E - V(r)]\psi = 0$$

$$(1.14)$$

This equation is much easier to handle if the Cartesian coordinate system is replaced by polar coordinates whose origin is chosen to be at the center of mass of the system. (Since the hydrogen nucleus is about 1836 times as heavy as the electron, the center of mass is actually very close to the nucleus.) In the polar coordinate system, the position of any point is defined by means of its distance r from the origin and the two angles θ and φ which specify the direction in space in which the distance r is to be taken. It is easy to see that such a coordinate system is very convenient for handling problems which involve a potential energy depending only on the distance r between two particles and not on the other coordinates θ and φ.

After conversion to polar coordinates, and substitution of $V = -e^2/r$, the Schrödinger equation becomes

$$\frac{1}{r^2}\frac{\partial}{\partial r}\left(r^2 \frac{\partial \psi}{\partial r}\right) + \frac{1}{r^2 \sin^2 \theta}\frac{\partial^2 \psi}{\partial \varphi^2} + \frac{1}{r^2 \sin \theta}\frac{\partial}{\partial \theta}\left(\sin \theta \frac{\partial \psi}{\partial \theta}\right)$$

$$+ \frac{2m_e m_n}{\hbar^2(m_e + m_n)}\left(E + \frac{e^2}{r}\right)\psi = 0 \quad (1.15)$$

By some simple algebraic manipulation, this equation can be changed into a form in which each of the terms is a function of only one of the variables r, θ, and φ. In this form, the equation is of the type

$$F_1(r) + F_2(\theta) + F_3(\varphi) = \text{constant}$$

Such an equation can only be generally true for any values of r, θ, and φ if the three functions F_1, F_2, and F_3 are themselves separately equal to constants. By this argument the wave equation is separated into three equations which may then be integrated. The equation containing the variable r is the only one of the three which contains the energy terms E and $V(r)$, as we would expect, since V depends only on the distance r between the nucleus and the electron.

The solution of the three equations leads to the appearance of three whole numbers (quantum numbers). To illustrate this point, we will consider only the simplest case which is the equation involving the angle θ as its variable. The equation is

$$\frac{1}{\psi}\frac{d^2\psi}{d\theta^2} = -m^2 \qquad (1.16)$$

We have here set the one term in the full wave equation which contains θ as equal to a constant which we have chosen to write as $-m^2$. Equation (1.16) has the following solution:

$$\psi = \frac{1}{\sqrt{2\pi}} e^{\pm im\theta} = \frac{1}{\sqrt{2\pi}} (\cos m\theta + i \sin m\theta) \qquad (1.17)$$

where the i is the imaginary quantity $\sqrt{-1}$. Now θ can have any value between 0° and 360° (0 to 2π radians), and the function ψ must have the same value for $\theta = 0$ as for $\theta = 2\pi$, since these two values of θ represent the same point in space. Because the sine and cosine functions repeat themselves every 2π radians, the requirement that ψ can have only a single value at the point 0 or 2π can only be met if m is an integral quantity which may have any positive or negative value. In other words, there must be an integral number of oscillations of ψ in a full circle in order that ψ may have only a single value at any point.

The number m is known as the *magnetic quantum number*. The energy of the hydrogen atom does not depend on the value of this quantum number unless we place the atom in a magnetic field. Then the allowed energy levels split up into a number of new levels each of which has a different value for m. This phenomenon, which is known as the Zeeman effect, is responsible for the splitting of the lines in the hydrogen spectrum from a discharge tube operating in a magnetic field.

From the solution of the equation containing r, we derive both a quantum number given the symbol n and the name *total quantum number*, and values for the energy E for the various values of n. The result turns out to be the same as that found by Bohr (equation 1.5). From the equation involving φ, we obtain the *azimuthal quantum number l*, which is related to the angular momentum of the system by equation (1.4). The values of these three quantum numbers are related to each other according to the following scheme:

$$n = 1, 2, 3, \cdots$$

$$l = 0, 1, 2, \cdots, (n-1) \qquad (1.18)$$

$$m = -l, (-l+1), (-l+2), \cdots, -1, 0, 1, 2, \cdots, (l-1), l$$

n may have any integral value, but l must then lie between 0 and $(n-1)$. m may have any value between $+l$ and $-l$, including zero.

We have already mentioned the splitting up of the energy levels (and hence of the spectral lines) in magnetic fields (the Zeeman effect). The theory that we have described thus far cannot account for all the details of this effect. In 1925, Uhlenbeck and Goudsmit suggested that the electron must be regarded as spinning on an axis passing through itself. It possesses angular momentum due to this rotation, and in order to fit the observed Zeeman effect, it is necessary to assume that the angular momentum of the electron must be either $+\frac{1}{2}\hbar$ or $-\frac{1}{2}\hbar$. The two signs correspond to the two different possible directions of rotation of the electron. We may introduce a fourth quantum number s which can have only the values $+\frac{1}{2}$ or $-\frac{1}{2}$ corresponding to the two allowed values for the angular momentum of the electron due to its spin.* $\hbar$ is a natural unit of angular momentum (see Problem 9).

D. The Pauli Exclusion Principle

In 1925, Pauli stated the important principle that in any atom, no two electrons may have the same values for all the four quantum numbers n, l, m, and s. We are now in a position to see how this *exclusion principle* can be used to explain in a very simple way the arrangement of the chemical elements in the periodic table.

When the total quantum number n has the value 1, we are restricted by equation (1.18) to $l = 0$ and $m = 0$. The electron spin quantum number may have the two values $\pm\frac{1}{2}$, so that the maximum number of electrons with $n = 1$ will be two. In the element of atomic number 1 (hydrogen), we have one such electron. In the next element (helium), we have the maximum of two. In helium, therefore, we say that the $n = 1$ shell is filled. Such an arrangement is particularly stable. The helium atom therefore has little tendency to disturb its filled electron shell, which it must do in order to enter into chemical combination with other atoms. Helium is the lightest of the inert gases, which have virtually no tendency to form chemical compounds.

As we proceed to the next element (lithium), a third electron is added, and it must go into the $n = 2$ shell. This third electron is not as tightly bound to the atom as the first two electrons, and lithium can readily lose it with the formation of a positively charged lithium ion. The ease with which this can happen is the reason for the great chemical reactivity of lithium. When $n = 2$, equation (1.18) states that l may have the values 0 and 1, and m may be -1, 0, and $+1$. We may also have $s = \pm\frac{1}{2}$. Thus there are eight combinations available, as shown in Table 1.2.

By the time we reach element 10 (neon), we have filled both the $n = 1$

---

* More accurately, the spin angular momentum is $\hbar \sqrt{s(s + 1)}$ rather than $s\hbar$. Discussion of this point is deferred to Chapter 4.

and the $n = 2$ shells.   Neon, like helium, is therefore chemically inert.
The element which precedes it, however, is fluorine.   This element needs
one electron to complete the $n = 2$ shell, and a large amount of energy is
liberated when this last electron is added to the shell.   Fluorine is therefore chemically extremely reactive, and is energetically able to complete
the shell by robbing almost any other element of the required electron.

TABLE 1.2. Quantum Numbers of the First Ten Atomic Electrons

Electron	n	l	m	s
1	1	0	0	$+\frac{1}{2}$
2	1	0	0	$-\frac{1}{2}$
3	2	0	0	$+\frac{1}{2}$
4	2	0	0	$-\frac{1}{2}$
5	2	1	-1	$+\frac{1}{2}$
6	2	1	0	$+\frac{1}{2}$
7	2	1	$+1$	$+\frac{1}{2}$
8	2	1	-1	$-\frac{1}{2}$
9	2	1	0	$-\frac{1}{2}$
10	2	1	$+1$	$-\frac{1}{2}$

The extension of this reasoning to the rest of the periodic table of elements proceeds along the same lines, although the order in which the various possible shells fill up with electrons is not always quite the order that
would be expected from simple ideas.

The shell in which $n = 1$ is usually called the K shell.   An electron in
the K shell is referred to as a K electron.   The $n = 2$ shell is called the
L shell, and so on through the alphabet.   In order to specify the values of
the quantum numbers of an individual electron, there is a simple terminology which must be memorized.   The values of l are specified by certain
letters according to the scheme shown in Table 1.3.   The complete

TABLE 1.3. Spectroscopic Terminology for l Values

l	Spectroscopic terminology
0	s
1	p
2	d
3	f
4	g
5	h
6	i
.	.
.	.
.	.

designation of the quantum numbers is then written as shown in the following example. Thus a $2p_{3/2}$ electron is one for which $n = 2$, $l = 1$, and the total angular momentum of the electron (in units of $\hbar$) is $\frac{3}{2}$. The total angular momentum J, derived from both the electron spin and motion around the nucleus is $J = l + s = l \pm \frac{1}{2}$. (We shall return to the problem of adding angular momenta in Chapter 4.) To designate that a shell for which $n = 5$ and $l = 3$ contains seven electrons, we write $5f^7$.

E. The Uncertainty Principle

By solving the wave equation for a dynamical system, we obtain the functions from which we can calculate the expectation values of the dynamical quantities, but we do not obtain precise values for all these quantities. Heisenberg suggested that this uncertainty was in fact due to the operation of a fundamental principle, which became known as the *uncertainty principle*. He suggested that it is not possible to know the exact values of all the dynamical variables of a system at one and the same time. For example, even in the most exact measurements that can ever be made, the uncertainty Δp in the measured momentum of a particle and the uncertainty Δx in its position can never simultaneously be reduced to zero. Even under ideal conditions, Δp and Δx will be related by the equation

$$\Delta p \cdot \Delta x = \hbar \qquad (1.19)$$

The similar equation $\Delta E \cdot \Delta t = \hbar$ connects the uncertainty in the measured energy E of a system with the uncertainty in the time t at which the energy was measured. It must be emphasized that the uncertainty principle has nothing to do with ordinary experimental difficulties. Even with perfect equipment perfectly used, the uncertainties expressed in equation (1.19) would still exist. According to this equation, it is possible in principle to measure the momentum of a system with as much accuracy as desired, but then the position of the system, x, will become more and more uncertain the greater the precision of the momentum measurement.

As an example, consider the problem of measuring the position and momentum of an electron. Suppose that we could build such a perfect microscope that we could actually see the electron. The uncertainty in the position of the electron would be about equal to the wavelength of the light which we use in the experiment. Thus $\Delta x \simeq \lambda$. A photon of wavelength λ has momentum h/λ. The photon must be scattered by the electron if we are to "see" the electron, for this is the only way in which we could tell that there was an electron present. When this happens, the momentum of the electron will be altered by an amount $\Delta p \simeq h/\lambda$. Thus $\Delta x \cdot \Delta p \simeq h$ as required by equation (1.19). (We have lost the numerical factor 2π in this simple analysis.)   If we attempt to measure x more accurately, we must use light quanta of shorter wavelength and hence of greater momentum, so that the accuracy of measurement of p is decreased.   We may try to make the same measurements by a completely different method, but we will always find that the best results we can get are subject to the limitations of equation (1.19).   There have been many ingenious attempts to design "paper experiments" to avoid the consequences of the uncertainty principle, but they have never been successful.

F. The Composition of Nuclei

The atomic weights of many elements are close to integral multiples of the atomic weight of hydrogen.   It was therefore suggested by Prout in 1815 that the atoms of all elements are in fact built up from hydrogen atoms.

In recent times, this hypothesis was revived when it was suggested that atomic *nuclei* are built from hydrogen *nuclei*.   The hydrogen nucleus, which is called the *proton*, has a mass of almost exactly unity on the atomic weight scale, and an electrical charge equal to that of one electron, but positive in sign.   Nuclei containing only protons would therefore carry an electrical charge (in units of the electronic charge) equal numerically to their atomic weight.   We have already seen that the positive charge is in fact roughly equal to only one half of the atomic weight.   It was therefore natural to suggest that, in addition to the protons, nuclei contained a sufficient number of negatively charged electrons to neutralize part of the positive charge.   On this view, a nucleus of helium would contain four protons and two electrons.   However, there are several reasons why it is not possible to accept electrons as component parts of nuclei.

In 1932, Chadwick discovered that the bombardment of beryllium with α-particles from the decay of polonium produced a new kind of particle which carried no electric charge, and which was therefore named the *neutron*.   He found that its mass was very nearly equal to the mass of the proton.

Immediately after the discovery of the neutron, the new particle was incorporated into theories of the structure of nuclei, for it was clear that nuclei of any mass and charge could in principle be constructed from a suitable number of neutrons and protons.   The number of protons must be numerically equal to the positive electrical charge of the nucleus (in units of the electronic charge) and hence to the atomic number.   Thus the nucleus of helium would contain two protons to provide the charge, and two neutrons to make the mass up to the required value of four.   The nucleus of thorium, with atomic number 90 and atomic weight 232, would contain 90 protons and $(232 - 90)$ or 142 neutrons.

The hypothesis that nuclei contain protons and neutrons has proved to be very fruitful, and as we shall see, it forms the basis for all the detailed theories of nuclear structure.

G. Energy Units

The energy unit most commonly used in nuclear physics and chemistry is the *electron volt* (ev). It is the energy gained by a particle carrying an electric charge equal to that of one electron when it is accelerated by an electric potential of one volt. The electron volt is equal to 1.602×10^{-12} ergs. The kiloelectron volt (kev) and million electron volt (Mev) are very commonly used. Chemical energies (e.g., heats of reaction) are of the order of electron volts per molecule, but nuclear energies are typically a few million times greater.

The fundamental energy unit in the cgs system is the erg. The safest way to make numerical calculations is to use cgs units (or the mks system if it is more familiar) and to convert to other units such as Mev only at the very end. For example, to calculate the potential energy V of an electron at a distance r from a nucleus of atomic number Z by means of the equation $V = -Ze^2/r$, put r in cm and the electronic charge e in electrostatic units. V then appears in ergs; it can finally be divided by 1.602×10^{-12} to obtain a result in ev. Similarly, calculations by the equation $E = mc^2$ give E in ergs if m is in grams and c is measured in cm per sec.

REFERENCES

1. Schiff, L. I., *Quantum Mechanics*, McGraw-Hill Book Co., New York, 1955.

2. Pauling, L. and E. B. Wilson, *Introduction to Quantum Mechanics*, McGraw-Hill Book Co., New York, 1935.

3. Bohm, D., *Quantum Theory*, Prentice-Hall, Inc., Englewood Cliffs, N. J., 1951.

4. Rojansky, V., *Introductory Quantum Mechanics*, Prentice-Hall, Inc., New York, 1938.

5. Slater, J. C., *The Quantum Theory of Matter*, McGraw-Hill Book Co., New York, 1951.

6. Kimble, E. C., *Fundamental Principles of Quantum Mechanics*, McGraw-Hill Book Co., New York, 1937.

7. Harnwell, G. P., and W. E. Stephens, *Atomic Physics*, McGraw-Hill Book Co., New York, 1955.

8. Flügge, S. (ed.), *Handbuch Der Physik*, Julius Springer Verlag, Berlin, 1957: Vol. V/1, W. Pauli, "Die allgemeinen Prinzipien der Wellenmechanik"; Vol. XXXV, E. R. Cohen and J. W. M. Du Mond, "The Fundamental Constants of Atomic Physics," Vol. XXXV, H. A. Bethe and E. E. Salpeter, "Quantum Mechanics of One- and Two-Electron Systems."

9. Tolansky, S., *Introduction to Atomic Physics*, Longmans, Green, and Co., London, 1956.

10. Rutherford, E., J. Chadwick, and C. D. Ellis, *Radiations from Radioactive Substances*, Cambridge University Press, Cambridge, 1930.

PROBLEMS

1. At any angle of measurement, which foil will scatter more helium ions, gold 0.0001 cm thick or aluminum 0.0001 cm thick?

2. At any angle of measurement, which foil will scatter more helium ions, aluminum 0.0001 cm. thick or a gold foil with the same weight per unit area as the aluminum?

3. The density of copper is 8.92. Calculate the size of the copper atom, assuming that in copper metal the atoms are cubes packed together with no gaps. Compare your result with the known radius of the copper atom.

4. What would be the density of copper if it were composed of copper nuclei tightly packed together with no gaps? Assume for simplicity that the nuclei are cubes whose sides are 10^{-12} cm.

5. Calculate the wavelength of the light emitted by an atom when an electron makes a transition from one orbit to another orbit so that the energy of the atom changes by 10 electron volts.

6. What is the kinetic energy of an electron whose de Broglie wavelength is equal to 10^{-8} cm?

7. What is the greatest wavelength of light whose photons are energetic enough to cause the ejection of an electron from a sodium atom? The minimum energy required to remove an electron from a sodium atom is 5.12 electron volts.

8. Remembering that the force of attraction (F, dynes) exerted by a charge Ze on an electron (charge $-e$) at a distance of r cm is $F = Ze^2/r^2$, calculate the work done in moving an electron from 10^{-8} cm to infinity when $Z = 10$.

9. Show that Planck's constant has the same dimensions as angular momentum.

10. Calculate the wavelength of the line in the hydrogen spectrum corresponding to change of the principal quantum number from 3 to 2.

11. Calculate the velocity of a proton which is moving inside a nucleus in a circular orbit of radius 10^{-13} cm with angular momentum of one unit.

12. The wave function representing the motion of a particle of mass m and total energy E in a field-free region (i.e., no potential energy) is

$$\Psi(x,t) = A \sin\left[\frac{(x - x_0)}{\hbar}\sqrt{2mE}\right] e^{-iEt/\hbar}$$

where A and x_0 are the constants of integration which originate from integration of the wave equation.

(a) By differentiation with respect to x, show that the equation, without the exponential time-dependent part, represents a solution of the wave equation (1.10) with $V(x)$ set equal to zero.

(b) Use the equation to show that the wavelength of the particle is given by equation (1.6). (The wavelength is the distance between points in space at which the value of $\Psi(x,t)$ repeats itself.)

(c) Does the equation for $\Psi(x,t)$ in any way restrict the possible values of E? Note that sin θ is finite, single-valued, and continuous for all real value of θ.

(d) Use the wave function to calculate the expectation value of the kinetic energy T of the particle. Use the expression $T = p^2/2m$; the operator form for p^2 is $(\hbar/i)^2 d^2/dx^2$. Remember that $\int_{-\infty}^{+\infty} \Psi^*\Psi \, dx = 1$. Discuss the meaning of your result. (If, in solving this problem, you find that you are attempting a difficult integration, then you have already gone wrong.)

13. Draw a rough graph of $\Psi = \cos m\theta$ for $m = 1$, 1.5, and 2. Convince yourself that the value of Ψ is the same for $\theta = 0$ and $\theta = 360°$ (2π radians) only when m is an integer. [Refer to equation (1.17)].

14. By differentiation, confirm that equation (1.17) is a solution of equation (1.16).

CHAPTER 2

Radioactive Decay

A. The Discovery of Radioactivity

The discovery of X-rays by Roentgen in 1895 caused a lot of excitement in scientific circles. The origin of the X-rays was thought by some to be connected with the fluorescence of the glass discharge tube in which the rays were produced. Becquerel, among others, therefore began to investigate various fluorescent substances to see whether they too emitted X-rays. The test consisted simply of wrapping the sample in black paper and placing it under a silver plate above which there was a photographic plate. It was known that X-rays, if present, would pass through the silver plate and blacken the photographic plate. Becquerel had worked with fluorescent substances many years before, and one of the samples left from this work was potassium uranium double sulfate. He therefore tried this sample, and the photographic plate was darkened. Thus radioactivity was discovered in 1896 by a fortunate combination of chance and misconception.

Becquerel soon found that the darkening of the photographic plate had nothing to do with fluorescence, but was exhibited by all compounds of uranium, including those that did not fluoresce. The photographic method was a slow and inconvenient way of detecting the radiations from the uranium compounds, but Becquerel found that these radiations, like the X-rays, had the property of ionizing air, thus rendering it a conductor of electricity. Hence an electrically charged body, placed near a sample of uranium, soon lost its charge by conduction through the air, and this phenomenon provided a convenient and sensitive method for measuring the intensity of the radiations. A simple apparatus for making such measurements is shown in Figure 2.1, which is adapted from Madame Curie's *Traité de Radioactivité* published in 1910. It consists of a box B with a block of insulating substance I mounted in its top. Through the insulator runs a metal rod R to which is attached a strip of gold leaf L. To the top of the rod R is fastened a table T underneath a cover C. When the table, rod, and gold leaf are electrically charged (by means of a battery), the gold leaf is repelled from the rod and sticks out as shown in the figure. The radioactive substance is placed on the table, and by ionizing the air under the cover, causes the electrical charge to leak away at a rate proportional to the intensity of the radiation. The gold leaf therefore collapses towards the rod, and its motion may be followed by means of a low powered microscope. Such an instrument is known as a gold leaf electroscope.

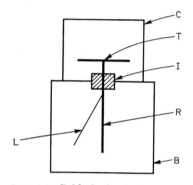

Fig. 2.1. Gold leaf electroscope, after M. Curie, 1910

With this simple equipment, Pierre and Marie Curie discovered that thorium is also radioactive. They investigated many uranium compounds and minerals and found that some of the minerals were much more strongly radioactive than pure uranium itself. This suggested that these minerals contained radioactive substances in addition to the uranium, and further investigation led to the discovery of the new elements polonium (atomic number 84) and radium (atomic number 88) in 1898. Both these elements were intensely radioactive.

B. Nature of the Radioactive Rays

Soon after the discovery of radioactivity, it was found that three kinds of radiations were emitted by the radioactive substances. These rays could be distinguished from each other in two ways, first by the difference in the ease with which the rays could pass through matter, and second by the direction in which the path of the rays was bent by the application of a magnetic field. The most easily absorbed rays were given the name α-particle. In 1903, Rutherford found that the α-particles were deflected by both electric and magnetic fields. By measuring the deflections, he was able to determine the ratio of the electric charge of the particles to their mass, as well as the velocity of the particles. The most reasonable interpretation of his observations was that the particles were atoms of helium, bearing a charge twice that of the electron, but positive rather than negative. Their velocity was about 2×10^9 cm per sec.

It was already known that helium gas is associated with radioactive minerals. In 1909, Rutherford and Royds obtained a direct experimental proof of the nature of the α-particles by the method shown in Figure 2.2. The tube T contained a sample of the radioactive gas radon, which provided the α-particles. The walls of the tube were thin enough to allow the α-particles to escape from T into the space S. By raising the level of the mercury in S, the products could be compressed into the discharge tube D and analyzed by exciting their characteristic spectra. Rutherford and Royds were able to observe the gradual appearance of the whole spectrum of ordinary helium in the discharge tube. The α-particles, therefore, are nuclei of helium. After slowing down and stopping in the glass walls of the space S, the helium nuclei capture two electrons from their surroundings, thus becoming ordinary neutral helium atoms.

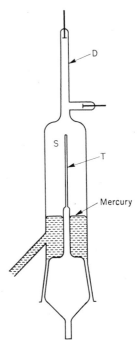

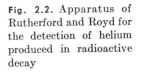

Fig. 2.2. Apparatus of Rutherford and Royd for the detection of helium produced in radioactive decay

Whereas the α-particles can be stopped by a piece of paper, the second type of radiation requires roughly 1000 times as much matter to bring it to rest. These rays were given the name β-rays. They are deflected much more readily by magnetic fields than the α-particles, but in the opposite direction. They therefore carry a negative electrical charge. The β-rays were identified by Becquerel with ordinary electrons traveling with high velocities. Many radioactive substances emit β-particles whose velocities are very close to the velocity of light.

The third type of radiation, called γ-rays, is even more penetrating than β-particles. The γ-rays emitted by some radioactive substances can only be stopped by several centimeters of lead. The rays are not deflected by magnetic or electric fields. They are electromagnetic radiations of the same kind as X-rays, light, and radio waves, but of very short wavelength. The γ-ray photons are therefore of high energy, usually between a few kilovolts and a few Mev.

Immediately after the discovery of radioactivity, it was realized that the emission of the various types of radiations must be an atomic property rather than a molecular or bulk phenomenon, because the rate of emission does not depend on the state of chemical composition of the radioactive element concerned. The appearance of helium nuclei among the rays indicates that the phenomenon probably involves the atomic nucleus. Now if a nucleus emits an α-particle, whose charge is $+2$ and whose mass is 4 on the atomic weight scale, then obviously the nucleus that remains after the event will carry two units less positive charge and four units less mass. Thus a nucleus of uranium of charge 92 and atomic weight 238 will, after the emission of a α-particle, become a nucleus of thorium (charge 90) with atomic weight 234. This transformation may be written

$$_{92}U^{238} \rightarrow {}_{90}Th^{234} + {}_{2}He^{4} + Q$$

The subscript numbers in front of the chemical symbols of the elements represent the nuclear charge (i.e. the atomic number, for which the symbol Z is used), and the superscript numbers following the chemical symbols are the atomic weights rounded off to the nearest whole number. These rounded atomic weights are called *mass numbers*. They are given the symbol A. Q represents the energy released in the transformation.

Since a β-particle is negatively charged, its emission by a nucleus will cause an increase of one unit in the nuclear positive charge Z. There will be no change in the mass number A, since the mass of the β-particle is only 0.00055 on the atomic mass scale. A typical transformation may be represented as follows:

$$_{90}Th^{234} \rightarrow {}_{91}Pa^{234} + \beta^{-} + Q$$

As we shall see later, many nuclei emit positively charged electrons (positrons). An example of such a transformation is

$$_{11}Na^{22} \rightarrow {}_{10}Ne^{22} + \beta^{+} + Q$$

It is usual to represent electrons emitted from nuclei by the symbols β^{-}

and β^+. In many cases, orbital atomic electrons are expelled from the atom as a secondary consequence of a radioactive decay process. These electrons are usually represented by the symbol e^-. They are of course exactly the same as the β^--particles emitted from nuclei, but the different symbols are useful in distinguishing the origin of the electrons.

The emission of a γ-ray produces no change in the atomic number or mass number of the nucleus, but only a decrease in its energy content. In most cases the emission of the γ-rays is a secondary consequence of either an α-decay or a β-decay. Following the initial decay, the residual nucleus is frequently left with excess energy which it subsequently emits as one or more γ-rays until it has reached its lowest energy level, which is called the *ground state*.

C. The Discovery of Isotopes

The study of the various radioactive substances present in uranium and thorium minerals showed that there were several pairs of radioactive species which were chemically indistinguishable from each other, but which differed in their radioactive decay properties. As an example of this, consider the series of radioactive decays which starts with $_{92}U^{238}$:

$$_{92}U^{238} \rightarrow {}_2He^4 + {}_{90}Th^{234} \rightarrow \beta^- + {}_{91}Pa^{234} \rightarrow \beta^- + {}_{92}U^{234} \rightarrow {}_{90}Th^{230} + {}_2He^4$$

The emission of an α-particle and then two successive β^--particles must leave a nucleus of the same charge as the initial nucleus, but four mass units lighter. If the two nuclei have the same charge, the atoms of which they are a part must have the same number and arrangement of orbital electrons. Since the electrons determine the chemical properties of the atom, these two atoms will be chemically indistinguishable except for certain extremely small effects. Such species, which have the same atomic number but differ in mass number, are called *isotopes*.

The first direct proof of the existence of isotopes came from atomic weight measurements. Both uranium and thorium, after several successive decays involving the emission of α- and β^--particles, finally turn into lead. However, it was expected that the lead obtained from uranium would have a different atomic weight from that obtained from thorium, and that both of them would be different from ordinary lead, whose atomic weight is 207.21. In 1914, Soddy and Hyman obtained a value of 207.74 for the atomic weight of lead obtained from the thorium mineral thorite. Richards and co-workers obtained a value of 206.08 for lead extracted from the uranium mineral clevite.

The first observation of isotopy in a light element, which did not involve the phenomenon of radioactivity, was made in 1912 by Thomson. His method involved the deflection of a beam of charged neon ions by magnetic and electric fields.   Measurement of the extent of the deflection permitted the calculation of e/m, the ratio of the charge of the ions to their mass.   Thomson showed that the inert gas neon contained two isotopes whose mass numbers were 20 (the more abundant) and 22.   He was able to obtain a slight separation of the two isotopes by repeatedly allowing neon to diffuse through a clay pipe.   According to the kinetic theory, the diffusion rate of a gas should be inversely proportional to the square root of its molecular weight.   Therefore the lighter isotope of neon should diffuse slightly faster than the heavier isotope.   This was exactly what was observed.   Thomson was able to obtain two neon fractions whose atomic weights were 20.15 and 20.28.   In 1919, Aston began to use a much improved magnetic and electric deflection apparatus which he called a *mass spectrograph*.   He found that many elements consist of mixtures of isotopes, whose masses are always very close to integral numbers on the atomic weight scale.   For example, the atomic weight of ordinary chlorine is 35.457 (on the chemical scale which uses oxygen = 16 as standard), but chlorine contains the two isotopes Cl^{35} (abundance 75.4% by atoms) and Cl^{37} (abundance 24.6%).   The exact masses of these two isotopes are 34.9688545 and 36.9658959.   These numbers are very close to integers, as indeed they must be if their nuclei are composed of protons and neutrons not too tightly bound together.

D. Isobars, Isotones, Isomers, and Nuclides

The term *isobar* is used to express the relationship between nuclear species which share the same mass number A but differ in atomic number Z.   For example, $_{19}K^{40}$ and $_{20}Ca^{40}$ share mass number 40, but differ by one unit in Z.   Although isobaric atoms share the same mass number, they do not have *exactly* the same mass.   Thus the mass of K^{40} is 39.9640079, while that of Ca^{40} is 39.9625892.   The difference seems slight, but as we shall see later it is very important because it is related to the difference in energy between the two atoms, and even a small mass difference corresponds to a considerable energy difference.   *Isotones* are nuclei which have the same number of neutrons but different numbers of protons.

The term *isomer* expresses the relationship between nuclei which share both the same mass number and the same atomic number.   Such nuclei differ only in their energy content.   The more energetic nucleus can decay to the less energetic nucleus by emission of energy, usually in the form of a γ-ray photon.   In most cases, the decay is extremely rapid and the existence of the more energetic nucleus is fleeting (less than 10^{-14} sec).   Such short-lived nuclei are usually called *excited states* or *metastable states*.   The term isomer is best reserved for those cases in which the more energetic nucleus has a life expectancy long enough to permit it to be observed. The dividing line between "isomer" and "metastable state" is quite nebulous.

As we have already seen, the word isotope is properly used to express a certain definite relationship between nuclei.   However, it is commonly used in a much looser sense.   Thus we often speak of "radioactive isotopes" when we really mean "radioactive nuclear species."   In this usage, the word isotope does not imply that all the species under discussion share the same atomic number, and it is therefore a misuse of the word.   To designate any nuclear species which differs from all others in any way at all, the term *nuclide* is often used.   Thus F^{19} and Ra^{226} are both nuclides, but they are not isotopic, isotonic, isobaric, or isomeric in their relationship.

E. The Kinetics of Radioactive Decay

We have already mentioned that the radioactive decay process is a property of the individual isolated nucleus.   The probability that a nucleus will decay in a certain time interval does not depend on the state of chemical combination, the temperature, pressure, or the presence of other atoms or nuclei.   (There are certain very minor exceptions to this statement when the radioactive decay involves the interaction of the nucleus with its own electron cloud.)   The probability that the nucleus will decay in a certain time interval does not depend on the age of the nucleus.   A radioactive nucleus remains unchanged, perhaps for billions of years, until it decays in one sudden act.

The rate of radioactive decay from a sample of any radioactive substance must be proportional only to the number of nuclei present, if radioactivity is a property of isolated nuclei.   In the language of chemical kinetics, the decay is a first-order reaction.   In a sample containing N nuclei, the rate of decay, $-dN/dt$, will be

$$- \frac{dN}{dt} = \lambda N \tag{2.1}$$

where λ is a constant called the decay constant.   It has a value which is characteristic of the nuclei under consideration.

Equation (2.1) can be integrated as follows:

$$\int - \frac{dN}{N} = \int \lambda \, dt$$

$$\therefore \quad - \ln N = \lambda t + \text{constant of integration} \tag{2.2}$$

To evaluate the constant, let N_0 be the number of nuclei present at some arbitrary zero time, and N the number at time t. When $t = 0$,

$$- \ln N_0 = \text{constant of integration}$$

$$\therefore \quad - \ln N = \lambda t - \ln N_0$$

$$\therefore \quad - \ln \frac{N}{N_0} = \lambda t$$

$$\therefore \quad \frac{N}{N_0} = e^{-\lambda t}$$

$$\therefore \quad N = N_0 e^{-\lambda t} \tag{2.3}$$

Thus, as in any first-order process, the number N of nuclei remaining *decreases exponentially with time.*

The characteristic decay rate of a nuclear species is usually quoted as the *half life*, which is the time required for one half of the initial number of nuclei to decay. If $t_{1/2}$ is the half life, then by substitution in equation (2.3),

$$\frac{N}{N_0} = \frac{1}{2} = e^{-\lambda t_{1/2}}$$

$$\therefore \quad t_{1/2} = \frac{(\ln 2)}{\lambda} = \frac{0.693}{\lambda} \tag{2.4}$$

The *mean life* τ of a nuclear species is $1/\lambda$ (see Problem 13).

It is often necessary to measure the half life of a radioactive substance, and there are many ways in which the measurement may be made. The method which is chosen in a particular case is usually determined by the value of the half life itself. Methods which can be used to measure half lives of many years are not suitable for half lives which are measured in microseconds.

Method 1. If some type of radiation detector is available which will measure the number of nuclei decaying per unit time, or some quantity which is proportional to that number, then by making measurements at suitable time intervals, the half life can be determined. For example, the electroscope described above will measure the amount of ionization caused by the emitted α-, β-, or γ-rays. This ionization is proportional to the number of these particles which are emitted per second, and hence it is also proportional to dN/dt. But by equation (2.1), dN/dt is proportional to N, the number of nuclei surviving at time t. Hence, according to equation (2.2), we may plot $\ln dN/dt$ against t and obtain a straight line whose slope is $-\lambda$. The value of $t_{1/2}$ may be obtained directly from the graph, by the procedure illustrated in Figure 2.3. The ordinate is the logarithm of any measurable quantity which is proportional to the number of nuclei remaining—in this case it is $\log_{10}$ (ionization intensity). We might equally well have used $\log_{10}$ (number of counts per minute)

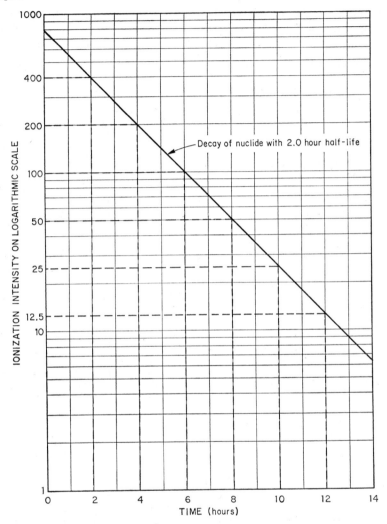

Fig. 2.3. Measurement of half-life from semi-logarithmic decay curve

recorded with some radiation detector such as a Geiger counter. The abscissa is the time at which the measurements were made. The half life may be read from the graph by determining the time at which the ionization intensity has fallen to one half of its initial value. Observe that in two half lives, the ionization intensity has fallen to one quarter of its initial value, or in three half lives to one eighth, and so on. If $\log_{10} dN/dt$ is plotted against t, the slope of the line will be $-\lambda/2.303$.

In many cases, a sample will contain two or more radioactive substances whose half lives will usually be different.　Each substance in the mixture will decay at its own characteristic rate, but if the radiation detector responds to the rays emitted by each component, then the decay curve

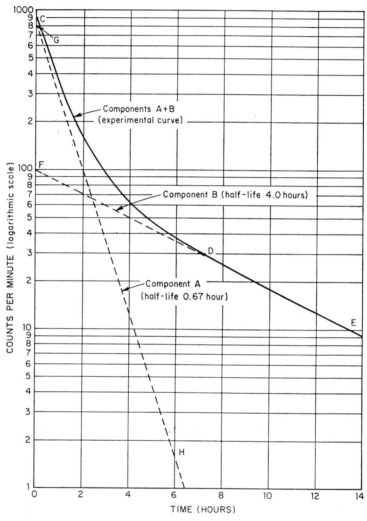

Fig. 2.4.　Resolution of complex decay curve

will no longer be a straight line.　Figure 2.4 shows the type of curve which is obtained from a mixture containing two components.　If the two half lives are sufficiently different, it may happen that the shorter-lived component A will decay almost completely while a substantial amount of the longer-lived component B still remains. The decay curve will then become a straight line (segment DE of Figure 2.4). The half life of the component B may then be measured from the slope of this line. If DE is extrapolated back to zero time, the line FD will represent the contribution of component B to the measured number of counts per minute. Hence the number of counts per minute of component B at any time may be subtracted from the number of counts per minute experimentally measured at the same time (line CD); the difference will be the number of counts per minute due to the component A. In this way the independent decay curve GH for component A may be constructed, and the half life of A determined. Note that the points G and F represent the number of counts per minute of A and B respectively at zero time.

This graphical procedure may in principle be extended to any number of components, but the resolution of the curve usually becomes very unreliable for more than three components unless their half lives differ very considerably. Of course it is useless even for two components if their half lives are nearly equal. In such a case, radiation detectors must be used which are sensitive to only one of the radiations, or which can distinguish between them.

Method 2. Accurate measurement of half lives by Method 1 will clearly fail if the half lives are so long that during the period of observation there is only a very small decrease in the quantity which is being measured. In such a case a quite different method may sometimes be used.

If the substance is available in sufficient quantity to permit its analytical determination by some suitable method, and if its atomic weight M is known, then the number of nuclei present can be calculated. It is equal to (weight of substance) $\times$ (Avogadro's Number) $\div M$. If in addition the number of nuclei decaying per unit time can be measured, then λ can be obtained from

$$\lambda = \frac{\text{Number of nuclei decaying per unit time}}{\text{Number of nuclei present}}$$

The number of nuclei decaying per unit time is of course equal to the number of particles emitted per unit time, and this is the quantity which is usually measured. Notice that in this method it is dN/dt itself which must be measured, and not just any quantity that is proportional to dN/dt as in Method 1. Such "absolute" measurements may be made fairly easily with an accuracy of 0.1% for substances which emit α-particles. The measurement of β-particles is much more difficult, and an accuracy of 1% would be considered rather satisfactory.

The number of nuclei decaying per unit time per unit weight of material present is called the *specific activity*. For a pure radioactive species, the specific activity is a function only of the half life. The shorter the half life the higher the specific activity.   If impurities are present—either other elements or other isotopes of the same element—then the specific activity will naturally depend on the quantity of these in the mixture.

F. Radioactive Equilibrium

Among the radioactive nuclides there are many examples of chains of decays in which a radioactive parent decays to a daughter which is also radioactive, and so on.   As an example, consider the sequence

$$\text{Ra}^{226} \text{ (1620 years) } \xrightarrow{\alpha} \text{Rn}^{222} \text{ (3.83 days) } \xrightarrow{\alpha} \text{Po}^{218} \text{ (3.05 min)}$$
$$\xrightarrow{\alpha} \text{Pb}^{214} \text{ (26.8 min)}$$

The numbers in parentheses are the half lives of the nuclides.

In a sample of pure Ra^{226} entirely free from Rn^{222} and the subsequent decay products, the radioactivity will naturally be entirely due to the Ra^{226} itself.   However, immediately after preparation of the sample, Rn^{222} will begin to appear.   The rate of formation of the Rn^{222} will be equal to the rate at which the Ra^{226} nuclei are decaying, and thus

$$\text{Rate of formation of Rn}^{222} = N_{\text{Ra}^{226}}\lambda_{\text{Ra}^{226}}$$

where the N and the λ are the number of nuclei and the decay constant of Ra^{226}.   But the Rn^{222} itself undergoes radioactive decay:

$$\text{Rate of decay of Rn}^{222} = N_{\text{Rn}^{222}}\lambda_{\text{Rn}^{222}}$$

Hence as the number of nuclei of Rn^{222} increases, so does the number of them that decay per unit time, until finally a state of equilibrium is reached.   The rate of formation of the Rn^{222} is then exactly equal to its rate of decay.

The number of nuclei of the parent Ra^{226} decreases with time according to the equation

$$N_{\text{Ra}^{226}} = N^0_{\text{Ra}^{226}}e^{-\lambda_{\text{Ra}^{226}}t}$$

and hence the rate of formation of Rn^{222} is

$$\text{Rate of formation of Rn}^{222} = N^0_{\text{Ra}^{226}}\lambda_{\text{Ra}^{226}}e^{-\lambda_{\text{Ra}^{226}}t}$$

Therefore at equilibrium,

$$N_{\text{Rn}^{222}}\lambda_{\text{Rn}^{222}} = N^0_{\text{Ra}^{226}}\lambda_{\text{Ra}^{226}}e^{-\lambda_{\text{Ra}^{226}}t} \tag{2.5}$$

The half life of the Ra^{226} is very long and hence $\lambda_{\text{Ra}^{226}}$ is small.   The quantity $e^{-\lambda_{\text{Ra}^{226}}t}$ will therefore be close to unity as long as the time t is not more than a few hundred years.   We can therefore simplify equation (2.5) to

$$N_{\text{Rn}^{222}}\lambda_{\text{Rn}^{222}} = N_{\text{Ra}^{226}}\lambda_{\text{Ra}^{226}}$$

or

$$\frac{N_{\text{Rn}^{222}}}{N_{\text{Ra}^{226}}} = \frac{t_{1/2}(\text{Rn}^{222})}{t_{1/2}(\text{Ra}^{226})} \tag{2.6}$$

According to equation (2.6), when radioactive equilibrium is established in a system in which the half life of the parent is much longer than that of the daughter, then the ratio of the number of nuclei of daughter present to the number of nuclei of the parent is equal to the ratio of their half lives.   Radioactive equilibrium of this type is known as *secular equilibrium*.

We must now consider how long it will take for equilibrium to be established.   To simplify the notation, we will use the symbols N_1 and λ_1 for the number of atoms and the decay constant of the parent, and N_2 and λ_2 for the daughter.   The net rate of production of the daughter, dN_2/dt, is its (rate of production) − (rate of decay), whence

$$\frac{dN_2}{dt} = (\lambda_1 N_1^0 e^{-\lambda_1 t}) - (N_2 \lambda_2) \tag{2.7}$$

This equation must now be solved for N_2, the amount of the daughter present at any time t.   Assume that the solution will be of the form

$$N_2 = u e^{-\lambda_2 t}$$

where u is some function of t.   Then differentiating this expression for N_2 with respect to t, we obtain

$$\frac{dN_2}{dt} = -u\lambda_2 e^{-\lambda_2 t} + e^{-\lambda_2 t}\frac{du}{dt}$$

Substituting for N_2 and dN_2/dt in equation (2.7),

$$-u\lambda_2 e^{-\lambda_2 t} + e^{-\lambda_2 t}\frac{du}{dt} = \lambda_1 N_1^0 e^{-\lambda_1 t} - u\lambda_2 e^{-\lambda_2 t}$$

or

$$e^{-\lambda_2 t}\frac{du}{dt} = \lambda_1 N_1^0 e^{-\lambda_1 t}$$

or

$$\frac{du}{dt} = \lambda_1 N_1^0 e^{-(\lambda_1 - \lambda_2)t}$$

$$\therefore \quad u = \frac{\lambda_1}{\lambda_2 - \lambda_1} N_1^0 e^{-(\lambda_1 - \lambda_2)t} + C$$

$$\therefore \quad N_2 = u e^{-\lambda_2 t} = \frac{\lambda_1 N_1^0}{\lambda_2 - \lambda_1} e^{-\lambda_1 t} + C e^{-\lambda_2 t}$$

The constant C may be evaluated by the condition that the amount of the daughter shall be N_2^0 at $t = 0$.   Then

$$N_2^0 = \frac{\lambda_1 N_1^0}{\lambda_2 - \lambda_1} + C$$

$$\therefore \quad N_2 = \frac{\lambda_1 N_1^0}{\lambda_2 - \lambda_1} \left(e^{-\lambda_1 t} - e^{-\lambda_2 t} \right) + N_2^0 e^{-\lambda_2 t} \tag{2.8}$$

If the amount of the daughter is initially zero, then of course the last term in equation (2.8) vanishes.

For a case such as Ra^{226} and Rn^{222}, $\lambda_2 \gg \lambda_1$, and $e^{-\lambda_1 t} \simeq 1$.   Equation (2.8) therefore simplifies to

$$N_2 = \frac{\lambda_1 N_1^0}{\lambda_2} \left(1 - e^{-\lambda_2 t} \right) \tag{2.9}$$

This equation gives the amount of the daughter which has "grown in" at any time t.   It can be put into a very convenient form by expressing this amount as a fraction of the final equilibrium amount.   From equation (2.6), the equilibrium amount will be

$$N_2^{\text{equil}} = N_1^0 \frac{\lambda_1}{\lambda_2}$$

Therefore at any time t,

$$\frac{N_2}{N_2^{\text{equil}}} = \left(1 - e^{-\lambda_2 t} \right) \tag{2.10}$$

Substitution of values of t into this equation shows that, if there is initially no daughter present, then after a lapse of time equal to one half life of the daughter, one half of the final equilibrium amount will be present.   After two half lives, three quarters of the equilibrium amount will be present, and so on.   Figure 2.5 shows the growth of Rn^{222} in initially pure Ra^{226}, for a case where the final equilibrium amount of the Rn^{222} is 800 counts per minute.

Equations (2.9) and (2.10) are valid only for the special case where $\lambda_2 \gg \lambda_1$, since we made this assumption in their derivation.   Observe that the rate of approach towards the equilibrium depends only on the half life of the daughter, but that the amount of daughter present at equilibrium depends on the ratio of the half lives of parent and daughter, as well as on the amount of parent present.

Now return to consider the general equation (2.8), in which there are no restrictions on the values of λ_1 and λ_2.   If $\lambda_2 > \lambda_1$, but not so much greater that we can ignore the decay of the parent during the growth of the daughter, then the situation is called *transient equilibrium*.   Figure 2.6 shows the growth and decay of a daughter whose half life is 1 hour from a parent whose half life is 10 hours.   The amount of the daughter at first increases, then reaches a maximum, and finally decreases at the same rate as the parent with which it is in transient equilibrium.

Figure 2.7 shows the growth and decay of a daughter which has a half life of 2 hours from a parent whose half life is 1 hour. In this case, the parent and daughter are never in equilibrium. The amount of daughter present still shows a maximum, but it finally decays away at a rate characteristic of its own half life rather than that of its parent.

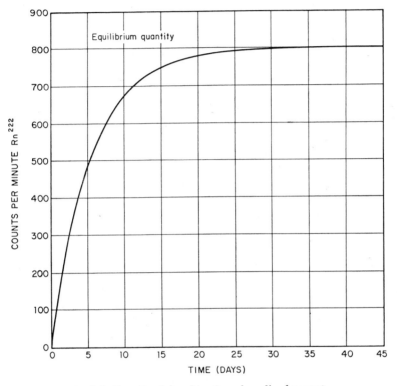

Fig. 2.5. Growth of daughter from long-lived parent

Equations similar to (2.8) may be derived for the growth and decay of the third or later members of a decay sequence. The general solution for the number of nuclei of the nth product at time t, N_n, is

$$N_n = C_1 e^{-\lambda_1 t} + C_2 e^{-\lambda_2 t} + C_3 e^{-\lambda_3 t} + \cdots C_n e^{-\lambda_n t} \qquad (2.11)$$

where

$$C_1 = \frac{\lambda_1 \lambda_2 \lambda_3 \cdots \lambda_{n-1} N_1^0}{(\lambda_2 - \lambda_1)(\lambda_3 - \lambda_1) \cdots (\lambda_n - \lambda_1)}$$

$$C_2 = \frac{\lambda_1 \lambda_2 \lambda_3 \cdots \lambda_{n-1} N_1^0}{(\lambda_1 - \lambda_2)(\lambda_3 - \lambda_2) \cdots (\lambda_n - \lambda_2)}$$

$$C_3 = \frac{\lambda_1 \lambda_2 \lambda_3 \cdots \lambda_{n-1} N_1^0}{(\lambda_1 - \lambda_3)(\lambda_2 - \lambda_3)(\lambda_4 - \lambda_3) \cdots (\lambda_n - \lambda_3)}$$

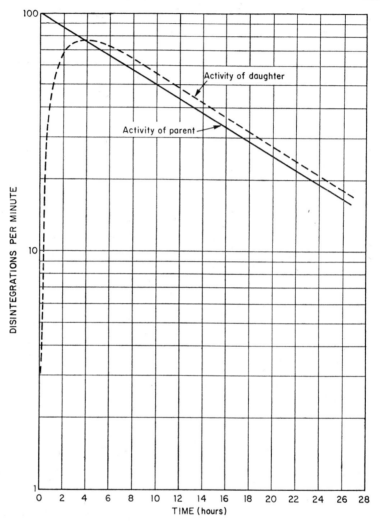

Fig. 2.6. Growth and decay of daughter in transient equilibrium with parent

and so on. This solution was first obtained by Bateman in 1910. Calculations by the use of equation (2.11) become very tedious for systems of several components, but digital or analog electronic computers are sometimes used. The discharge of a condenser through a resistance is exponential, and therefore makes a simple electrical analog for the radioactive decay process. The amount of charge lost by the condenser represents the amount of the daughter formed, and this charge may itself be stored

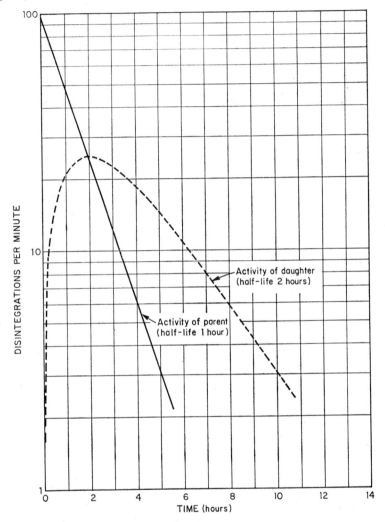

Fig. 2.7. Growth and decay of daughter from short-lived parent

in a second condenser which is discharging through a second resistance to represent the decay of the daughter, and so on.

G. Branching Decay

Many nuclei are unstable to decay by more than one mode. For example, Cs^{130} decays with a total half life of 30 min by the emission of both positive and negative electrons in the ratio of 27.5 positive to 1 negative electron. To each mode of decay we may assign a partial decay constant. The overall decay constant will then be the sum of all the partial decay constants

$$\lambda_{total} = \lambda_1 + \lambda_2 + \cdots + \lambda_n \tag{2.12}$$

The partial half lives for the different decay modes are related to the partial decay constants by the equations

$$t_{1/2}(n) = \frac{(\log_e 2)}{\lambda_n} \tag{2.13}$$

The fraction of the decays which occur by a given mode will be

$$\text{Fraction decaying by } n\text{th mode} = \frac{\lambda_n}{\lambda_{total}} \tag{2.14}$$

For Cs^{130}, λ_{total} will be 3.85×10^{-4} sec^{-1}, and since the fraction decaying by β^--emission is $1/28.5$, λ_{β^-}, from equation (2.14), will be $(3.85 \times 10^{-4}) \div 28.5$, or 1.35×10^{-5} sec^{-1}. The partial β^--decay half life will, from equation (2.13), be 14.3 hours.

H. Units of Radioactive Intensity

A sample of any radioactive substance which is decaying at the rate of 3.700×10^{10} disintegrations per second is said to contain one curie of the substance. Originally, the curie was supposed to represent the rate of decay of 1 gm of Ra^{226}. However, the value of the unit then depended on the accuracy with which the half life of radium could be measured. Therefore, in 1950, the definition was changed to its present form, which contains no reference to the properties of radium. 10^{-3} and 10^{-6} curies are called the millicurie and microcurie respectively. 10^6 curies is called 1 megacurie.

The unit is commonly used in medical practice, and in the sale and purchase of radioactive substances. Unfortunately, attempts to introduce a more sensible unit have not been successful.

While physicists usually express decay or counting rates in terms of disintegrations or counts per second, chemists usually use the minute as the unit of time. In this unit, one curie is 2.22×10^{12} disintegrations per minute.

REFERENCES

1. Rutherford, E., *Radioactive Substances and Their Radiations*, Cambridge University Press, Cambridge, 1910.

2. Curie, M., *Traité de Radioactivité*, Paris, 1910.

3. Curie, Mme. P., *Radioactivité*, Hermann et Cie., Paris, 1935.

4. Rutherford, E., J. Chadwick, and C. D. Ellis, *Radiations from Radioactive Substances*, Cambridge University Press, Cambridge, 1930.

5. Segrè, E. (ed.), *Experimental Nuclear Physics*, John Wiley & Sons, New York, 1959: Vol. III/8, E. Segrè, "Radioactive Decay."

PROBLEMS

1. The decay of a radioactive sample is measured with a counter. The results are as follows:

Time after starting experiment, hr	Observed disintegrations per min
0	173
6	115
10	85
17	58
24	48
30	40
40	27
50	20
60	19
84	10
90	9
100	6.6
120	4.0

Plot these results on semilogarithmic paper and evaluate the half lives of the substances present. How many disintegrations of each was present at time zero?

2. In an experiment designed to produce a new isotope, the amount obtained might be as low as $10\beta^-$ disintegrations per minute. To how many grams of the isotope does this correspond, if its half life is 1 hour and its mass number is 120?

3. Ra^{226} (half life 1622 years) decays to produce Rn^{222}, which itself is radioactive (half life 3.825 days). A sample containing 10^{-3} gm of Ra^{226} was purified completely from its Rn^{222} daughter, and then left undisturbed for 24 hours. How much Rn^{222} was present at this time, measured in (a) disintegrations per minute (b) weight?

4. U^{239} decays with a half life of 23.5 min to produce Np^{239}, which in turn decays with a half life of 2.33 days to produce Pu^{239}. The half life of Pu^{239} is 2.436×10^4 years.

(a) If a pure sample of U^{239} contains 10^{10} disintegrations per minute, how many disintegrations per minute of Pu^{239} will be present at the end of a few weeks?

(b) How many grams of Pu^{239} does this represent?

5. The half life of Na^{22} is 2.58 years. It decays either by the emission of positive electrons or by the capture into the nucleus of a negative electron from an atomic orbit, with a ratio of 89% positive electron emission to 11% electron cap-

ture.   Calculate the partial decay constant and half life for each of the modes of decay.

6. Calculate the number of grams and the number of radioactive atoms contained in one millicurie of (a) Na^{24} (b) P^{32} (c) Ra^{226}.

7. A uranium ore contains 1% by weight of U^{238}.   What weight of Ra^{226} would be found in 1000 kg of the ore if the Ra^{226} is in radioactive equilibrium with the U^{238}?

8. P^{32} decays with a half life of 14.22 days to form S^{32}.   If 1 curie of pure P^{32} is stored for one day, what weight of S^{32} will it then contain?

9. Radioactive C^{14} is produced in the earth's atmosphere as a result of bombardment with cosmic rays from outer space.   The radioactive carbon is taken up by living things, with the result that they contain 10 disintegrations per minute of C^{14} per gm of carbon.   On their death, this C^{14} decays with a half life of 5568 years, and no fresh C^{14} is absorbed.   Carbon derived from wood taken from an Egyptian tomb proved to have a C^{14} content of 7.62 disintegrations per minute per gm.   What was the age of the tomb?

10. A freshly purified radioactive substance showed an initial counting rate of 4000 counts per minute.   The activity at intervals of time thereafter was as follows:

Time, hr	Activity, counts/min
0	4000
2	4440
4	4800
8	5430
16	6340
24	6930
40°	7550
60	7850

Determine graphically the half life of the daughter substance which is "growing in."

11. A sample of plutonium consists of Pu^{239} and Pu^{240} in unknown proportions. The specific activity was found to be 1.72×10^8 disintegrations per minute per milligram.   What is the composition of the sample?   The half lives of Pu^{239} and Pu^{240} are 2.436×10^4 years and 6.58×10^3 years respectively.

12. Calculate the total energy released (in calories) during the complete decay of 1 curie of Co^{60}.   The energy released in each decay event is 2.82 Mev.

13. Prove that the average life of the nuclei in a radioactive substance (the mean life τ) is given by $\tau = 1/\lambda$.   *Hint:*

$$\tau = \frac{\int_{t=0}^{\infty} [(\text{Number of nuclei reaching age } t \text{ and then decaying in time } dt) \times t]}{(\text{Initial number of nuclei})}$$

CHAPTER 3

Nuclear Masses and
Nuclear Stability

A. Mass Scales

It is very convenient to measure the masses of atoms on a relative scale. (If masses of individual atoms are expressed in grams, the numbers are inconveniently small.) Unfortunately, three relative atomic mass scales are in use. In the *chemical scale*, the mass of naturally occurring oxygen is taken to be exactly 16. This was a very convenient scale to use when atomic weights were measured by chemical methods. However, when this scale was chosen, it was not known that natural oxygen consists of a mixture of three isotopes, whose abundances in ordinary air are: O^{16} 99.759%, O^{17} 0.037%, O^{18} 0.204%. For very precise work, the use of such a mixture as a standard substance is always danger-ous, since the composition of a mixture may vary. In fact the O^{18} content is somewhat variable. It may be as low as 0.198% in river water and as high as 0.208% in carbon dioxide.

These difficulties were avoided in the *physical scale* by the choice of the single isotope O^{16} as the standard substance whose mass is exactly 16 by definition. The standard substance of the physical scale is thus slightly lighter than that of the chemical scale, and physical scale atomic masses are therefore numerically slightly greater. The ratio of the O^{16} physical scale to the chemical scale is 1.000278.

In 1960, the International Union of Pure and Applied Physics changed the standard substance of the physical scale from O^{16} to C^{12}, whose mass is taken to be exactly 12 by definition. The main reason for the change was the greater convenience of C^{12} in the experimental measurement of atomic masses in mass spectrometers (Chapter 13). The ratio between the O^{16} and C^{12} scales is 0.99968218. We shall use the C^{12} physical scale (see Appendix II), but care must be used because many published mass tables are based on the old O^{16} scale.

The masses of nuclei are naturally slightly less than the masses of the atoms of which they form a part. The mass difference is mainly due to the electron masses. Although we shall be primarily interested in the masses of nuclei rather than of atoms, it is customary to express all mass values as *atomic masses*, including the mass contribution of the atomic electrons.

B. Relation Between Mass and Energy

The masses of nuclei or atoms are chiefly of interest to us because of the intimate relationship between mass and energy which was discovered by Einstein. According to the special theory of relativity, the mass of a body moving with velocity v is

$$m = \frac{m_0}{\left(1 - \dfrac{v^2}{c^2}\right)^{1/2}} \tag{3.1}$$

where m_0 is its mass when it is at rest, and c is the velocity of light (2.998×10^{10} cm per sec). The fraction v/c is usually given the symbol β.

According to equation (3.1), the mass of a body is not constant but depends on the velocity of the body relative to the observer who is meas-uring the mass. This result is in complete disagreement with Newtonian mechanics, in which it was assumed that the mass of a body was constant. Notice, however, that for very small values of v relative to the velocity of light, m becomes equal to m_0.   For bodies in rapid motion, the equations of relativity must be used in place of Newton's laws.

The mass of a body increases with velocity, becoming infinite when $v = c$.   It is impossible to accelerate a body to a velocity greater than c, because the infinite mass at $v = c$ would require an infinite force to produce any further increase in velocity.   In particle accelerators such as cyclotrons, the particles often reach velocities which are very close to the velocity of light, and the large mass increase causes considerable complication in the design of the machines.

The kinetic energy T of a moving body is given by the equation

$$T = m_0 c^2 \left(\frac{1}{\sqrt{1 - \beta^2}} - 1 \right) = (m - m_0)c^2 \qquad (3.2)$$

For small values of β, this equation reduces to the familiar form $T = \frac{1}{2}mv^2$. According to equation (3.2), increasing the energy of a body automatically produces an increase in its mass, and the energy and mass changes are related by the equation

$$\text{Increase in energy} = (\text{Increase in mass}) \times c^2 \qquad (3.3)$$

Equation (3.3) is more familiar in the form $E = mc^2$.   This result actually applies to any form of energy, not only to kinetic energy.

For example, when an exothermic chemical reaction takes place with liberation of the heat of reaction ΔH, the total mass of the products must be less than the mass of the reactants by the amount $\Delta H/c^2$.   This at first sight appears to be contrary to experience, but c^2 is a very large number, so that even for very exothermic reactions, the change in mass is far too small to be measured even with the most sensitive balances.

Nuclear transformations involve energy changes that are about 10^6 times larger than those found in chemical reactions, and the mass changes are therefore quite easy to detect and measure.

C. The Mass Excess

If the masses of atoms can be measured accurately enough, then it is possible to use equation (3.3) to calculate the total amount of energy with which the nucleus is bound together.   As an example, consider the atom O^{16}.   It consists of eight neutrons, eight protons, and eight electrons, and on the C^{12} physical scale its atomic mass is 15.99491494.   The mass of a neutron is 1.00866544, and that of a hydrogen atom (i.e., a proton plus an electron), is 1.00782522; eight neutrons and eight hydrogen atoms together have a mass of 16.13192528.   The mass of O^{16} is therefore deficient by 16.13192528 − 15.99491494) or 0.13701034 mass units. This deficiency represents the quantity of energy which would be released if an atom of O^{16} were synthesized from its constituents.   This energy is called the *total binding energy* of the O^{16} atom, because it is a measure of how strongly the components of the atom are held together.   Since one mass unit (C^{12} physical scale) is equal to 931.4 Mev, the total binding energy of O^{16} is 0.13701034 $\times$ 931.4 or 127.6 Mev.   It is important to remember that in the "synthesis" of an O^{16} atom, all but a very small part

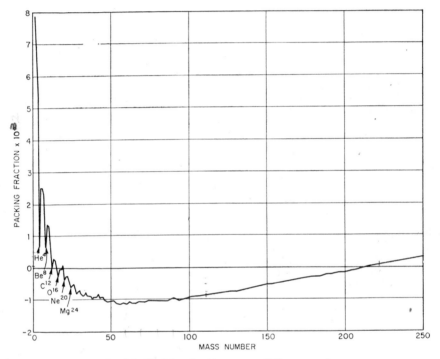

Fig. 3.1. Packing fraction curve, C^{12} mass scale

of this energy comes from the formation of the nucleus itself.   The binding energy of the atomic electrons is trivial.   For oxygen, it amounts to about 1 kev.

A quantity related to the total binding energy of the atom is the *binding energy per nucleon*.   This is the total binding energy divided by the total number of neutrons and protons (collectively known as nucleons) in the nucleus.   For O^{16}, it is (127.6 ÷ 16) or 7.97 Mev.   The total binding energy and the binding energy per nucleon may be readily calculated from the atomic masses listed in Appendix II.

For any atom of mass M, the total binding energy in mass units is $M - (ZM_H + NM_N)$, where Z and N are the numbers of protons and neutrons respectively in the nucleus, and M_H and M_N are the masses respectively of the hydrogen atom and the neutron. A quantity closely related to the total binding energy is the *mass excess*, which is defined as $M - (Z + N)$, or $M - A$. For O^{16}, for example, the mass excess given in Appendix II is -0.00508506 mass units. The mass excess is closely related to the total binding energy, but it has the advantage that it is easier to calculate. Appendix II is a table of mass excess values in units of both kilovolts and μu ($1\ \mu$u $= 10^{-6}$ atomic mass units). The standard substance is C^{12}.

A further quantity is the *packing fraction* which is related to the mass excess as the binding energy per nucleon is related to the total binding energy. It is defined as $(M - A)/A$—i.e., the mass excess per nucleon. It is a convenient quantity to use as a measure of the average energy with which the nucleons are bound together in the nucleus. A large packing fraction value means that the nucleons are loosely bound.

The packing fraction varies in an interesting way with the mass number A, as shown in Figure 3.1. The main feature of the curve is the broad minimum in the region of $A = 60$. For higher A values, the packing fraction rises slowly, indicating that the nucleons are less tightly bound. This effect is due to the mutual Coulomb repulsion of the protons in the nucleus. The higher the value of Z (and hence of A), the greater is the effect of this repulsion in reducing the stability of the nucleus. Superimposed on the smooth packing fraction curve are sharp minima for the nuclei He^4, Be^8, C^{12}, O^{16}, and Ne^{20}. These nuclei possess greater stability than their neighbors, and as we shall see, the packing fraction curve is one of the many pieces of evidence for the existence of filled shells of nucleons analogous to the stable, inert-gas, filled shells of atomic electrons.

D. Mass and Stability

Strictly speaking, a stable nucleus is one which cannot spontaneously decay or change in any way whatsoever. However, it is convenient to define a more limited type of stability, by specifying with respect to which type of change the nucleus is stable. Thus U^{238} is unable to decay spontaneously by emission of β^- or β^+ particles to give Np^{238} or Pa^{238} respectively. In either process, energy would have to be supplied to the system in order to bring about the change. Therefore U^{238} is said to be β-stable. However, it is not stable with respect to other types of decay, since it can emit α-particles, forming Th^{234}. This process is exothermic to the extent of 4.27 Mev per nucleus, almost all the energy appearing as kinetic energy of the α-particle. U^{238} can also spontaneously disintegrate into two smaller nuclei of roughly equal size (spontaneous fission), and this type of decay takes place with the liberation of about 200 Mev of energy.

Actually, all the nuclides in the heavier half of the periodic table are in principle unstable with respect to α-decay, but very few nuclei lighter than Pb^{208} are in fact observed to decay in this manner. Failure to observe a change does not always mean that a system is thermodynamically stable—it may only mean that the change is taking place too slowly to be observed, perhaps because a large activation energy is involved. For example, a mixture of hydrogen and oxygen gases at room temperature will remain apparently unchanged for a long period of time, and yet the mixture is not thermodynamically stable with respect to the formation of water.

When accurate mass values are available, they may be used to provide a precise definition of stability. If a nuclear transformation is exothermic, then the total mass of all the products must be less than the total initial mass. A few examples will help to clarify this statement.

Consider the nucleus Na^{22}. Its atomic mass is 21.994435. The mass of eleven neutrons and eleven hydrogen atoms would be 22.18139726, and since this is greater than the mass of Na^{22} by 0.187 mass units, or 174 Mev, then Na^{22} cannot spontaneously disintegrate into neutrons and hydrogen atoms. 174 Mev would have to be supplied from an external source of energy. If Na^{22} emitted an α-particle, the products of the reaction would be He^4 and F^{18}, whose masses add up to 22.0035535, which is more than the mass of Na^{22} by 0.009118 mass units, or 8.49 Mev. Therefore the spontaneous emission of an α-particle is not possible. The mass of Ne^{22} is 21.9913845, which is less than the mass of Na^{22}, so that if Na^{22} could find a way to transform itself into Ne^{22}, the process should be exothermic. This transformation does in fact occur in two different ways, and we shall consider the energetics of these decays in Section E.

It must again be emphasized that just because a process is energetically possible we cannot conclude that it will take place at a measurable rate. However, if it is energetically *impossible*, then it is certain that the process will not occur spontaneously at all. As an example of a decay which is energetically possible but is not actually observed, consider the α-decay of W^{182}, whose mass is 181.94647. The combined masses of the products, He^4 and Hf^{178}, would be 181.94509, which is less than the mass of W^{182}. The process is not in fact observed to occur, presumably because the half life of W^{182} is so long that the number of α-particles emitted per minute from samples of a reasonable size is below the limits for detection with present techniques.

E. Beta-Decay Energies

The use of atomic masses to calculate the energies available for β-decay processes sometimes causes a certain amount of confusion.

Consider first the β^--decay process, of which Na^{24} provides a suitable example.   The atomic mass of Na^{24} is 23.9909669.   This mass, of course, includes the mass of the Na^{24} nucleus and of the eleven atomic electrons. Na^{24} decays by emission of a negative electron (β^--particle) to form Mg^{24}, whose atomic mass is 23.9850446.   This mass includes the mass of the Mg^{24} nucleus plus the mass of the twelve atomic electrons.   However, when a nucleus of Na^{24} decays, the product must be Mg^{24} with only the eleven atomic electrons originally present.   The β^--particle itself escapes from the vicinity of the Mg^{24} nucleus, so that the product is the ion Mg^+. At first glance it would seem that, since a complete neutral Mg^{24} atom is not formed in the β^--decay, it is not proper to use the atomic mass of Mg^{24} to calculate the energy available for the decay process.   However, although the Mg^{24} has one electron missing, the system as a whole does not: the β^--particle itself makes up the deficiency.   The overall transformation may then be written

$$\underbrace{Na^{24} \text{ nucleus} + 11 \text{ electrons}}_{\text{Mass} = Na^{24} \text{ atomic mass}} \rightarrow \underbrace{Mg^{24} \text{ nucleus} + 11 \text{ electrons}}_{\text{Mass} = Mg^{24} \text{ atomic mass}} + 1 \beta^-$$

$$+ \text{ Energy}$$

The energy available for the β^--decay process is therefore just the mass difference between the initial and final atoms:

$$E(\beta^-) = (\text{Mass } Na^{24}) - (\text{Mass } Mg^{24}) = 0.005922 \text{ mass units} = 5.5 \text{ Mev}$$

Next consider the β^+-decay process, taking the decay of Na^{22} to Ne^{22} as an example.   The product in this case is an element of lower atomic number, so that one of the eleven electrons of the Na^{22} will be superfluous. The reaction may be written thus:

$$\underbrace{Na^{22} \text{ nucleus} + 11 \text{ electrons}}_{\text{Mass} = Na^{22} \text{ atomic mass}} \rightarrow \underbrace{Ne^{22} \text{ nucleus} + 10 \text{ electrons}}_{\text{Mass} = Ne^{22} \text{ atomic mass}}$$

$$+ 1 \text{ electron} + 1 \beta^+ + \text{ Energy}$$

The energy available for the transformation will be, as usual, the difference in mass between the initial and the final system.   In this case, the energy is

$$E(\beta^+) = (\text{Mass } Na^{22}) - (\text{Mass } Ne^{22} + \text{Mass 1 electron} + \text{Mass } \beta^+)$$

The masses of the positive and negative electron are each equivalent to 0.511 Mev, so that the energy may be written

$$E(\beta^+) = (\text{Mass } Na^{22} - \text{Mass } Ne^{22}) \times 931.4 - 2 \times 0.511 \text{ Mev}$$

Thus the energy available for β^+-decay is less than the atomic mass difference by 1.022 Mev, and unless the mass difference exceeds this amount, the emission of a positron is energetically impossible.

There is a third type of β-decay process which we now meet for the first time. Many nuclei decay by capturing an atomic electron from one of the shells close to the nucleus instead of emitting a positron. The effect of capturing a negative electron into the nucleus is to reduce the (positive) nuclear charge by one unit, and of course the emission of a positron from the nucleus would have the same effect. Hence the result of either electron capture or β^+-decay is to form a nucleus the same in mass number but one unit lower in atomic number than the initial nucleus. Electron capture is classified as a β-decay, since, like the other two types, it involves the interaction between the nucleus and an electron. Many nuclei decay by both electron capture and positron emission. Na^{22}, for example, decays 89% by positron emission and 11% by electron capture (EC). The product is Ne^{22} in both cases. There is a difference, however, in the energy balance. By capturing one of its own electrons, the Na^{22} transforms itself into an atom of Ne^{22} with just the required ten atomic electrons. One electron has disappeared from the system, and we can represent the transformation thus:

$$\underbrace{Na^{22}\text{ nucleus} + 11\text{ electrons}}_{\text{Mass} = Na^{22}\text{ atomic mass}} \rightarrow \underbrace{Ne^{22}\text{ nucleus} + 10\text{ electrons}}_{\text{Mass} = Ne^{22}\text{ atomic mass}} + \text{Energy}$$

The energy available is therefore just equal to the difference between the two atomic masses:

$$E(\text{EC}) = (\text{Mass } Na^{22} - \text{Mass } Ne^{22}) \times 931.4 \text{ Mev}$$

To summarize, the difference between the two atomic masses is equal to the energy available for the transformation in both the electron capture and β^--decay processes. For β^+-decay, the energy available is less than the mass difference by two electron masses, or 1.022 Mev. The 1.022 Mev is "locked up" as the mass of one positive and one negative electron. Actually, it reappears as energy after a short delay, because the positron comes to rest and then annihilates itself with a negative electron. Both the particles disappear and their mass is converted into the energy of a pair of photons of 0.511 Mev each.

F. Proton-Neutron Ratio

We now consider the way in which the ratio of the number of protons to the number of neutrons in a nucleus affects the mass of the nucleus, and therefore affects the types of decay which the nucleus may undergo.

There is a very convenient diagram by means of which it is possible to display certain nuclear properties and to relate them to the proton and neutron numbers. This diagram, which is called a Segrè Chart, is included in the back of the book.   The proton number Z is plotted vertically, and the neutron number N horizontally.   Each nuclide is represented by a square large enough to contain a brief summary of some of its properties.   Thus in any horizontal row, all the nuclides share the same value of Z and are isotopic.   In any vertical column, they share the same value of N and are isotonic.   Shaded squares represent nuclides which are stable to all types of β-decay (i.e., β^+, β^-, and electron capture).

A very important regularity in nuclear properties appears in almost every horizontal row.   For a given value of Z, the lighter isotopes are found to decay by either positron emission or by electron capture (or both).   One or more isotopes of intermediate mass number are stable, and the heaviest isotopes decay by β^--emission.   This typical behavior may be observed anywhere on the chart, but its simplicity is confused in the elements heavier than lead by the appearance of α-decay.   On the Segrè chart, the β-stable nuclides are joined together by a line which is called the stability line, or the line of maximum stability.   Almost all the β^+- and electron capture nuclides lie to the left of the line, and almost all the β^--emitters to the right of the line.

It appears, then, that for a given proton number, a nucleus must contain a number of neutrons lying within rather close limits in order to be β-stable.   If the nucleus contains too many neutrons, it takes steps to reduce the neutron-proton ratio by emitting a β^--particle, which transforms a neutron into a proton.   If the initial nucleus has Z protons and mass number A, the neutron-proton ratio will be $(A - Z)/Z$, and after the emission of the β^--particle, the ratio becomes $(A - Z - 1)/(Z + 1)$.   The latter ratio is smaller than the former for any values of A and Z.

If the initial nucleus is deficient in neutrons, decay by β^+-emission or by electron capture will change the neutron-proton ratio from $(A - Z)/Z$ to the larger value $(A - Z + 1)/(Z - 1)$.

Inspection of the chart shows that for the nuclides lighter than $_{20}Ca^{40}$, the stability line consistently runs through nuclides whose proton and neutron numbers are nearly *equal*.   This ratio therefore represents the most stable arrangement for light elements.   Among the heavier elements, the increasing nuclear charge tends to repel the protons, so that they are less tightly bound.   The most stable arrangement therefore tends to contain relatively more neutrons than protons.   In the region of uranium, for example, the stability line passes through U^{235}, which contains 143 neutrons and only 92 protons.

Since the nuclides which lie on the line of stability are the most stable, they must also be the lightest isobars.   This point may be illustrated by considering the masses of a series of isobars such as Se^{83}, Br^{83}, Kr^{83}, Rb^{83} and Sr^{83}.   Such a series is represented in the Segrè chart as a diagonal line crossing the line of stability almost at a right angle.   In this series of isobars, the following decays occur:

$$_{34}\mathrm{Se}^{83} \xrightarrow{\beta^-} {}_{35}\mathrm{Br}^{83} \xrightarrow{\beta^-} {}_{36}\mathrm{Kr}^{83}\ (\text{stable}) \xleftarrow{\text{EC}} {}_{37}\mathrm{Rb}^{83} \xleftarrow{\text{EC},\beta^+} {}_{38}\mathrm{Sr}^{83}$$

Since the Se^{83} decays to Br^{83}, and Br^{83} to stable Kr^{83}, their masses must decrease in the order $\mathrm{Se}^{83} > \mathrm{Br}^{83} > \mathrm{Kr}^{83}$. On the other side, the masses must decrease in the order $\mathrm{Sr}^{83} > \mathrm{Rb}^{83} > \mathrm{Kr}^{83}$, and thus Kr^{83} is the lightest isobar of mass number 83.

If both members of a pair of adjacent isobars were β-stable, we should be forced to conclude that they were exactly equal in mass. An exact identity is extremely unlikely, and in fact there are only two pairs of apparently stable adjacent isobars: $(_{48}\mathrm{Cd}^{113},\ _{49}\mathrm{In}^{113})$ and $(_{51}\mathrm{Sb}^{123},\ _{52}\mathrm{Te}^{123})$. One member of each pair is almost certainly unstable with respect to β-decay into its partner, but in each case the half life for the decay is expected to be too long to permit experimental detection of the radiations.

The total binding energy (or stability) of a nucleus is affected not only by the ratio of the proton and neutron numbers, but also by whether these numbers are even or odd. It is convenient to use terms such as "even-odd" to describe nuclei. The first adjective describes the proton number, and the second the neutron number. Thus $_{90}\mathrm{Th}^{234}$ is of the even-even type, $_{11}\mathrm{Na}^{23}$ is odd-even, $_{50}\mathrm{Sn}^{123}$ is even-odd, and $_{91}\mathrm{Pa}^{234}$ is odd-odd. The most stable nuclides are of the even-even type; the least stable are odd-odd. Even-odd and odd-even nuclei are about equally stable, and intermediate between the other two types. Notice that even-odd and odd-even nuclei must have odd A, while the other two types must have even A.

The simplest evidence for the effect of odd-even character on nuclear stability comes from counting the numbers of β-stable nuclides of each type which are known. The results of such a count are shown in Table 3.1. The four odd-odd nuclides are $_1\mathrm{H}^2$, $_3\mathrm{Li}^6$, $_5\mathrm{B}^{10}$, and $_7\mathrm{N}^{14}$; there are no β-stable odd-odd nuclides heavier than these.

TABLE 3.1. Frequency of Occurence of Nuclear Types

Nuclear type	Number of β-stable nuclides
Even-Even	201
Even-Odd	69
Odd-Even	61
Odd-Odd	4

The numbers in Table 3.1 may be explained by the important assumption that energy is released (and thus stability is increased) when two nucleons of the same type join together to form a pair. In even-even nuclei, all the nucleons of both types can be paired off. In even-odd and odd-even types, there must be one nucleon which has no partner. The great instability of the odd-odd nuclei suggests that the nucleon pairing does not take place between a neutron and a proton. If it did, there would be no reason why the stability of odd-odd nuclei should not be as great as even-even nuclei.

G. Semiempirical Mass and Binding Energy Equation

The masses of many atoms have been measured by mass spectroscopic and other methods, but there are many atomic species whose masses have not, and perhaps cannot be measured, for example because their half lives are so short. It is therefore useful to be able to calculate the masses of atomic species for which no measurements exist. A method for making this type of calculation was devised by von Weizsacker in 1935. Since there exists no detailed nuclear theory which will permit the calculation to be made accurately from first principles, it is necessary to resort to plausible equations containing constants which can be adjusted to give a good fit to the mass values which have been measured experimentally. Such equations are called "semiempirical" because the constants must be adjusted. The "semi" implies that the form of the equations is at least theoretically plausible.

With suitable values for the constants a, b, c, d and e, the atomic mass of the atom with mass number A and atomic number Z can be calculated from an equation of the type

$$M(Z,A) = (A - Z)M_N + ZM_H$$
$$- aA + bA^{2/3} + \frac{cZ^2}{A^{1/3}} + \frac{d(A - 2Z)^2}{A} - \frac{e}{A} \quad (3.4)$$

M_N and M_H are the masses of the neutron and the hydrogen atom respectively. The last constant e must be given a value which depends on the odd-even character of the nucleus. For even-even nuclei, the value is positive, for even-odd and odd-even nuclei it is zero, while for odd-odd nuclei it is negative.

The total binding energy E_b is usually of greater interest than the atomic mass. Since E_b is given by

$$E_b = [ZM_H + (A - Z)M_N - M(Z,A)] \times 931.4 \text{ Mev}$$

equation (3.4) may be rewritten to permit the direct calculation of E_b values:

$$E_b(Z,A) = aA - bA^{2/3} - \frac{cZ^2}{A^{1/3}} - \frac{d(A - 2Z)^2}{A} + \frac{e}{A} \quad (3.5)$$

The constants can be evaluated by comparing the equation with experimental results, but unfortunately no one set of values for the constants gives a satisfactory fit over the whole range of A values. For values of $A > 80$, the following equation yields fairly satisfactory values of E_b in Mev:

$$E_b(Z,A) = 14.1A - 13A^{2/3} - \frac{0.6Z^2}{A^{1/3}} - \frac{20(A - 2Z)^2}{A} \pm \frac{125}{A} \quad (3.6)$$

The last term is positive for even-even nuclei, negative for odd-odd nuclei, and zero for the other two types, for reasons which will be discussed in the next section.

H. Justification of the Binding Energy Equation

In the theoretical discussion of nuclear properties, a great deal of use is made of "nuclear models." A model is some simplified, plausible way of looking at the nucleus so that some understanding of a particular class of phenomena may be gained. Thus certain nuclear phenomena suggest that certain nuclei contain filled or "closed" shells of nucleons somewhat analogous to the closed shells of atomic electrons of the inert gases. Other phenomena suggest that the nucleus behaves like a droplet of an incompressible fluid. There is not necessarily any inconsistency in these apparently divergent viewpoints. As a crude analogy, consider some more familiar complex structure such as an automobile. From one point of view, the object consists of four wheels and a motor so that it may be propelled along a smooth surface. From another point of view, it is a device for extracting a small amount of useful work and a great amount of heat by the combustion of an organic fuel. Certain phenomena connected with the automobile could be understood from these points of view, but of course they are not a complete description of the mechanism. We shall consider the semiempirical binding energy equation in terms of the liquid drop model of the nucleus, making the following assumptions:

(1) All nuclei have the *same density*, and therefore the nucleons in all nuclei are at the same average distance apart. The volume of the nucleus, under this assumption, will be proportional to A, and hence its radius R will be

$$R = R_0 A^{1/3} \quad (3.7)$$

where R_0 is a constant which can be evaluated by experimental measurement of the radii of nuclei. There are several ways in which this can be done, and it is indeed found that R_0 is roughly constant for all nuclei. Its numerical value is found to be

$$R_0 \simeq 1.4 \times 10^{-13} \text{ cm}$$

(2) The forces binding nucleons together in the nucleus *saturate* in a manner analogous to chemical bonds. Nucleons interact with only a

limited number of those nucleons which are close to them.   In this respect
the nuclear forces are different from the Coulomb force, which is proportional to the square of the distance between two electrostatic charges.
The Coulomb force extends (although with decreasing strength) to
infinite distance.

(3) The forces between the nucleons are *independent of charge:* i.e., the
force between two neutrons is the same as between two protons or
between a proton and a neutron.   Two protons, of course, suffer a
Coulomb repulsion in addition to the attraction due to the nuclear force.
This repulsion is quite feeble compared with the attraction.   However,
it is a long-range force and therefore becomes increasingly important in
large nuclei containing many protons, since all the protons act together to
determine the strength of the Coulomb repulsion.

With these assumptions, we can now discuss the various terms in the
semiempirical binding energy equation (3.5).

1. aA.   By assumption (2), each of the A nucleons is bound only to a
certain definite number of its nearest neighbors, and the number of neighbors does not depend on A.   The total binding energy will therefore be
proportional to A.   Note that if the nuclear forces were of long range, so
that each nucleon could interact with all the other $(A - 1)$ nucleons, then
the total binding energy would be proportional to $A(A - 1)$.

2. $bA^{2/3}$.   As in a droplet of liquid, those nucleons which are close to
the surface are not surrounded by as many close neighbors as are nucleons
in the interior of the drop.   Hence they are less tightly bound, and we
must subtract an amount of binding energy which is proportional to the
number of nucleons at the nuclear surface.   This, in turn, will be proportional to the surface area, and thus to R^2 or $A^{2/3}$ by equation (3.7).   This
term is entirely analogous to the surface energy of a liquid drop, and it is
quite proper to think of a nucleus as having a surface tension.

3. $cZ^2/A^{1/3}$.   The loss of binding energy due to the Coulomb repulsion
between the protons must also be subtracted.   If the charge of the Z
protons is considered to be uniformly spread in a sphere of radius R, then
the potential energy due to the charge is proportional to Z^2/R, and therefore to $Z^2/A^{1/3}$ by equation (3.7).

4. $d(A - 2Z)^2/A$.   The quantity $(A - 2Z)$ is equal to the excess of
neutrons over protons, $(N - Z)$.   For $N = Z$, the term becomes zero.
We have already noticed that for a given value of A there exists a most
stable neutron-proton ratio, which for light nuclei is equal to unity.   A
negative term is therefore required which will increase both when the
number of protons or the number of neutrons increases above the most
stable value.   This requirement is met empirically by a term of the form
$(A - 2Z)^2/A$.

5. $\pm e/A$.   This term expresses the experimental observation that
even-even nuclei (in which every nucleon can be paired off with another

of the same kind) are more stable than the other types. For this nuclear type, the term is therefore a positive contribution to the binding energy. For the odd-odd nuclei, the term must be taken as negative, while for the other nuclear types it is zero. The form e/A is chosen to fit approximately the experimental values of this pairing energy in the heavier part of the periodic table.

I. Application of the Semi-empirical Binding Energy Equation

The equation may be used to tabulate calculated values of atomic masses or binding energies of nuclides whose masses have not been meas-

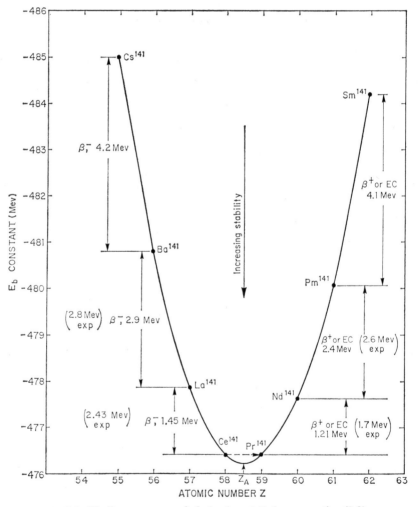

Fig. 3.2. Binding energy parabola for A = 141, from equation (3.8)

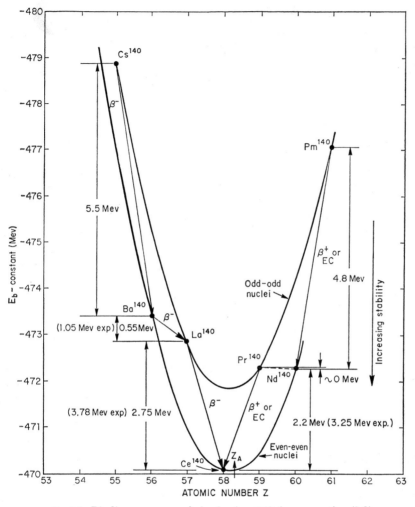

Fig. 3.3. Binding energy parabolas for A = 140, from equation (3.8)

ured.   A very complete table, calculated from a semi-empirical equation containing more terms than equation (3.5) was published by P. A. Seeger, *Nuclear Physics*, **25**, 1 (1961).   From the tabulated masses, calculations of the energy released in nuclear transformations can be made by the method of Sections 3D and E.

For β-decay processes of all kinds, A does not change.   For constant A, equation (3.6) reduces to:

$$E_b(\text{constant } A) = \text{constant} - \frac{0.6Z^2}{A^{1/3}} - \frac{20(A - 2Z)^2}{A} \pm \frac{125}{A} \quad (3.8)$$

Equation (3.8) contains terms in Z and Z^2 only, and is therefore the equation of a parabola. For a fixed odd value of A (that is, odd-even or even-odd nuclei), E_b therefore varies in a parabolic fashion with Z and the last term of equation (3.8) is zero. For a fixed, even value of A (that is, even-even or odd-odd nuclei), there will be two parabolas corresponding to positive and negative values of the last term in equation (3.8). The parabolas will be separated in energy by $2 \times 125/A$. Figures 3.2 and 3.3 show the parabolas calculated from equation (3.8) for $A = 141$ and $A = 140$, respectively. The differences between the binding energies for adjacent values of Z are equal to the energies available for β-transitions. Thus, from Figure 3.2, the value of (E_b − constant) for Ba^{141} is −480.8 Mev, while for La^{141} it is −477.9 Mev. La^{141} is therefore more stable than Ba^{141}, and the energy available for the transition $Ba^{141} \rightarrow La^{141} + \beta^-$ is (480.8 − 477.9) or 2.9 Mev. The experimentally determined figure is 2.8 Mev. The agreement is not always so close! According to Figure 3.2, Ce^{141} and Pr^{141} have very nearly equal binding energies and it is an open question which of them would decay into the other. Actually, Ce^{141} is observed experimentally to decay by β^--emission to Pr^{141}, the available energy being 0.581 Mev.

For even values of A (Fig. 3.3), β-decay processes cross from one parabola to the other, since β-decay transforms even-even nuclei into odd-odd, and vice versa. The most stable isobar of $A = 140$ is correctly predicted to be Ce^{140}; all other isobars are unstable with respect to β-decay of one type or another. Figure 3.3 shows Pr^{140} and Nd^{140} as having about equal binding energy. Experimentally, Nd^{140} is found to decay by electron capture (EC) to Pr^{140}, but the energy available for this decay is probably not very great.

The points on the Z axis marked Z_A in Figures 3.2 and 3.3 represent the most stable values of Z (vertices of the parabolas) for $A = 141$ and 140 respectively. Values of Z_A may be calculated by differentiating E_b with respect to Z, keeping A constant, and setting the derivative equal to zero. Applying this procedure to equation (3.8) gives

$$Z_A = \frac{40A}{80 + 0.6A^{2/3}} \qquad (3.9)$$

Naturally, equation (3.9) may give nonintegral values of Z_A. The most stable isobar will be the one whose atomic number is closest to Z_A.

Inspection of the parabola for odd A (Fig. 3.2) shows that there can only be one β-stable isobar for any odd value of A. Obviously, only one isobar can be the lowest on the parabola, and although there may be a pair like Ce^{141} and Pr^{141} with almost equal binding energy, one of them must always be slightly higher than the other, and therefore unstable with respect to β-decay.

Since the pairing energy term in equation (3.6) or (3.8) causes the parabola for odd-odd isobars to lie above that for even-even isobars, it will be unlikely that any odd-odd isobar will be β-stable.   In principle there might be one stable odd-odd isobar if the parabolas happened to fall as those shown in Figure 3.4.   However, we have already seen that there are only four β-stable odd-odd nuclei, and none heavier than N¹⁴. In fact the pairing energy term is too large to permit a case like that shown in Figures 3.4 to arise very often.

In the example shown in Figure 3.3, there is only one β-stable even-

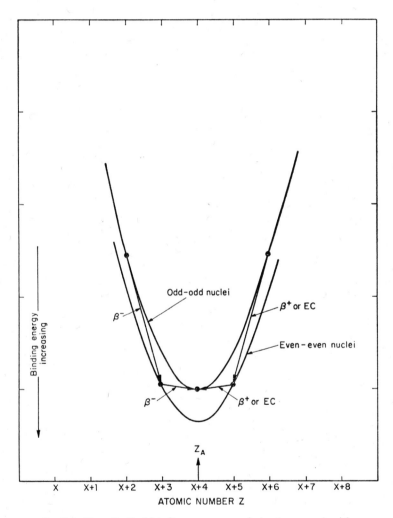

Fig. 3.4. Hypothetical binding energy parabolas for even A with stable odd-odd isobar

even isobar (Ce¹⁴⁰). However, if the parabolas fell as shown in Figure 3.5, there could be as many as three β-stable even-even isobars.

The semiempirical binding energy equation is a smooth function of Z and A. Hence if any nuclei contain arrangements of protons or neutrons which for any reason are specially stable, their binding energies will be underestimated by the smooth equation. Such special arrangements are in fact observed; they correspond to the formation of closed shells of nucleons analogous in some respects to the closed shells of atomic electrons

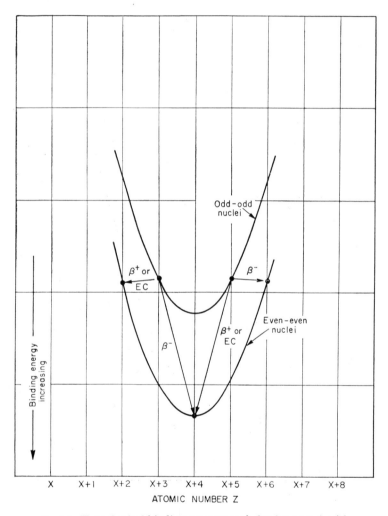

Fig. 3.5. Hypothetical binding energy parabolas for even A with three β-stable even-even isobars

in the inert gas atoms.   The difference between the measured binding energy and the value calculated from the semiempirical binding energy equation is a measure of the extra stability due to the formation of the closed shell.   We shall return to this subject in Chapter 5.

REFERENCES

1. Segrè, E. (ed.), *Experimental Nuclear Physics*, John Wiley & Sons, New York, 1953: Vol. I/5, K. T. Bainbridge, "Relative Isotopic Abundances of the Elements: Isotopic Masses."

2. *Table of Levy's Atomic Masses*, Report CRP 654, Atomic Energy of Canada Ltd., Chalk River, Ontario.

3. Strominger, D., J. M. Hollander, and G. T. Seaborg, *Revs. Modern Physics*, **30**, 585 (1958) (table of isotopes).

4. Everling, F., L. A. König, J. H. E. Mattauch, and A. H. Wapstra, *Nuclear Physics*, **18**, 529 (1960) (relative nuclidic masses).

5. Feather, N., *Nuclear Stability Rules*, Cambridge University Press, Cambridge, 1952.

6. Flügge, S. (ed.), *Handbuch der Physik*, Julius Springer Verlag, Berlin, 1958: Vol. XXXVIII/1, A. H. Wapstra, "Atomic Masses of Nuclides."

7. Hintenberger, H. (ed.), *Nuclear Masses and Their Determination*, Pergamon Press, London, 1957.

8. *Proceedings of the Hamilton Conference on Nuclidic Masses*, University of Toronto Press, Toronto, 1960.

9. Seeger, P. A., *Nuclear Physics*, **25**, 1 (1961).   (Semi-empirical atomic mass law and large table of mass values.)

PROBLEMS

1. Calculate the total binding energy of C^{12}.

2. How much energy would be absorbed or released if two atoms of O^{16} were fused together to make one atom of S^{32}?

3. Calculate the amount of energy required to dissociate one atom of C^{12} into three atoms of He^4.

4. For the following known or unknown nuclides, predict the mode or modes of β-decay (β^-, β^+, or EC) which are likely to take place: $_8O^{20}$, $_{23}V^{50}$, $_5B^9$, $_{16}S^{30}$.

5. Using equation (3.7) to obtain a rough estimate of the distance between the nucleons in a nucleus, calculate
   (a) The relative Coulomb potential energy between two adjacent protons;
   (b) The gravitational potential energy between two adjacent nucleons.

(c) Finally, calculate the binding energy per nucleon for any convenient nucleus, and satisfy yourself that it is much larger than the energies which you calculated in (a) and (b).

6. The stable isotopes of magnesium and their mass excesses on the C^{12} physical scale are:

$$Mg^{24} \quad -14,955.4 \; \mu u$$
$$Mg^{25} \quad -14,160.3 \; \mu u$$
$$Mg^{26} \quad -17,409.1 \; \mu u$$

Their abundances, in atoms percent, are 78.60, 10.11, and 11.29 respectively. Calculate the atomic weight of magnesium on the chemical scale.

7. By computing the appropriate parabolas, predict the types of decay and their energies for the isobars of $A = 180$. (Use four-figure logarithm tables.) Which isobar or isobars are stable? Compare your predictions with the Segrè chart.

8. Show by calculation in which direction the following reaction would be exothermic:

$$2Mg^{26} \leftrightarrow Cr^{52}$$

9. Answer the following questions by studying the Segrè chart:
(a) How many nuclides on the neutron-deficient side of the stability line decay by β^--emission?
(b) Would you expect Ho^{155} to be heavier or lighter than Dy^{155}?
(c) How many cases can you find in which there are three β-stable isobars for a given A?

10. The loss of binding energy due to surface effects [$A^{2/3}$ term in equation (3.6)] should be relatively more serious for light nuclei, which have a greater ratio of surface area to volume than heavier nuclei. Satisfy yourself that this is so by calculating the loss of binding energy due to the surface effect for $A = 50$ and $A = 200$.

11. The Coulomb repulsion term in equation (3.6) should be more important for heavy nuclei than for light. Satisfy yourself that this is so by calculating the loss in binding energy due to the Coulomb effect for $A = 50$ and $A = 200$, choosing reasonable values for Z in each case.

12. The two effects mentioned in Problems 10 and 11 work in opposite directions as a function of A. At some value of A, the losses in binding energy due to the two terms combined should be a minimum. Locate approximately the element for which this will occur. Compare your results with the broad minimum of the packing fraction curve of Figure 3.1.

13. Avogadro's Number and the Faraday have values of 6.0248×10^{23} and 96,522 coulombs respectively if the O^{16} physical scale is used. What would their values be on the C^{12} physical scale?

14. Assume that all the sun's energy is produced by the reaction

$$4_1H^1 \rightarrow {}_2He^4 + 2\beta^+$$

The sun yields 2 calories per minute per square centimeter at the surface of the earth.   The distance of the earth from the sun is 1.49×10^6 km.   How much helium does the sun produce per year?

15. The red giant stars, which are cooler than the sun, produce energy from reactions such as

$$\text{Be}^9 + \text{H}^1 \rightarrow \text{Li}^6 + \text{He}^4 + \text{energy}$$

From mass values in Appendix II, calculate
  (a) The energy release in Mev for this reaction;
  (b) The percentage of the initial mass converted into energy;
  (c) The energy released in kilocalories per mole;
  (d) The packing fraction of Be^9.

16. Show that the binding energy per nucleon can be expressed as

$$\frac{E_b}{A} = 0.00853 - P + 0.0004 \frac{A - 2Z}{A}$$

where P is the packing fraction.

17. Calculate the energy (in Mev) which is equivalent to the mass of an electron.

18. Calculate the mass of an electron which is moving at 99% of the velocity of light.   What is its kinetic energy?

CHAPTER 4

Nuclear Spin and Moments

A. Angular Momentum

In the theory of nuclear properties, angular momentum plays such an important part that we must now carry somewhat further the discussion of Chapter 1, Section B.

When a particle is moving under the influence of a force which is spherically symmetrical (i.e., the force depends only on the distance of the particle from the center of the force), then the orbital angular momentum of the particle will be constant. In Figure 1.2 (a), the angular momentum of the moving body about the point O was constant, because in this example the force was zero in all directions about O. The Coulomb force between an electron and the nucleus of hydrogen is spherically symmetrical, since it depends only on the distance of separation.

For systems of this kind, the quantum mechanical value of the angular momentum is found to be

$$\text{Angular momentum} = \hbar[l(l+1)]^{1/2} \qquad (4.1)$$

where l is an integer (the azimuthal quantum number), which may have any value from zero to infinity. Thus the angular momentum is *quantized*—that is, it can have only certain discrete values. Like all quantum mechanical results, this is true for very large systems as well as for atoms or nuclei. For example, the angular momentum of the moon is quantized, but in this case, the angular momentum is so large compared with the size

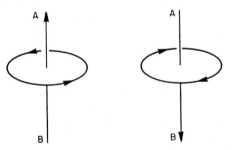

Fig. 4.1. Vector representation of angular momentum

of the "steps" between adjacent allowed values that the quantization is quite unobservable.

Angular momentum is a vector quantity, i.e., it has both a magnitude and a direction. A convenient way to represent it is shown in Figure 4.1. The angular momentum of a particle rotating in a plane at right angles to the plane of the page is represented as the line AB which lies along the axis of rotation. The length of the line AB is equal to the magnitude of the angular momentum. Its direction is arbitrarily chosen to be the direction in which an ordinary right-handed screw would advance if rotating in the same direction as the particle.

The vector AB can be split up into components in other directions in just the same way as any other vector, such as velocity or force. If a definite direction in space is selected, then it is possible to specify the component of an angular momentum vector in the chosen direction. Common sense would seem to say that this component may have any value between $-\hbar[l(l+1)]^{1/2}$ and $+\hbar[l(l+1)]^{1/2}$, depending on the angle between the angular momentum vector and the chosen direction. However, quantum mechanics leads to a different result. The angular momentum component in a fixed direction can only have the set of values $m\hbar$, where m is an integer whose values lie in the range $-l \cdots 0 \cdots +l$. The actual value of m in any case depends on the angle between the chosen direction and the angular momentum vector. The integer m may have any one of a set of $(2l + 1)$ different values, whereas in classical mechanics, there would be an infinite number of different possible values for the projection of a vector onto a fixed direction in space. Notice that the maximum projected value of the angular momentum is $l\hbar$ rather than $\hbar[l(l + 1)]^{1/2}$. In any experiment designed to measure the angular momentum, $l\hbar$ is the largest result that could ever be obtained, no matter in which direction the measurement is made. In the rest of the discussion, therefore, we shall use the term "angular momentum" to mean the "maximum projected value of the angular momentum." Figure 4.2 shows a graphical representation of the seven possible values of the angular momentum projection when $l = 3$.

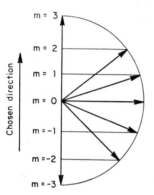

Fig. 4.2. The $(2l + 1)$ possible projected values of the angular momentum in a fixed direction when $l = 3$

In Chapter 1, we saw that the electron possesses spin angular momentum in addition to any angular momentum due to its orbital motion. The magnitude of the spin angular momentum is $\hbar[\frac{1}{2}(\frac{1}{2} + 1)]^{1/2}$. Just as there are $2l + 1$ possible projected values of the orbital angular momentum, so there are $(2 \cdot \frac{1}{2}) + 1$, or *two* possible projected values for the spin vector. These are often referred to as "spin up" and "spin down." In each case, the projected magnitude of the spin angular momentum is the same, $\frac{1}{2}\hbar$.

Like electrons, neutrons and protons have spin $\frac{1}{2}$. In addition to their spin, they may have an orbital angular momentum due to their motion within the nucleus. The total angular momentum of a neutron or proton will be equal to the vector sum of the angular momenta due to the orbital motion and the spin. According to classical mechanics, there will be an infinite number of resultants of this sum, but quantum mechanics leads to a much simpler result. The addition of the angular momentum vectors l_1 and l_2, where $l_1 \geq l_2$, can only give the resultants $(l_1 + l_2)$, $(l_1 + l_2 - 1)$, $(l_1 + l_2 - 2) \cdots$, (l_1), $(l_1 - 1)$, $(l_1 - 2)$, $\cdots$, $(l_1 - l_2)$. Thus if $l_1 = 5$ and $l_2 = 3$, the possible values of their sum are 8, 7, 6, 5, 4, 3, and 2. Notice that there are $(2l_2 + 1)$ different values. If s represents the spin of an electron, neutron or proton, then by the same arguments, the total angular momentum of the particle can only have the values $(l \pm s)$ or $(l + \frac{1}{2})$ and $(l - \frac{1}{2})$, since $+\frac{1}{2}$ and $-\frac{1}{2}$ are the only two values of the projection of the spin angular momentum on the vector representing the orbital angular momentum l.

The quantum mechanical total angular momentum I obtained in this way is actually the *maximum projected value*. The total angular momentum is $\hbar[I(I + 1)]^{1/2}$. We shall actually use the term "total angular momentum" to mean the maximum projected value. When applied to nuclei, I is often called the *nuclear spin*. Even though the orbital part of the total angular momentum becomes meaningless if the internal field of force is not spherically symmetrical, the total angular momentum I must remain constant in any system which is not under the influence of external forces.

The nucleus as a whole will possess angular momentum which is the vector sum of the orbital and spin angular momenta of all the neutrons and protons of which it is composed. The orbital angular momenta $m\hbar$ are always integral multiples of $\hbar$. No matter how they may be oriented with respect to one another, all the orbital angular momentum vectors must add up to an integral number of $\hbar$ units. The spin angular momenta, being half-integral, must also add to an integral number of $\hbar$ units if the nucleus contains an even number of nucleons (i.e., an even value of A), or to a half-integral number of units if the number of nucleons is odd (odd A). The spins of a large number of nuclei have been measured, and there are no exceptions to these rules. For example, the spins of the odd-A nuclei C^{13} and Sr^{87} are $\frac{1}{2}$ and $\frac{9}{2}$ respectively. The even-A nuclei C^{12} and Cs^{134} have spins 0 and 4 respectively. There is an extension of the rules which is found experimentally always to be true: that the lowest energy level of an even-even nucleus always has spin zero, which of course is a special case of the rule that even-A nuclei must have integral spin.

B. Spin and Magnetism

A charged particle moving within an atom or nucleus represents electricity in motion, and it is therefore not surprising that such particles generate magnetic fields. It is possible to observe the interaction of these atomic or nuclear magnetic fields with each other or with external applied magnetic fields in a great variety of important ways.

The magnitude of the magnetic effect is measured by the magnetic dipole moment of the system. For a simple bar magnet of length L and pole strength p, the magnetic dipole moment μ is equal to pL. If such a magnet is placed in a magnetic field of strength H so that the length of the magnet makes an angle θ with the direction of the field, then it experiences a couple which tends to rotate it so that its axis will be in the direction of the magnetic field. This situation is shown in Figure 4.3. The force on each pole of the magnet can be resolved into two components, one perpendicular to the magnet and the other along its length. The latter forces cancel out, leaving a turning couple which is equal to $HpL \sin \theta$.

The potential energy of the magnet when it is at a angle θ with respect to the magnetic field is

$$V = \int_{\theta}^{0} HpL \sin \theta \, d\theta \tag{4.2}$$

and this quantity is equal to $HpL(1 - \cos \theta)$. For an atomic or nuclear magnet, the potential energy can be measured in a great variety of ways which will be discussed later, so that if H is known, the value of the magnetic dipole moment $\mu = pL$ is obtained. Observe that neither p nor L can be measured separately, but only their product.

The magnetic dipole moment due to the motion of an electric current i in a circular orbit of radius r is $\pi r^2 i$. If the current is due to the motion of an electron of charge e, and its angular velocity is ω radians per second, then $i = e\omega/2\pi$. In electromagnetic units, the magnetic moment μ is

$$\mu = \frac{e\omega r^2}{2c}$$

where c is the velocity of light. The angular momentum of the electron is

$$p = m_e\omega r^2$$

where m_e is the mass of the electron, and hence

$$\mu = \frac{pe}{2m_ec} \tag{4.3}$$

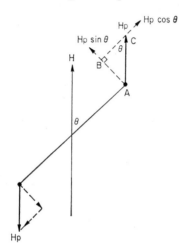

Fig. 4.3. Forces experienced by a bar magnet in a uniform magnetic field

Thus the magnetic moment is proportional to the angular momentum. But the angular momentum is restricted to the quantized values $l\hbar$, and hence

$$\mu \text{ (electron orbital motion)} = \frac{l\hbar e}{2m_ec} \tag{4.4}$$

The quantity $\hbar e/2m_ec$ is thus a natural unit of magnetic moment for an orbital electron. It is known as the Bohr magneton. Its value is 9.2732 $\times$ 10^{-21} erg per gauss.

The magnetic moment of an electron due to its spin can also be calculated. It is found to be very slightly greater than one Bohr magneton:

$$\mu \text{ (electron spin)} = 2.0032 \times \text{(electron spin)} \times \frac{\hbar e}{2m_ec}$$

$$= 9.2838 \times 10^{-21} \text{ erg per gauss} \tag{4.5}$$

For a free proton, it might be expected that the spin magnetic moment μ (proton spin), would be given by an equation similar to equation (4.5), but with the proton mass replacing the electron mass. This turns out to be too simple a view; the magnetic moment of the proton is actually

$$\mu \text{ (proton spin)} = 2.793 \text{ nuclear magnetons} \qquad (4.6)$$

The nuclear magneton is defined as the quantity $e\hbar/2m_p c$, where m_p is the mass of the proton. Its value is 5.05038×10^{-24} erg per gauss, which is less than the Bohr magneton by the ratio m_e/m_p.

The neutron carries no net electrical charge, but this is no guarantee that there are no circulating electric currents within its structure. The neutron is in fact found experimentally to have a magnetic moment due to its spin:

$$\mu \text{ (neutron spin)} = -1.913 \text{ nuclear magnetons} \qquad (4.7)$$

The negative sign means that the agent responsible for the magnetic moment is a negative charge circulating in the direction of the neutron spin. Since the neutron as a whole is not charged, its orbital motion cannot produce a magnetic moment, and therefore

$$\mu \text{ (neutron orbital motion)} = 0 \qquad (4.8)$$

We now expect that the magnetic moments of nuclei will be made up by vector addition of the following component magnetic moments:

(1) Proton angular momentum component
(2) Proton spin component
(3) Neutron spin component

By and large, the spins and magnetic moments of nuclei are consistent with the view that nucleons form pairs in such a way that their individual spins and magnetic moments cancel out. (This pairing was responsible for the last term in the semiempirical binding energy equation of the last chapter.) Thus the spins and magnetic moments of even-even nuclei are always zero. The spin and magnetic moment of an odd-A nucleus will in many cases be entirely due to the motion and spin of the single unpaired nucleon. This concept of nuclear structure is known as the single particle model. We shall discuss it in more detail in Chapter 5. Table 4.2 gives a comparison of some experimental magnetic moments with the values calculated from the single particle model.

The spin $(\pm\frac{1}{2})$ of the unpaired nucleon can only have two directions in space relative to the direction of the orbital angular momentum vector. If the orbital angular momentum is l units, then the total nuclear angular momentum I due to the single unpaired nucleon in an odd-A nucleus must be

$$I = l + \tfrac{1}{2} \quad \text{or} \quad I = l - \tfrac{1}{2} \qquad (4.9)$$

With these simple ideas, it is possible to calculate the magnetic moment which would be expected for nuclei with either a single unpaired proton or a single unpaired neutron. The expected values, which are known as the Schmidt limits, are given in Table 4.1.

TABLE 4.1. Magnetic Moments of Nuclei with a Single Unpaired Nucleon (Schmidt Limits)

Nuclear spin I	Magnetic moment	
	Odd proton	Odd neutron
$l + \frac{1}{2}$	$\mu_p + I - \frac{1}{2}$	$\mu_n \ (-1.913 \text{ n.m.})$
$l - \frac{1}{2}$	$\left(\dfrac{I}{I+1}\right)(I + \frac{3}{2} - \mu_p)$	$-\left(\dfrac{I}{I+1}\right)\mu_n$

The measured nuclear magnetic moments usually lie close to the values shown in Table 4.1. However, if the theory were exact, they should be *exactly* equal to either the $(l + \frac{1}{2})$ or the $(l - \frac{1}{2})$ value. There are two ways in which the theory may be imperfect. First, the magnetic moment of the unpaired neutron or proton may not be exactly the same as that of a free particle. It might be modified by the presence of the other (paired) nucleons in the nucleus. Second, the presence of the unpaired nucleon may itself alter the properties of the rest of the nucleus so that it also contributes to the magnetic moment. Probably both of these effects occur.

For many nuclei, the values of I and l are known, so that the magnetic moment may be calculated by substitution in the appropriate part of Table 4.1. Table 4.2 shows a comparison of magnetic dipole moments calculated in this way with the corresponding experimentally measured values. The agreement is fairly good.

TABLE 4.2. Comparison of Measured Nuclear Magnetic Dipole Moments and Values Calculated from Table 4.1

Nuclide	Spin I	Odd particle	$I = l \pm \frac{1}{2}$	Magnetic moment	
				Calculated	Experimental
$_6C^{13}$	$\frac{1}{2}$	Neutron	−	+0.64	+0.702
$_8O^{17}$	$\frac{5}{2}$	Neutron	+	−1.913	−1.894
$_{19}K^{39}$	$\frac{3}{2}$	Proton	−	+0.124	+0.391
$_{36}Kr^{83}$	$\frac{9}{2}$	Neutron	+	−1.913	−0.969
$_{51}Sb^{121}$	$\frac{5}{2}$	Proton	+	+4.793	+3.360
$_{81}Tl^{205}$	$\frac{1}{2}$	Proton	+	+2.793	+1.63
$_{83}Bi^{209}$	$\frac{9}{2}$	Proton	−	+2.62	+4.08

C. Electric Quadrupole Moments

We wish now to examine the way in which the electric charge due to the protons may be distributed within the nucleus. Let the nucleus contain a point charge e, at a distance r from the center of the nucleus, and let the coordinates of e be x, y and z, the origin being at the center of the nucleus. We wish to calculate the electrostatic potential φ at some point on the z axis outside the nucleus in terms of the magnitude and coordinates of the charge e inside the nucleus. It is just this potential, well outside the nucleus, which we can observe experimentally.

It can be shown that at a distance D from the center of the nucleus, the value of φ is

$$\varphi = \frac{e}{D} + \frac{er}{D^2} \cos \theta + \frac{er^2}{D^3}\left(\frac{3}{2}\cos^2 \theta - \frac{1}{2}\right) + \cdots \tag{4.10}$$

where $\cos \theta = z/r$.

The first term e/D of equation (4.10) equals the potential at a distance D from a charge e. The part er of the second term is a product (charge $\times$ length). It is called the electric dipole moment. (Compare with the definition of magnetic dipole moment.) The er^2 of the third term is a product (charge $\times$ length^2). It is the electric quadrupole (or 2^2-pole) moment. The next term [omitted from equation (4.10)] contains the electric octupole moment (2^3-pole), and so on. We could have used a similar method in the discussion of magnetic moments, but it was not necessary; only magnetic dipole moments are required to explain nuclear magnetic properties.

It can be shown that the moments of even order, such as the quadrupole (2^2-pole), the 2^4-pole, the 2^6-pole, and so on, must be zero unless the nuclear spin $I \geq n/2$, where n is the multipole order. Therefore only nuclei with $I \geq 1$ can have a measurable quadrupole moment. Furthermore, if the nucleus has an axis of symmetry in any direction and a plane of symmetry at right angles to it, and if its centers of mass and charge coincide, then all the odd multipoles, such as the dipole moment, the 2^3-pole moment and so on, must be zero. In fact, the first and third terms of equation (4.10) are found by experiment to be the only terms required to describe the electric potential outside nuclei.

As an example of the use of multipoles to describe a distribution of electric charges, consider Figure 4.4. In example (a), the total charge is $+2e$, the dipole moment is zero, and the quadrupole moment is $2d^2e$. In example (b), the total charge is zero, the dipole moment is $2de$, but the quadrupole moment—which is $-e(-d)^2 + e(+d)^2$—is zero.

The existence of a nonzero quadrupole moment necessarily implies that the nucleus in question is not spherical. Such nuclei may be thought of as spheroidal in shape, either prolate or oblate. These two shapes are illustrated in Figure 4.5. The prolate spheroid will have a positive quadrupole moment, the oblate spheroid a negative value. If the semi-axes of the spheroid are c and a respectively, and the total charge is Ze

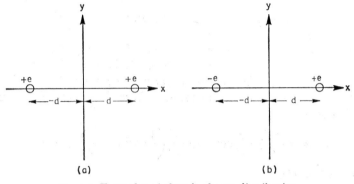

Fig. 4.4. Examples of electric charge distribution

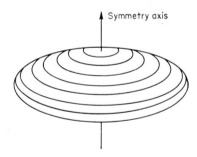

Prolate spheroid (football-shaped)

Oblate spheroid (bun-shaped)

Fig. 4.5. Prolate and oblate spheroids

(uniformly distributed), then the quadrupole moment Qe is

$$Qe = \frac{2Z}{5(c^2 - a^2)} \tag{4.11}$$

The mean square radius of the nucleus will be $R^2 = \frac{1}{2}(a^2 + c^2)$.

From its definition in equation (4.10), it is apparent that the dimensions of the electric quadrupole moment will be (electrical charge × area). It is usual to divide the measured values by the proton charge, so that quadrupole moments are reported in units of area. [It was for this reason that the quadrupole moment was written as Qe in equation (4.11).] Values often lie in the region 10^{-26}–10^{-24} cm², or about the same as the cross-sectional areas of nuclei. (The area 10^{-24} cm² is usually known as the "barn"; 10^{-27} cm² is the "millibarn.")

D. Measurement of Nuclear Spin and Moments

According to equation (4.2), the potential energy of a magnetic dipole μ will depend on its orientation relative to an applied magnetic field H. A nucleus of spin I can only orient itself so as to give $(2I + 1)$ different projections in the direction of the magnetic field, and each different orientation will correspond to a different potential energy. These potential energy differences depend on μ, I, and H. Therefore, if transitions from one orientation to another can be induced, there exists the possibility of measuring μ and I. This can in fact be done by the application of high frequency electromagnetic radiation from a suitable radio-wave generator. If the generator is tuned to a frequency ν such that the photon energy $h\nu$ which it generates is exactly equal to the energy difference between adjacent orientations of the nuclear magnetic dipoles, then transitions between orientations will be induced, and energy will be absorbed from the generator.

In an analogous manner, the nuclear electric quadrupole moment will interact with an electric field. In this case, however, the potential energy of the system will only be a function of its orientation when the nucleus is subjected to an electric field which is *nonuniform* (i.e., a field whose strength varies from place to place). Nonuniform electric fields of sufficient strength are often found in crystals, but they cannot be generated by means of high voltage equipment. The quadrupole resonance method therefore consists of measuring the frequency of the electromagnetic radiation from a high frequency radio wave generator which induces transitions from one nuclear orientation to another in a crystalline solid.

The principles outlined in the preceding paragraphs have been applied in a confusing variety of elegant experiments. The separate disciplines of chemistry, atomic physics, nuclear physics, and solid state physics often approach each other very closely at this point, and a complete understanding of all the experimental methods requires a good knowledge of all these subjects. The following brief review gives only a general impression of the subject.

Method 1: *Optical Spectroscopy.* The orbital motion and spin of the electrons of an atom produce a magnetic field in the neighborhood of the nucleus, so that the potential energy of the atom will depend on the orientation of the nuclear magnetic dipole with respect to the total angular momentum vector of the system of electrons.   Hence the energy levels of the atom, each corresponding to a definite electronic state, will be split into a number of separate levels, each corresponding to the same electronic state but with different relative nuclear orientations.   Accordingly, the spectral lines will be similarly split up into a series of closely spaced lines, which are known as the hyperfine structure (hfs) of the lines. The number of components into which a given electronic energy level is split depends on the nuclear spin I and on the total angular momentum J (spin plus orbital) of the system of electrons.   For $J = 0$, there is no hfs splitting.   For $J < I$, the level splits into $(2J + 1)$ hyperfine components, while for $I < J$, it splits into $(2I + 1)$ components.   By studying the optical spectrum with sufficiently high resolution to resolve the hyperfine structure of the lines, it may therefore be possible to determine the nuclear spin I.

The energy separation between the separate hfs lines depends on μ, I, and the strength of the magnetic field at the nucleus due to the atomic electrons.   According to equation (4.2), the change in potential energy in the rotation through 180° of a magnet of dipole moment μ in a field H is

$$\Delta V = \int_0^{180°} H\mu \sin \theta \, d\theta$$

$$= 2H\mu \qquad (4.12)$$

For a nucleus of spin I, there will be $(2I + 1)$ allowed orientations with $2I$ "gaps" between them, each gap corresponding to a transition from one orientation to the next.   Therefore the energy separation ΔE between adjacent orientations will be $2H\mu/2I$, or

$$\Delta E = \frac{H\mu}{I} \qquad (4.13)$$

By means of equation (4.13), μ can be calculated from the energy separation ΔE between the hfs components of a line provided that H is known.   A method of calculating H has been devised by Goudsmit, Fermi, and Segrè, and values of μ may be calculated with an accuracy of about 10%.

Method 2: *Rotational Spectra.*   If a molecule consists of two identical atoms whose nuclei have spin I, then the total nuclear spin quantum number S for the molecule will be the vector sum of the two nuclear spins I.   It can have the values $2I$, $2I - 1$, $2I - 2$, $\cdots$, 1, 0.   In this series, alternate terms are even and odd.   In the spectrum of such a molecule, the lines corresponding to the transition of an electron from one energy level to another are split up because of the possibility of a simultaneous change in the rotational energy of the molecule.   The lines in this splitting are due alternately to molecules with even and odd total spin quantum numbers S.

The probability that a molecule will have a particular value S for the total nuclear spin quantum number is $(2S + 1)$ because there are $(2S + 1)$ allowed orientations of S, all equally probable.   Hence the ratio R of the probability that the value of S will be even to the probability that S will be odd is

$$R = \frac{[2(2I) + 1] + [2(2I - 2) + 1] + \cdots}{[2(2I - 1) + 1] + [2(2I - 3) + 1] + \cdots}$$

and for any value of I (integral or half-integral), it is easy to show that

$$R = \frac{(I + 1)}{I} \tag{4.14}$$

Thus the probabilities of even and odd values of S are not equal, since $(I + 1)/I$ is greater than 1 for any value of I.   Since even and odd S values are associated with alternate lines in the spectrum, then the alternate lines must have different intensities (since the molecular species which give rise to them are present in different amounts).   The intensity ratio will be $(I + 1)/I$, which permits the determination of I by measurement of this ratio.

In the case of the molecule H_2, $I = \frac{1}{2}$, and hence S can only have the two values 0 or 1.   The two species of molecules are well known as para and ortho hydrogen; at normal temperatures the ratio of the ortho to the para form is $(I + 1)/I = 3$.

There are several ways in which molecular rotational transitions may be observed directly rather than as a fine structure in electronic transitions.   The energies of the rotational transitions often correspond to photons of wavelengths in the centimeter range, which can be generated by high frequency radio techniques.   The absorption of these photons as a function of their energy can be studied in a way entirely analogous to the study of optical absorption spectra.   Instead of measuring the effect of nuclear spin on the intensity of lines, it is possible to measure directly the hfs splitting of the lines.

Method 3: Atomic Beams.   If an atom whose nucleus has a magnetic moment is placed in a uniform magnetic field, we have already seen (Fig. 4.3) that the resulting force on the nucleus is a pure rotation.   However, if the field is not uniform, one end of the magnetic dipole will experience a stronger field than the other end, and there will be an additional force of translation in addition to the turning couple.   It is possible to generate magnetic fields which are sufficiently nonuniform that even a dipole as small as an atom will experience an appreciable force.

If a beam of atoms whose nuclei have spin I is allowed to stream from a small hole in an oven through such a magnetic field, the atoms will suffer a deflection, and the beam will be split into $2(2I + 1)$ beams. This effect may be exploited by means of the apparatus shown in Figure 4.6 (a). The atoms stream from the oven 0 into the magnet A whose field is about 6000 gauss, with a field gradient of 6000 gauss per centimeter. After leaving the magnet A, the atoms pass through a collimator and into the field of

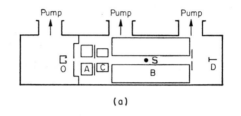

(a)

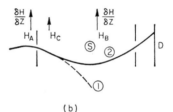

(b)

Fig. 4.6. Atomic beam method. (a) Experimental arrangement. (b) Path of atoms through apparatus. From W. A. Nierenberg, Annual Reviews of Nuclear Science, **7**, 364 (1957)

magnet C. This magnet has a uniform field. At right angles to the field, there is a weak oscillating magnetic field supplied by a loop of wire which is connected to a high frequency generator. In the field of the C magnet, the normal hyperfine structure of the atomic energy levels is broken down by the Zeeman effect into a multiplicity of magnetic sublevels. Transitions between some of these levels may be induced by the oscillating magnetic field if the frequency of the oscillator, ν, is adjusted so that $h\nu$ is exactly equal to the energy change in the transition. This energy change depends mainly on the atomic magnetic moment, the nuclear spin, and the field of the C magnet, but it is also slightly affected by the nuclear magnetic moment.

After leaving the C magnet, the atoms pass through a second inhomogeneous field in magnet B. Those that suffered no change in the orientation of their atomic magnetic dipole moment in magnet C will be deflected in the same direction in magnet B as they were in magnet A (path 1 of Fig. 4.6 (b)). Those that changed orientation will be deflected in the opposite direction (path 2), will successfully avoid the stop-wire S, and will eventually arrive at the detector D.   Unless the frequency of the oscillator is set at exactly the right value to induce the proper transition, no atoms can arrive at the detector.

Various types of detector have been used to suit the circumstances of the particular experiment.   If the nucleus under study is radioactive, then its atoms may be caught on buttons of sulfur (to which the atoms stick very well) placed in the detector position, and the number of atoms caught may be subsequently estimated by counting their radiation.   In this way, nuclei whose half lives are as short as 30 minutes have been studied.   The amount of material required for a measurement may be as little as 10^{10} atoms.

By studying as a function of the C magnet field the resonant frequencies which induce transitions permitting atoms to reach the detector, both the nuclear spin I and the nuclear magnetic dipole moment μ may be measured.   The forces which act on the atoms in the inhomogeneous magnetic fields are actually due almost entirely to interaction of the magnetic fields with the *magnetic moment of the atom* caused by the orbital electrons, because the atomic magnetic moment is much larger than the nuclear magnetic moment.   However, the way in which the forces split the atomic beam depends also on the nuclear spin and magnetic moment, so that these quantities can be measured.

Method 4: *Nuclear Magnetic Resonance.*   In this method, the sample— a diamagnetic liquid or solid, or a gas at high pressure—is placed in a uniform magnetic field, and the frequency ν required to induce transitions from one nuclear orientation to another is measured.   At the resonant frequency, the sample absorbs energy from the radiofrequency generator. The relationship between ν, H, μ, and I is again given by equation (4.13).

When μ and I are both known, as for the proton, for example, a measurement of ν (which can be made with very great precision) serves to measure H.   This method is often used in the measurement or control of magnetic fields in instruments such as mass spectrometers.

Many chemical compounds contain atoms of the same element in more than one state of combination.   For example, ethyl alcohol contains hydrogen in a CH_3— group, a —CH_2— group, and an —OH group.   The protons in the three different states of combination "invert their spins" at a slightly different frequency—or at a fixed frequency they pass through resonance at slightly different values of the magnetic field.   In order to observe this effect, extremely uniform magnetic fields must be used. The group of three absorption lines in ethyl alcohol is shown in Figure 4.7. The width of the group is only 0.05 gauss.   With even higher resolution, even more splitting may be observed.   These effects are of great value in studies of chemical kinetics and the structure of compounds.

Method 5: *Paramagnetic Resonance (Electron Spin Resonance).* In a field of H gauss, the proton resonance frequency is

proton ν (kilocycles per second) $= 4.26H$

For values of H in the region of 10,000 gauss, therefore, frequencies of about 40 Mc/sec are required to observe the proton spin resonance. At very much higher frequencies, the spin resonance of the unpaired electrons

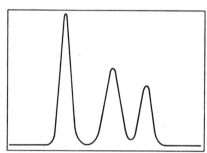

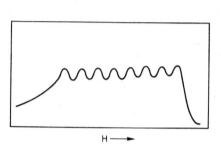

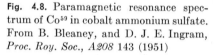

Fig. **4.7.** Proton resonance spectrum of ethyl alcohol. From J. T. Arnold, S. S. Dhermatti, and M. E. Packard, *Journ. Chem. Phys.*, **19**, 507 (1951)

Fig. **4.8.** Paramagnetic resonance spectrum of Co^{59} in cobalt ammonium sulfate. From B. Bleaney, and D. J. E. Ingram, *Proc. Roy. Soc.*, *A208* 143 (1951)

in paramagnetic substances can be observed. The resonant frequency in this case is

electron ν (kilocycles per second) $= 2.80 \times 10^3 H$

Electron spin (paramagnetic) resonance can be observed in organic free radicals, and is an important tool in the study of organic and inorganic compounds and their reactions. Nuclear information has for the most part been obtained by the incorporation of paramagnetic ions into the crystal lattice of some isomorphous diamagnetic compound. For example, a paramagnetic lanthanide ion such as Nd^{+++} may be incorporated into the crystal lattice of a diamagnetic compound such as $LaCl_3$. The dilution of the paramagnetic ion is necessary in order to obtain sharp resonances.

The paramagnetic resonance frequency is split by interaction of the spinning electron with the nuclear magnetic moment. However, the effect of the strong electric fields in the crystals introduces considerable complication. The number of hfs components is again $(2I + 1)$, so that I may be determined by counting this number. Values of μ and Q (the nuclear quadrupole moment) can sometimes be obtained, but the results are not reliable. Figure 4.8 shows the paramagnetic resonance spectrum of Co^{++} in the compound cobalt ammonium sulfate. The eight partly resolved hfs components correspond to $I = \frac{7}{2}$ for Co^{59}.

Method 6: *Nuclear Quadrupole Resonance.* In this case, the electric field gradient due to the crystal lattice interacts with the nuclear quadrupole moment, so that the energy of the system depends on the orientation of the nuclear spin with respect to the direction of the field gradient. Again the frequency of the oscillating electric field required to induce transitions from one orientation to the next may be measured. The frequencies required are in the neighborhood of a few hundred megacycles per second. The main difficulty in obtaining the electric quadrupole moment is in calculation of the electric field gradient due to the crystal lattice.

Method 7: *Radioactive Decay Properties.* Since this topic forms a major part of Chapters 6, 7, and 8, it will suffice merely to mention here that the decay properties of a nucleus are profoundly influenced by the spin difference between the decaying nucleus and its daughter. It is often possible to decide with reasonable certainty what the spin of a nucleus must be if that of its parent or daughter is known.

Some of the nuclear spins measured by the method above are listed in Appendix III.

REFERENCES

1. Feenberg, E., *Shell Theory of the Nucleus*, Princeton University Press, Princeton, 1955.

2. Mayer, M. G., and J. H. D. Jensen, *Elementary Theory of Nuclear Shell Structure*, John Wiley & Sons, New York, 1955.

3. Kopfermann, H., *Nuclear Moments*, Academic Press, New York, 1958.

4. Nierenberg, W. A., "Spins and Moments of Radioactive Nuclei," *Ann. Revs. Nuclear Sci.*, **7**, 349 (1957).

5. Segrè, E. (ed.), *Experimental Nuclear Physics*, John Wiley & Sons, New York, 1953: Vol. I, N. F. Ramsey, "Nuclear Moments and Statistics."

6. Herzberg, G., *Atomic Spectra and Atomic Structure*, Dover Publications, New York, 1944.

7. Flügge, S. (ed.), *Handbuch der Physik*, Julius Springer Verlag, Berlin: Vol. XXXVII/1 (1959), P. Kusch and V. W. Hughes, "Atomic and Molecular Beam Spectroscopy"; Vol. XXXVIII/1 (1958), F. M. Kelly, "Determination of Nuclear Spins and Magnetic Moments by Spectroscopic Methods"; L. Wilets, "Isotope Shifts"; D. Laukien, "Kernmagnetische Hochfrequenz-Spektroskopie"; C. H. Townes, "Determination of Nuclear Quadrupole Moments."

8. Siegbahn, K. (ed.), *Beta- and Gamma-Ray Spectroscopy*, North Holland Publishing Co., Amsterdam, 1955.

9. Rose, M. E., *Elementary Theory of Angular Momentum*, John Wiley & Sons, New York, 1957.

10. Edmonds, A. R., *Angular Momentum in Quantum Mechanics*, Princeton University Press, Princeton, 1957.

PROBLEMS

1. Calculate the magnetic dipole moment which you would expect for the following nuclei: Cs^{137}, Eu^{153}, Cl^{37}, F^{19}, V^{51}, and Nb^{93}. For the first three nuclei, $I = l - \frac{1}{2}$; for the last three, $I = l + \frac{1}{2}$. Schmidt's limit

2. Which of the nuclides in Problem 1 might have a nuclear quadrupole moment? $I \geqslant 1$

3. Calculate the electric monopole, dipole, and quadrupole moments of the arrangements of charges shown in Figures 4.9 (a) and (b).

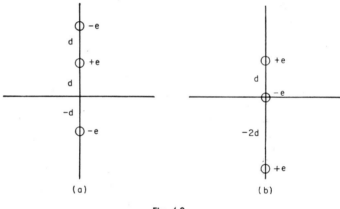

Fig. 4.9

4. If the origin in Figure 4.9 (a) were displaced downward by a distance d, would the values of the three electric moments change? If so, what would they become?

5. The spin of the deuteron is 1. What possible values exist for the total nuclear spin quantum number S of the molecule D_2? What would be the relative frequency of occurrence of the several S values in deuterium at room temperature?

6. How many hfs components would you expect to see for an atomic energy level having $J = 2$ and $I = \frac{3}{2}$? p. 74

7. Calculate the frequency of (a) proton spin resonance, (b) electron spin resonance, in a magnetic field of 10,000 gauss. p. 78

8. Calculate the work done in turning a bar magnet 10 cm in length, pole strength 10 units, through 45° in a uniform magnetic field of 100 gauss. Assume that the magnet was initially lying in its position of lowest potential energy.

9. For the magnet of Problem 8, in its initial position, calculate the net force acting on the magnet when the field has a gradient of 10 gauss per cm.

10. The electric quadrupole moment of Lu^{175} ($Z = 76$) is 5.90 barns. Calculate the ratio of major to minor semiaxes of the nucleus. The mean square radius may be obtained from the equation $R = 1.40 \times 10^{-13} A^{1/3}$ cm.

CHAPTER 5

The Structure of Nuclei

A. Introduction

In this chapter we shall explore further the structure of nuclei, using as the basis of the discussion several of the models of nuclei which have been proposed. Reference was made in Chapter 3, Section H to the utility of imaginary models of the nucleus as an aid in correlating and understanding the properties of nuclei. In that section, the liquid drop model was introduced, and it will therefore be unnecessary to mention it again in the present chapter. It will be useful later on in the discussion of fission.

B. The Nuclear Potential

Neutrons and protons are both attracted by nuclei when the distance of separation is small.   The force of attraction is exerted over only a short distance: if the nucleon is more than about 1 fermi $(1 \text{ fermi} = 10^{-13} \text{ cm})$ from the surface of the nucleus, the force is negligible.   A proton which is too far from a nucleus to feel the short-range attractive force may yet experience a repulsion due to the Coulomb force between its positive charge and that of the nucleus.

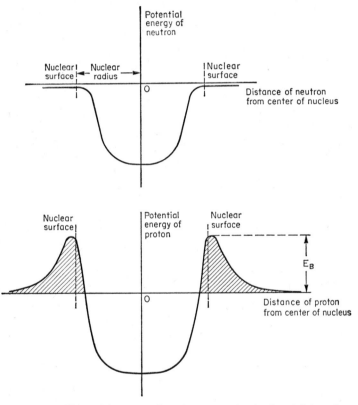

Fig. 5.1. Potential energy of neutron or proton in the vicinity of nucleus

As a result of these forces, the potential energy of a nucleon approaching a nucleus will be a function of the distance of separation.   Figure 5.1 shows the variation of this potential energy with separation for both a proton and a neutron.   The potential energy of the nucleon at infinite separation is arbitrarily taken as the energy zero.

In the region from the nuclear surface out to infinite distance, the potential energy of a neutron suffers almost no change.   Close to the nuclear surface the neutron begins to feel the strong attraction of the short-range nuclear forces and its potential energy therefore drops rapidly.

If the neutron continues to travel through the nucleus, its potential energy will rise again as it approaches the nuclear surface on the side opposite to its point of entry. Naturally, energy must be conserved; the drop in potential energy appears as kinetic energy of the neutron. However, if the neutron loses some of this kinetic energy in its passage through the nucleus, then it may be unable to accumulate sufficient potential energy to escape again. (Loss of kinetic energy may readily take place by collision with a second nucleon.) The neutron may then be permanently "trapped" inside the nucleus.

The potential energy curve for the proton in Figure 5.1 is modified by the Coulomb force, which causes the potential energy to increase as the proton approaches the nuclear surface. The shaded portion of the proton potential energy diagram is called the Coulomb barrier, since it has the effect of a barrier preventing the approach of a proton (or any other positively charged particle) to the nucleus. The increase of potential energy of the proton as it approaches the Coulomb barrier is obtained at the expense of its kinetic energy; the proton slows down. If the particle approaches the nucleus with a kinetic energy which is less than E_b, the height of the barrier, then it will not be able to reach the nuclear surface. It will be reflected (Coulomb-scattered) by the barrier. (There is a quantum mechanical effect which permits some of the particles to enter the nucleus even though they have insufficient kinetic energy to surmount the barrier. We shall return to this phenomenon of barrier "penetration" in the discussion of α-decay.)

The height of the Coulomb barrier, E_b, is

$$E_b = \int_R^\infty \frac{z_1 z_2}{r^2}\, dr = \frac{z_1 z_2}{R} \text{ ergs} \qquad (5.1)$$

where z_1 and z_2 are the charges of the incident particle and nucleus in esu, and R is the distance (in cm) between their centers when they are in contact. R may be calculated approximately as follows:

$$R = \text{radius incident particle} + \text{radius of nucleus}$$

$$= 1.4 \times 10^{-13}(A_1^{1/3} + A_2^{1/3}) \text{ cm} \qquad (5.2)$$

where A_1 and A_2 are the mass numbers of the incident particle and nucleus. For protons incident upon a heavy element such as uranium, the height of the barrier is about 10 Mev.

Potential energy curves which have a minimum, such as those of Figure 5.1, are called potential wells. The foregoing discussion of the interaction between nuclei and protons or neutrons illustrates the possibility of describing some of the properties of nuclei by specifying the dimensions of their potential wells. For ease of calculation, a nucleus may be approximately described by means of a "square well" such as that shown in Figure 5.2. Such a well represents a nucleus with a "sharp" surface. That is to say, the density of nuclear matter has a constant value up to the nuclear surface, where it instantly falls to zero. Wells such as those of Figure 5.1 represent a more realistic state of affairs. The density of nuclear matter remains almost constant throughout most of the nuclear volume, but near the surface it diminishes gradually to zero. Note that the term "square well" does not imply that the *nucleus* is square in shape.

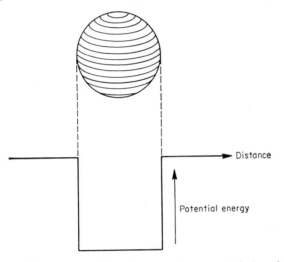

Fig. 5.2. Square potential well representing a spherical nucleus

It is actually spherical, or nearly so. The "square" well is intended to represent a potential energy which is zero outside the well, but drops instantly to some constant negative value inside the well.

The shape and depth of the nuclear potential well are determined by the nature of the forces acting between all the nucleons in the nucleus. The concept of the potential well is a crude approximation to a real nucleus, in which we attempt to replace the individual effect of each nucleon by an average which represents approximately the effect of all of them acting together. It is an important objective of research to try to relate the properties of the potential well to the individual forces between the nucleons, and considerable progress in this direction has been made by Brueckner and his co-workers.

Experimental studies of the scattering of protons and neutrons by nuclei show that the nuclear potential well must have a depth of about 30 Mev. As we observed in Chapter 3, the energy required to remove a nucleon from a typical nucleus is only about 7–8 Mev. Hence we are forced to conclude that the nucleons within the potential well are not all

lying at the bottom of the well.   In fact they occupy a series of discrete
energy levels.   This situation is illustrated (for a square well) in Figure
5.3.   Because the Coulomb repulsion acts on the protons within the
nucleus but not on the neutrons, the depth of the well is about 5 Mev
less for protons than for neutrons.   The levels marked E_f (protons or
neutrons) represent the energy of the highest level which contains a
nucleon.   A nucleon in the energy level at E_f will be the easiest nucleon

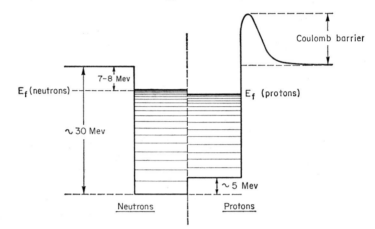

Fig. 5.3. Energy levels for neutrons and protons in a nuclear
potential well (schematic)

to remove from the nucleus since it already possesses the most energy.
The energy required to remove a nucleon from the levels E_f must be
equal to the binding energy of a nucleon to the nucleus, and as we have
seen already, this amounts to about 7–8 Mev.   Hence E_f must lie at an
energy of about 7–8 Mev below the potential energy zero.   In Figure 5.3,
E_f(proton) is shown slightly below E_f(neutron).   In other nuclei this
order may be reversed, but in any case the energy difference between
E_f(proton) and E_f(neutron) must always be small.   The energy E_f,
which is called the Fermi energy, is a function of A and Z.   It will be
discussed in more detail in Section E.

C. The Shell Model

We mentioned in Chapter 3 that certain nuclei are particularly stable.
For example, the energy required to remove a neutron from the various
isotopes of lead drops very sharply between Pb^{208} (126 neutrons) and
Pb^{209} (127 neutrons). Pb^{208} is therefore much more stable than Pb^{209}.
The energies required to remove a neutron from the various lead isotopes
are shown in Table 5.1.   In addition to the sudden drop at a neutron

number of 126, observe the alternation in the values in Table 5.1.   In
each case, the energy required to remove a neutron from an even nucleus
is greater than the energy required for either of its two neighboring odd
nuclei.   This energy difference represents the cost of breaking up a neutron pair in the even nucleus.

TABLE 5.1. Energies Required to Remove a Neutron from the Lead Isotopes

Isotope	Neutron number	Energy to remove one neutron, Mev
Pb^{205}	123	6.64
Pb^{206}	124	8.16
Pb^{207}	125	6.73
Pb^{208}	126	7.38
Pb^{209}	127	3.87
Pb^{210}	128	5.23
Pb^{211}	129	3.77

The result contained in Table 5.1, and much additional evidence which
will be mentioned later, suggests that the structure of the Pb^{208} nucleus
(with 126 neutrons) is particularly stable.   Throughout the periodic system there are other cases of a similar nature, each associated with a particular number of protons or neutrons.   These numbers are called
"magic numbers."   They are listed in Table 5.2.   A nucleus with a
magic number of protons or neutrons is called a magic nucleus; Pb^{208} with
82 protons and 126 neutrons is doubly magic, and so is Ni^{56} with 28
nucleons of each type.

TABLE 5.2. Proton and Neutron Magic Numbers

Protons	Neutrons
2	2
8	8
20	20
28	28
50	50
82	82
	126

The shell model of the nucleus starts with the assumption that each
nucleon moves in a potential well which is an approximate representation
of the interaction of that nucleon with all the others.   If the Schrödinger
equation is solved for the case of a nucleon confined in a well, it is found
that, just as in the case of the electron of the hydrogen atom, the nucleon
can occupy only one of a set of discrete energy levels.   Each level is

characterized by four quantum numbers, $\nu, l, j,$ and m_j. The radial quantum number ν is equal to the number of loops or nodes in the wave function ψ across the width of the well.* Figure 5.4 shows the behavior of ψ for a

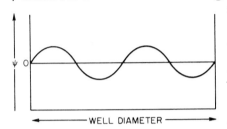

nucleon occupying a level for which $\nu = 4$. There are four loops, two above and two below the $\psi = 0$ line.

The quantum number l is related to the orbital angular momentum of the nucleon by the usual equation:

Orbital angular momentum
$$= \hbar[l(l + 1)]^{1/2}$$

Fig. 5.4. Behavior of ψ for a nucleon with quantum number $\nu = 4$. (After L. Pauling, and E. B. Wilson, *Introduction to Quantum Mechanics*, McGraw-Hill Book Co., New York, 1935

As before, the value of l is designated by the appropriate letter from Table 1.3.

The quantum number j is related to the total angular momentum (spin plus orbital), whose magnitude is $\hbar[j(j + 1)]^{1/2}$. Since nucleons of either kind have spin $\frac{1}{2}$, j and l must be related by

$$j = l \pm \tfrac{1}{2} \tag{5.3}$$

The value of j is written as a subscript. Thus a $2f_{5/2}$ nucleon is one which occupies a level for which $\nu = 2$, $l = 3$, and $j = l - \frac{1}{2} = \frac{5}{2}$.

m_j, the magnetic total angular momentum quantum number, is the magnitude of the projection of j on an arbitrary direction in space, for example the direction of a magnetic field. Thus it is related to j in the same way as the atomic electron magnetic quantum number m is related to the azimuthal quantum number l.

The energy of a nucleon in a potential well depends only on the values of the quantum numbers ν and l. For any value of l, j may have the two values $l \pm \frac{1}{2}$, and for each value of j there are $(2j + 1)$ values of m_j. Hence the total number of nucleons *of each kind* that can share a given value of ν and l is $[2(l + \frac{1}{2}) + 1] + [2(l - \frac{1}{2}) + 1]$, or $2(2l + 1)$. A level which contains more than one particle with the same energy is said to be *degenerate*.

Table 5.3 shows the quantum numbers for the energy levels of nucleons in a potential well of infinite depth. The levels at the bottom of the table correspond to the bottom of the well. The second column shows the number of nucleons of each type which may occupy each level, and the third column gives the sum of all the nucleons of each type starting at the bottom of the well. We may hope that these last numbers will include the

---

* In the past, some authors have used the quantum number n $(= \nu + l)$ rather than ν.

magic numbers of Table 5.2.   The result is unsatisfactory, since the numbers 28, 50, and 126 do not appear.

The difficulty was resolved by Haxel, Jensen, and Suess and independently by M. G. Mayer.   Their procedure may be illustrated by considering the $1p$ level of Table 5.3.   This level may contain up to six nucleons

TABLE 5.3. Energy Levels of Nucleons in an Infinite Potential Well

Level	Nucleons in filled level	Sum of nucleons
$2g$	18	156
$1i$	26	138
$3p$	6	112
$2f$	14	106
$1h$	22	92
$3s$	2	70
$2d$	10	68
$1g$	18	58
$2p$	6	40
$1f$	14	34
$2s$	2	20
$1d$	10	18
$1p$	6	8
$1s$	2	2

of each type, and each of the six nucleons will have the same energy. (A level such as this is said to be sixfold degenerate.)   Each nucleon has an orbital angular momentum of one unit ($l = 1$) and spin $\frac{1}{2}$ unit.   Four of them must have the orbital angular momentum vector pointing in the same direction as the vector representing the spin.   For the other two, the vectors point in opposite directions from each other.   Haxel, Jensen, and Suess and M. G. Mayer proposed that the energies of these two groups of nucleons would in fact be different.   The group whose vectors are coupled to give a total angular momentum j of $\frac{3}{2}$ units would have an energy lower than the group whose total angular momentum is $\frac{1}{2}$ unit.   This same energy splitting applies to all the energy levels with $l \geq 1$, but the energy difference between the pairs of levels formed in this way increases as l increases.   Thus the $1i$ level is split into a level with $j = \frac{13}{2}$ and a level with $j = \frac{11}{2}$.   In this case, the energy separation between these two levels is considerably greater than between the two levels into which the $1p$ level is split.

With these assumptions, the order of the levels is rather extensively rearranged from that shown in Table 5.3.   The new sequence which is obtained with this "spin-orbit" coupling is shown in Figure 5.5.   The subscript numbers are the total angular momentum j of each nucleon in the level.

The characteristic discontinuities in properties which indicate the

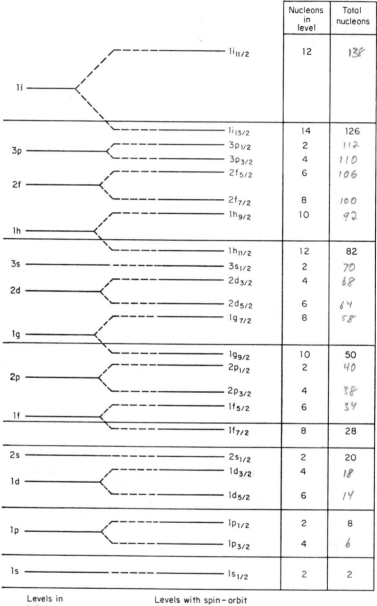

	Nucleons in level	Total nucleons
$1i_{11/2}$	12	138
$1i_{13/2}$	14	126
$3p_{1/2}$	2	112
$3p_{3/2}$	4	110
$2f_{5/2}$	6	106
$2f_{7/2}$	8	100
$1h_{9/2}$	10	92
$1h_{11/2}$	12	82
$3s_{1/2}$	2	70
$2d_{3/2}$	4	68
$2d_{5/2}$	6	64
$1g_{7/2}$	8	58
$1g_{9/2}$	10	50
$2p_{1/2}$	2	40
$2p_{3/2}$	4	38
$1f_{5/2}$	6	34
$1f_{7/2}$	8	28
$2s_{1/2}$	2	20
$1d_{3/2}$	4	18
$1d_{5/2}$	6	14
$1p_{1/2}$	2	8
$1p_{3/2}$	4	6
$1s_{1/2}$	2	2

Levels in infinite well   Levels with spin–orbit coupling (shell model)

Fig. 5.5. Comparison of levels in an infinite potential well with spin-orbit coupling level sequence

completion of a shell (either of atomic electrons or of nucleons) are due to the existence of levels (or groups of levels) which are separated by a large energy gap from the closest levels above them. If all the levels are closely spaced in energy, then there may not be any dramatic change in properties when the first nucleon enters a new level.

The spin-orbit coupling scheme depresses the energies of the levels whose total angular momentum j is $(l + \frac{1}{2})$ so much, for the larger l values, that these levels join the group of levels below. For example, the $1g$ level is split into the $1g_{9/2}$ and $1g_{7/2}$ levels, and these levels are so widely separated in energy that a recognizable magic number of 50 nucleons appears, corresponding to the filling of the $1g_{9/2}$ level. The next nucleon enters the $1g_{7/2}$ level, which is at a considerably higher energy. The energy separation between the levels which are split by spin-orbit coupling may be as great as 2 Mev for the higher l values.

D. Evidence for the Shell Model

The experimental evidence for the existence of energy gaps in the nuclear level scheme is overwhelming. We shall summarize briefly only a small part of it.

1. *Number of Stable Isotopes and Isotones.* Nuclei with a magic number of protons or neutrons possess extra stability which is reflected in the appearance of an unusually large number of stable nuclides. For example, calcium ($Z = 20$) has six stable isotopes whereas the neighboring even-Z elements argon and titanium have three and five respectively. There are six stable isotones with $N = 50$, but only three with $N = 48$ and four with $N = 52$. The numbers of stable isotones are also unusually large for $N = 20$ (five), $N = 28$ (five), and $N = 82$ (seven). The extra stability of magic nuclei is responsible for the sharp minima in the packing fraction curve (Fig. 3.1).

2. *Natural Abundances of Nuclides.* Nuclides with a magic number of neutrons or protons often occur in nature in an abundance much greater than would be expected. The abundance of an isotope with even A is rarely greater than 60% of the naturally occurring even-Z element, except among the lighter elements. For example, natural selenium ($Z = 34$) contains 0.87% Se^{74}, 9.02% Se^{76}, 23.52% Se^{78}, 49.82% Se^{80}, and 9.12% Se^{82}. No isotope is present in as much as 60%. The only three exceptions to this rule are nuclides which contain a magic number of neutrons: $_{38}Sr^{88}$ ($N = 50$), $_{56}Ba^{138}$ ($N = 82$) and $_{58}Ce^{140}$ ($N = 82$), whose abundances are 82.56%, 71.66%, and 88.48% respectively. The abundance of $_{82}Pb^{208}$ ($Z = 82$, $N = 126$) is 52.3% of natural lead, and this is much higher than average for an even-even isotope, although not high enough to make a fourth exception to the 60% rule.

3. *Radioactive Decay Properties.*   The radioactive decay properties of the heavy elements show a very clear anomaly at $N = 126$.   (We shall return to this point in the discussion of α-decay in Chapter 7.)   The naturally occurring decay series among the heavy elements all end with an isotope of lead ($Z = 82$).   The two heaviest stable nuclides ($_{82}Pb^{208}$ and $_{83}Bi^{209}$) both have $N = 126$.

4. *Emission and Capture of Neutrons.*   The emission of a neutron from a nucleus requires that the nucleus first be excited to an energy greater than the binding energy of the neutron to the nucleus, which is normally about 7–8 Mev.   Although nuclei in excited states are very commonly produced as a result of a radioactive decay, excitation energies as high as 7 Mev are not obtained in this way.   However, the nuclei Kr^{87} ($N = 51$) and Xe^{137} ($N = 83$) both contain one neutron above a magic number.   This neutron is very loosely bound.   (Compare with the alkali metals, which all have one easily lost electron beyond an inert-gas, closed electron shell.)   When Kr^{87} and Xe^{137} are formed in excited states by the β^--decay of Br^{87} and I^{137} respectively, the loosely bound neutron is emitted spontaneously.

All nuclei can capture a low energy neutron when exposed to a beam of these particles.   Their tendency to do so is measured by a "cross section," which is the effective target area each nucleus presents to the neutrons.   A large cross section represents a large tendency to capture a neutron, and vice versa.   Nuclei which already contain a magic number of neutrons tend to have small cross sections for the capture of an additional neutron.   (This does not mean that the nuclei themselves are actually smaller than normal.)   For example, the cross section of Pb^{208} ($N = 126$) is 0.0006 barns, while that of Pb^{207} is 0.69 barns.   For Xe^{136} ($N = 82$) it is 0.15 barns, while for Xe^{135} it is 3.5×10^6 barns.   (One barn $= 10^{-24}$ cm^2.)

5. *Nuclear Quadrupole Moments.*   Magic nuclei and their neighbors are nearly spherical in shape, while nuclei which are far removed from a magic number appear to be spheroidal and therefore often have large electric quadrupole moments.   Particularly large positive quadrupole moments (corresponding to nuclei of prolate spheroidal shape) occur in the region of the heavy rare earth elements.   In this region, Z is roughly half way between the $Z = 50$ and $Z = 82$ magic numbers, while N is roughly half way between 82 and 126.

6. *Spins and Parities of Nuclei.*   We introduce here for the first time the quantum mechanical concept of parity.   The wave function ψ which describes a particular system such as an atom or a nucleus in a particular energy state is a function of the coordinates (x,y,z) which define a point in space.   For example, in equation (1.17), the function ψ, which was associ-

ated with the appearance of the magnetic quantum number m of the hydrogen atom, was a function of the polar coordinate θ. If now we change (x,y,z) in a wave function to $(-x,-y,-z)$, either ψ will change its sign or it will remain unchanged. If the system is such that the sign of ψ remains unchanged, then it is said to have even parity. If the sign of ψ changes, then the parity of the system is said to be odd. (The terms positive and negative are also commonly used instead of even and odd.)

The importance of the parity of a system is that, like energy and momentum, it is conserved as long as the system remains isolated from outside influence. (An exception to the principle of conservation of parity has been experimentally demonstrated for certain special cases. It will be discussed in Chapter 8.) A nucleus has a definite parity, and the parity can change only when a particle or photon enters or leaves the nucleus. The rules governing the emission of particles or of photons from nuclei are profoundly influenced by the presence or absence of a parity difference between the parent nucleus and its daughter.

The spins of nuclei in their ground states can be predicted with a fair degree of certainty by the shell model, with the following assumptions:

(1) The order of filling of the energy levels is given by the shell model (Fig. 5.5). In each completely filled level, the spins and orbital angular momenta of the nucleons add together to give a zero resultant.

(2) In the levels which are not completely filled, the nucleons form pairs in such a way that the spins and orbital angular momenta of the two nucleons in each pair add together to form a resultant total angular momentum which is zero. *No analogue of Hund's Rule here.*

(3) The spin of a nucleus with an odd number of neutrons or protons is equal to the total angular momentum, j, of the odd nucleon. The parity of the nucleus is determined by the l value of the odd nucleon. If l is even, the parity is even $(+)$. If l is odd, the parity is odd $(-)$.

The situation is more complicated for nuclei of the odd-odd type, which have both an odd proton and an odd neutron. We will return to these nuclei after illustrating the statements made above. The assumptions (2) and (3) constitute an extreme form of the single particle model of the nucleus, in the sense that the spin and parity of the ground state of the nucleus are determined entirely by the single unpaired nucleon.

Consider the nucleus $_8O^{17}$, containing eight protons and nine neutrons. By assumptions (2) and (3), the spin and parity of O^{17} can both be predicted if the energy level of the ninth neutron is known. Reference to Figure 5.5 shows that the ninth nucleon is to be found in the $1d_{5/2}$ level, for which $l = 2$ and $j = \frac{5}{2}$. Hence the spin and parity of O^{17} should be $\frac{5}{2}(+)$. The measured spin is indeed $\frac{5}{2}$. As a second example, consider the nuclei $_{49}In^{113}$ and $_{49}In^{115}$. In both these nuclei, the forty-ninth proton is the odd nucleon, and Figure 5.5 shows that the forty-ninth nucleon should be in the $1g_{9/2}$ level. Therefore these two nuclei should have spin and parity $\frac{9}{2}(+)$, and indeed they do.

There are, however, many failures of this simple theory. For example, the ninth proton of $_9\text{F}^{19}$ should be in the $1d_{5/2}$ level, but the spin of F^{19} is actually $\frac{1}{2}$ rather than $\frac{5}{2}$. In some cases, assumption (1) may fail. The order of levels shown in Figure 5.5 may be at fault, especially when two levels lie close together in energy. Under these conditions, it is hard to predict in which of two close levels a nucleon may be found. Further, the assumptions (2) and (3) frequently fail. In F^{19} for example, the nuclear spin is not determined by the ninth proton alone. There are two neutrons in addition to the closed shell of eight neutrons, and they couple their angular momentum with that of the ninth proton to give the nucleus a resultant spin of $\frac{1}{2}$ unit.

Assumptions (2) and (3) fail badly when the odd nucleon should have, according to the shell model, a high angular momentum. For example, among the heavier elements there should be many nuclei with spin $\frac{11}{2}$ corresponding to an odd nucleon in the $1h_{11/2}$ level. However, not a single example is found experimentally. It appears that the energy of an unpaired nucleon is particularly high when it occupies a level of high angular momentum. A lower energy state of greater stability can be formed by promoting a second nucleon from a level of lower angular momentum into the high angular momentum level so that a pair can be formed. This situation may be illustrated by the example of $_{56}\text{Ba}^{137}$, whose spin, parity, and magnetic moment are $\frac{3}{2}(+)$ and 0.9311 n.m. respectively. The odd nucleon is the 81st neutron, which should be in the $1h_{11/2}$ level. However, it appears that a neutron is removed from a pair in the $2d_{3/2}$ level to form a pair with the $1h_{11/2}$ neutron. The odd particle is therefore a $d_{3/2}$ neutron. By reference to Table 4.1 we obtain a value of $+1.148$ n.m. for the magnetic dipole moment of Ba^{137}, which is in fairly good agreement with the experimental value. If the state of the odd neutron were one for which $j = l + \frac{1}{2}$ (such as the $h_{11/2}$), then the magnetic moment would be negative instead of positive.

In odd-odd nuclei, there will be at least the two odd nucleons which couple their spins and angular momenta together to determine the spin of the nucleus. They may do this in a variety of ways. For example, a proton in the $2s_{1/2}$ level could couple with a neutron of the $1f_{7/2}$ level to give a resultant nuclear spin of 3 or 4. The nuclear spin may have any value between $|j_1 - j_2|^*$ and $(j_1 + j_2)$, where j_1 and j_2 are the total angular momenta of the two odd nucleons. Two rules due to Nordheim usually yield the right result. If the two nucleons have orbital angular

---

* The symbol $|j_1 - j_2|$ means the absolute magnitude of $(j_1 - j_2)$ without regard to whether it is a positive or a negative quantity.

momenta l_1 and l_2 and total angular momenta j_1 and j_2, then

    I. If $(l_1 + l_2 + j_1 + j_2)$ is even, then $I = |j_1 - j_2|$.

    II. If $(l_1 + l_2 + j_1 + j_2)$ is odd,

           then I will be large, probably near $(j_1 + j_2)$.   (5.3)

handy

If l_1 and l_2 are both even or both odd, the nucleus will have even parity. If one of them is even and the other is odd, then the parity of the nucleus will be odd.

$j = l \pm \frac{1}{2}$

As an example of the use of Nordheim's rules, consider $_{29}Cu^{64}$. The 29th proton is in the $1f_{5/2}$ level according to Figure 5.5, so that $l_1 = 3$ and $j_1 = \frac{5}{2}$. The 35th neutron is in the $2p_{3/2}$ level, so that $l_2 = 1$ and $j_2 = \frac{3}{2}$. Hence $l_1 + l_2 + j_1 + j_2 = 8$, and the spin of Cu^{64} should be equal to the magnitude of $(j_1 - j_2)$, or 1. This is in agreement with the value obtained by the atomic beam method. Since l_1 and l_2 are both odd, the parity of Cu^{64} will be even.

In $_{37}Rb^{86}$, the odd proton and neutron should be in the $2p_{3/2}$ and $1g_{9/2}$ levels respectively, so that $l_1 + l_2 + j_1 + j_2$ should be odd. The predicted spin is therefore 6, but the experimental value is only 2. Since the spins of Rb^{85} and Rb^{87} are $\frac{5}{2}$ and $\frac{3}{2}$ respectively, we may suspect that the 37th proton of Rb^{86} might be in the $1f_{5/2}$ level rather than in the $2p_{3/2}$. If this were so, then $l_1 + l_2 + j_1 + j_2$ would be even, and the spin of Rb^{86} would be 2, in agreement with the experimental value. The parity would be odd with either assumption about the level of the 37th proton.

Notice in Figure 5.5 that nearly all the levels within a given shell have the same parity. Hence, even if we are not sure in a particular case in which level within the shell an odd nucleon lies, we can still be almost certain of the parity.

E. The Fermi Gas Model

In this model, the nucleus is again regarded as a potential well like that of Figure 5.3, in which the protons and neutrons move. Nuclear forces between the nucleons are completely ignored, except of course that these forces are responsible for the existence of the well. Instead of attempting to make detailed calculations about the nature of the individual levels (as in the shell model), we treat the nucleus statistically in a way which resembles the statistical treatment of a gas in the kinetic theory. We cannot expect that this model will yield any information about nuclear spins and parities, but it is able to give a valuable interpretation of the behavior of nuclei at high levels of excitation where the shell model is of little use.

Starting at the bottom of the well, each energy level is regarded as being completely filled with as many protons or neutrons as the exclusion principle will allow. There are no vacancies, and the nucleus is thus in its lowest possible energy state. It therefore resembles a gas at the absolute zero on the temperature scale. If the nucleus is excited to some higher energy state, then one or more of the nucleons must be transferred from its normal energy level to some higher unoccupied level (i.e. to some level above E_f). The "nuclear temperature" is now no longer 0° A but has some higher value. The temperature of the nucleus is a measure of the extent to which nucleons occupy energy levels in the well above E_f. It is usual to express nuclear temperatures in units of kT, which has the dimensions of energy, rather than in degrees. In these units of energy, temperatures of a few Mev are commonly met. Note that the temperature in energy units is not at all the same thing as the excitation energy of the nucleus above its ground state. The two quantities are related in the same way as the temperature of a gas is related to its heat content.

Using the analogy of the nucleus to a gas, one may apply the methods of statistical mechanics. In this way, the value of the Fermi energy E_f may be calculated. The result is

$$E_f(\text{protons}) = 33.8 \left(\frac{Z}{A}\right)^{2/3} \text{Mev}$$

$$E_f(\text{neutrons}) = 33.8 \left[\frac{(A-Z)}{A}\right]^{2/3} \text{Mev}$$

(5.4)

In calculating the numerical coefficients in equation (5.4), the nucleus was assumed to have a radius $R = 1.5 \times 10^{-13} A^{1/3}$ cm.

The nuclear temperature T must vary with excitation energy E in such a way that the nuclear specific heat dE/dT becomes zero at $T = 0°$ A. (This is required by the Third Law of Thermodynamics.) The simplest equation connecting T with E which will satisfy this requirement is found to be

$$E = aT^2 \qquad (5.5)$$

a is an empirical constant which may be measured experimentally. It is a function of the mass number A of the nucleus. Typical values are shown in Table 5.4.

A model using statistical methods can be expected to yield information only about average nuclear properties. One property of interest is the average energy spacing D between energy levels. The reciprocal of D is the average number of nuclear energy levels in a given energy interval. It is usually given the symbol ρ and the name "level density." According to the Fermi gas model, the spacing between the energy levels decreases very rapidly as the nuclear excitation energy increases, especially if the nucleus is heavy. This was represented schematically in Figure 5.3 by drawing the levels closer and closer together as the Fermi energy E_f was approached. The relationship between the level density ρ and the excitation energy E according to the Fermi gas model is

$$\rho = Ce^{2\sqrt{aE}} \quad \text{levels per Mev} \qquad (5.6)$$

a is the same constant as that appearing in equation (5.5), and C is a new constant which decreases with increasing A. Values of C in a few typical cases are shown in Table 5.4.

TABLE 5.4. Values of the Constants a and C of Equation (5.6)
(After J. M. Blatt and V. F. Weisskopf*)

Mass number A	a, Mev^{-1}	C, Mev^{-1}
27	0.45	0.5
63	2	0.3
115	8	0.02
181	10	0.01
231	12	0.005

*See Reference 7 at the end of this chapter.

Nuclear temperatures and level densities may be measured experimentally by studying the energy spectra of protons and neutrons which are emitted from highly excited nuclei. However, many of the values which have been reported are of very dubious accuracy, and new measurements are badly needed. We shall return to this topic in Chapter 9.

F. The Collective Model

In the shell model, many of the properties of the nucleus are ascribed to the nucleon or nucleons which lie outside the filled shells. The shell model seems to bear little resemblance to the liquid drop model which was described in Chapter 3. The collective model incorporates features of both the shell and liquid drop models. It arose mainly as a result of the work of A. Bohr and B. R. Mottelson. (A. Bohr is the son of N. Bohr, whose work was mentioned in Chapter 1.)

In the language of the shell model, an excited state of a nucleus is formed when one or more nucleons are raised from their normal levels into higher energy levels. However, many excited states of nuclei are known which do not appear to be formed in this way. The collective model interprets some of these levels in terms of the collective motion of many nucleons acting together. It therefore differs considerably from the single particle version of the shell model.

The collective motion of the nucleons may be described as either a rotation or a vibration. We shall confine the discussion to rotations, since these motions are better understood. A collective rotation might be either the rotation of a group of nucleons around the surface of the nucleus, or it might be thought of as a wave motion traveling around the surface of the nucleus just as a ripple might travel around the surface of a drop of liquid. In this type of motion, the group of nucleons would oscillate up and down at right angles to the surface of the nucleus. Both types of motion are associated with quantized values of energy and angular momentum. In the initial formulation of the theory, the wave type of motion was preferred, but it now appears that the collective motion of groups of nucleons is about half way between the two extreme types of motion.

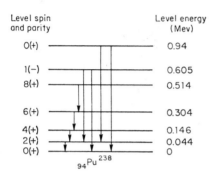

Fig. 5.6. Level scheme of Pu^{238} showing rotational band

The collective model is particularly valuable in accounting for the energy levels of nuclei in regions which are far removed from magic numbers. Such nuclei might be expected to deform rather easily, and hence the energy required to excite a collective motion of the nucleons is small. In such nuclei, rotational motion frequently causes the appearance of a set of energy levels which are analogous to the rotational energy levels of molecules. For example, the nucleus $_{94}$Pu^{238} (far removed from the magic numbers 82 and 126) has the series of energy levels shown in Figure 5.6. In this figure, the spin and parity are shown at the left end of the horizontal lines which represent the energy levels. The energy of the level in Mev is shown at the right end of the line; the lowest energy level (the ground state) is taken as the zero of the energy scale. The vertical arrows represent the transitions from the higher to the lower levels which have been experimentally observed. In most cases the transition takes place by emission of a γ-ray photon whose energy is equal to the energy difference between the initial and final level.

The sequence of levels in Pu^{238} with spin and parity 0(+), 2(+), 4(+), 6(+), and 8(+) represent a rotational band. Similar bands have been observed in a very large number of nuclei. For example, Pu^{239} has a band of this type, but in this case the spins and parities of the levels are $\frac{1}{2}(+)$, $\frac{3}{2}(+)$, $\frac{5}{2}(+)$, $\frac{7}{2}(+)$. We may distinguish two types of energy levels in nuclei: single particle levels due to the excitation of a single nucleon (or occasionally more than one nucleon) from one energy level in the potential well to a higher level, and collective levels due to some collective motion involving many nucleons. The relationship between single particle and collective levels thus bears some resemblance to the relationship between electronic and rotational states of molecules.

For rotational bands in even-even nuclei, the energy E_I of the level of spin I is given by

$$E_I = \frac{\hbar^2}{2\Im} I(I + 1) \qquad (5.7)$$

where $\Im$ is the moment of inertia of the nucleus. $\Im$ increases as the deformation of the nucleus away from a spherical shape increases, and hence the energy of the rotational levels decreases with increasing deformability (or "softness") of the nucleus. The values of I in equation (5.7) may be $0,2,4,6\cdots$. The ratio of the energy of the $4(+)$ level to that of the $2(+)$ level according to the equation will be $4(4 + 1)/2(2 + 1)$ or 3.33. For Pu^{238} (Fig. 5.6), the experimental value of this ratio is $0.146/0.044$, or 3.32. Table 5.5 shows the experimental values of the ratio for several other nuclei. Observe that the ratio E_4/E_2 is very close to the theoretical value for nuclei which are far from a magic number. For Pb^{208}, the ratio is too small, and the individual energies E_2 and E_4 are very large. This nucleus therefore has a very small moment of inertia, corresponding to a very rigid structure, hard to deform.

TABLE 5.5. Ratio of Energies of $4(+)$ to $2(+)$ Levels for Even-Even Nuclei

Nucleus	E_2 ($2(+)$ level), Mev	E_4 ($4(+)$ level), Mev	E_4/E_2
$_{62}Sm^{150}$	0.337	0.777	2.3
$_{72}Hf^{176}$	0.088	0.290	3.30
$_{72}Hf^{180}$	0.093	0.309	3.33
$_{82}Pb^{208}$	2.614	3.20	1.2
$_{88}Ra^{226}$	0.068	0.210	3.09
$_{90}Th^{228}$	0.057	0.186	3.26
$_{90}Th^{230}$	0.053	0.174	3.28
$_{98}Cf^{250}$	0.041	0.139	3.39

The first excited state of an even-even nucleus is almost invariably a $2(+)$ state. The energies of these levels above the $0(+)$ ground state show an interesting variation with the mass number. This is shown in Figure 5.7. The huge peak at $A = 208$ corresponds to the doubly magic nucleus Pb^{208}. Finer detail for the region beyond Pb^{208} is shown in Figure 7.8.

In the shell model with the single particle assumptions, the nuclear spin I was equal to the total angular momentum j of the odd nucleon. Clearly this is not true for rotational levels, and we require some new quantum numbers to describe these levels. The nuclei in which we are interested are deformed from their spherical shape to either a prolate or an oblate spheroid (see Fig. 4.5). However, they still have an axis of symmetry. The nuclear spin is made up by vector addition of the particle angular momentum j and the collective motion angular momentum R. The addition of these two vectors is shown in Figure 5.8. The projection of the vectors j and I on the axis of symmetry of the nucleus are given by two new quantum numbers Ω and K respectively. Within any rotational band, all the levels are characterized by the same values of Ω and K.

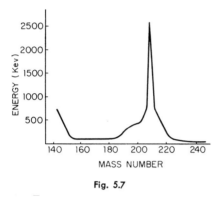

Fig. 5.7

For odd-A nuclei in which the ground state spin $I_0 = \Omega = K \geq \frac{3}{2}$, the energy E_I of the rotational level of spin I is given by

$$E_I = \frac{\hbar^2}{2\Im} [I(I + 1) - I_0(I_0 + 1)], \qquad I = I_0, I_0 + 1, I_0 + 2, \cdots$$

$$(5.8)$$

(For rotational bands in which $\Omega = K = \frac{1}{2}$, the situation is more complicated.)

In regions of strongly deformed nuclei far from magic numbers, the nuclear electric quadrupole moments sometimes reach values which are

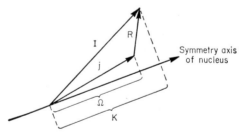

Fig. 5.8

far too large to be explained in terms of a single particle model. The electric quadrupole moment Q_j to be expected for a nucleus which has a single proton of total angular momentum j outside a closed shell is

$$Q_j = -\frac{2j - 1}{2(j + 1)} \cdot \frac{3}{5} R^2 \qquad (5.9)$$

R is the radius of the nucleus. Often the experimental values of quadrupole moments are far larger than this. By dividing the measured value by the magnitude of the value calculated from equation (5.9), we obtain a crude estimate of the number of nucleons which must be moving collectively to account for the measured quadrupole moment. Values as high as 40 are obtained in the region of strongly deformed nuclei between the magic numbers 82 and 126. Such large values lend strong support to the concept of collective motion in nuclei.

G. Nucleon-Nucleon Forces

In the discussion of the liquid drop model and the binding energies of nuclei in Chapter 3, we mentioned some of the properties which the force between nucleons must have if it is to be consistent with the observed properties of nuclei. We summarize these conclusions briefly:

(1) The nucleon-nucleon force shows the property of saturation, since nuclear densities and binding energies per nucleon are not a function of A. In this respect, the nuclear force resembles somewhat the force responsible for the chemical covalent bond.

(2) The forces between nucleons are independent of the charge of the nucleons: the n-n, p-p, and n-p forces are all equal.

In addition to these properties, the nucleon-nucleon force has the following characteristics:

(3) From experiments such as the Rutherford scattering of protons by nuclei, it appears that the nucleon-nucleon forces are exerted only over a very short range, of the order of 10^{-13} cm.

(4) From the binding energies of nuclei, it at once appears that the forces are far too strong to be of the familiar electrostatic, magnetic, or gravitational types.

A vast amount of experimental and theoretical work in nuclear physics has been concerned with the study of the nuclear forces by the use of scattering techniques. For example, the forces between two protons may be investigated by a detailed examination of the fate of a beam of protons from an accelerator when the protons are allowed to fall upon a target containing hydrogen (for example, a liquid hydrogen target). It is irrelevant that the target protons are actually hydrogen atoms or molecules, because the kinetic energy of the protons in the beam is so large compared with the energies in the chemical bonds. A beam of neutrons incident upon a hydrogenous target permits a study of the proton-neutron forces. Pure neutron targets are of course not available, but the forces between two neutrons may be studied by the bombardment of deuterium with neutrons. If the energy of the incident neutrons is large compared with the binding energy of the proton to the neutron in the deuteron (2.22 Mev), then the target nuclei will to a good approximation behave as a mixture of protons and neutrons. The effect of the protons on the neutron beam may be separated out by an independent study of the scattering of neutrons by protons in ordinary hydrogen targets.

As a result of all this experimental and theoretical work, several types of nucleon-nucleon forces have been distinguished, and apparently they are all involved simultaneously.

The first and simplest kind is an ordinary central force. Its strength depends only on the distance between the two nucleons and the orientation of their spins relative to one another. For example, the proton and neutron of the deuterium nucleus (deuteron) are bound together with a binding energy of 2.22 Mev. The nuclear spin is 1, and the orbital angular momentum of the nucleons is zero. The nuclear spin arises from the addition of the spins of the two nucleons. By the study of the scattering of slow neutrons in hydrogen, a second state of the deuteron has been found in which the spins of the two nucleons are antiparallel. However, in this state the binding energy of the neutron to the proton is much reduced—in fact, the spin 0 (spins antiparallel) state of the deuteron is actually unstable by about 50 kev, and the two nucleons do not remain together. This experiment clearly indicates that the strength of the nucleon-nucleon forces depends on the relative spin orientation of the two nucleons.

The same conclusion has been reached for the n-n and p-p forces. The dineutron (n-n) and the diproton (p-p) are both unstable. For both these nuclei, the spin 1 state is forbidden by the exclusion principle, and only the spin 0 state is permitted. As in the case of the deuteron, this spin 0 state is unbound.

A second kind of nuclear force is of the noncentral or tensor type. Its particular characteristic is that its strength depends not only on the distance between the two nucleons, but also on the angle which their spin vectors make with the line joining the two nucleons. The force between two isolated magnetic poles is a central force, but the force between two bar magnets is of the tensor type, since it depends not only on the distance between them, but also on their angles relative to the line joining their centers. The existence of a positive electric quadrupole moment for the deuteron requires that this nucleus must have a prolate spheroidal shape rather than spherical, and this is possible only if some tensor force is present in addition to the central force. The deuteron, under central forces alone, would be in a pure $^3S_1$ state (i.e. spins parallel, zero orbital angular momentum, and total angular momentum 1). In the presence of tensor forces, the total angular momentum and the sum of the spins remain meaningful quantities, but the orbital angular momentum does not (see Chapter 4, Section A). It is therefore possible for the deuteron wave function to contain a $^3D_1$ component (i.e., spins parallel, orbital angular momentum 2, total angular momentum 1). A P component (orbital angular momentum 1) cannot be present because it would be of the opposite parity, and the addition of tensor forces does not cause mixing in of components of different parity. The presence of the $^3D_1$ component permits the deuteron to have a quadrupole moment.

A third type of nuclear force is a "hard-core" repulsion which has been found to operate when two nucleons approach to within 0.5×10^{-13} cm. Its strength increases very rapidly with decreasing distance. It operates only between nucleons whose spins are antiparallel and whose total orbital angular momentum is zero (S state).

The repulsive force at small distances partly accounts for the constancy of nuclear density and the constancy of the binding energy per nucleon (saturation of nuclear forces), since it prevents nucleons in nuclei from packing closer and closer together as A increases. In the absence of a repulsive force, the close packing would cause the total binding energy to vary with some power of A greater than unity.

In addition to the forces already mentioned, there are probably others. For example, there is probably a force which depends on the magnitudes of, and the angles between, the orbital and spin angular momentum vectors. There may be forces which depend on the relative velocity of the pair of nucleons. Further, it may be that the total binding energy of a nucleus cannot be entirely represented as a sum of the effects of forces between pairs of nucleons; there may be forces which begin to act only when more than two nucleons are present.

So far, we have merely described the properties which the nucleon-nucleon forces must have in order to account for the experimental observations. The next step should be to construct a physical theory of the forces, but so far this step has been only partially successful.

Like nuclear forces, the forces holding the atoms together to form molecules show the phenomenon of saturation. Since the interatomic force can be thought of as due to the exchange of electrons between the atoms, Heisenberg suggested that the nucleon-nucleon force was also of the exchange type. It was discovered later that the object exchanged is actually a π-meson (pion). The π-meson may have $+1$, 0, or -1 electron charges. The rest mass of the neutral pion (π^0) is 264 electron masses; for the π^+ and π^-, the rest mass is 276 electron masses. The spin of all three types is zero.

The emission by a proton of a π^+, and its capture by a neutron, is equivalent to an interchange of positions of the two nucleons. The same result is obtained by the emission of a π^- by a neutron and its capture by a proton. In the interaction between two nucleons of the same type, a π^0 can be exchanged. The proton and neutron can each be thought of as continually emitting and reabsorbing pions. For an isolated particle, the permanent loss of a pion is energetically impossible, because no energy is available to provide the rest mass energy of the pion. Nevertheless, a "virtual" emission followed rapidly by reabsorption can occur. The uncertainty principle permits the law of conservation of energy to be broken by an amount of energy ΔE, provided that the time Δt for which the infraction lasts is such that $\Delta E \Delta t \leq \hbar$. In other words, there would never be any possibility of detecting the failure of energy conservation in such a short time. It is because the proton and neutron, even in isolation, are continually emitting and reabsorbing charged and uncharged pions, that their magnetic moments are not what would be expected for simple rotating particles. The pions occupy the same position in the theory of nuclear forces as the photon in the theory of electromagnetic forces.

If the emission and reabsorption of pions is coupled to the spins of the nucleons, then nucleons could exchange spins as well as positions. In fact four types of exchange interactions are theoretically possible, but no one of them, or combination of them, is in complete agreement with all the experimental observations. For example, the meson theory predicts a repulsion at short distances between nucleons with both parallel and antiparallel spins, whereas as we saw above, the repulsion is only observed when the spins are antiparallel.

The possibility that particles of mass intermediate between electrons and nucleons were involved in nuclear forces was first predicted by Yukawa in 1935. The first such particle to be discovered was the μ-meson, but it was soon realized that this could not be the Yukawa particle since it interacts very feebly with nucleons. Positive and negative μ-mesons are known. Their charges are identical with the electronic charge, they both have spin $\frac{1}{2}$, but their masses are 105.70 Mev. In 1947, Lattes, Ochialini, and Powell discovered the π-meson in the cosmic radiation falling on the earth from outer space. Pions are also produced in the bombardment of nuclei with high energy particle such as protons, and quite intense beams can be obtained in this way. The charged pion decays into a μ-meson of the same sign and a neutrino; its half life is 2.56×10^{-8} sec. (The neutrino is a particle of spin $\frac{1}{2}$ and zero mass and charge; it is discussed in Chapter 8.) The π^0 meson decays into two γ-rays, or more rarely into an electron, a positron, and a photon. The π^0 half life is less than 0.4×10^{-15} sec. The μ-meson is also unstable; it decays into an electron of the same sign and two neutrinos. The half life is 2.22×10^{-6} sec.

REFERENCES

1. Mayer, M. G., *Phys. Rev.*, **74**, 235 (1948); *ibid.*, **75**, 1969 (1949).

2. Haxel, O., J. H. D. Jensen, and H. Suess, *Phys. Rev.*, **75**, 1766 (1949).

3. Feenberg, E., *The Shell Theory of the Nucleus*, Princeton University Press, Princeton, 1955.

4. Mayer, M. G., and J. H. D. Jensen, *Elementary Theory of Nuclear Shell Structure*, John Wiley & Sons, New York, 1955.

5. Bohr, A., and B. R. Mottelson, "Collective and Individual Particle Aspects of the Nucleus," *Mat. Fys. Medd. Dan. Vid. Selsk.*, **27**, No. 16 (1953).

6. Villars, F., "The Collective Model of the Nucleus," *Ann. Revs. Nuclear Sci.*, **7**, 185 (1957).

7. Blatt, J. M., and V. F. Weisskopf, *Theoretical Nuclear Physics*, John Wiley & Sons, New York, 1952.

8. Orear, J., A. H. Rosenfeld, and R. A. Schluter, *Nuclear Physics (Fermi Lecture Notes)*, University of Chicago Press, Chicago, 1950.

9. Evans, R. D., *The Atomic Nucleus*, McGraw-Hill Book Co., New York, 1955.

10. Elton, L. R. B., *Introductory Nuclear Theory*, Isaac Pitman and Sons Ltd., London, 1959.

11. Endt, P. M., and M. Demeur, *Nuclear Reactions*, North Holland Publishing Co., Amsterdam, 1959.

12. Griffith, T. C., and E. A. Power (eds.), *Nuclear Forces and the Few Nucleon Problem*, Pergamon Press, London, 1960.

13. Flügge S. (ed.), *Handbuch der Physik*, Julius Springer Verlag, Berlin, 1957: Vol. XXXIX, *Structure of the Atomic Nucleus*.

14. Siegbahn, K. (ed.), *Beta- and Gamma-Ray Spectroscopy*, North Holland Publishing Co., Amsterdam, 1955.

PROBLEMS

1. What is the minimum energy which (a) a proton (b) a helium ion would require in order to penetrate the nucleus of Th^{232}?

2. It is found experimentally that the Coulomb barrier for helium ions approaching a nucleus of Bi^{209} has a height of 19.5 Mev. What would you conclude about the value of the radius parameter R_0 in the equation $R = R_0 A^{1/3}$ [Equation (3.7)]?

3. Calculate from the shell model the spins, parities, and magnetic moments of the following nuclei, and compare your results with the measured values: $_{16}S^{33}$, $_{19}K^{41}$, $_{20}Ca^{43}$, $_{27}Co^{59}$, $_{35}Br^{81}$, $_{53}I^{129}$.

4. Sb^{121} has spin $\frac{5}{2}$ and magnetic moment 3.36 n.m. What is the state of the 51st proton? What would the shell model predict?

5. How would you explain the spin $\frac{1}{2}$ and magnetic moment -0.8824 n.m. of Te^{125}?

6. Calculate the energy which you would expect for the $4(+)$, $6(+)$, $8(+)$, and $10(+)$ members of a rotational band in an even-even nucleus if the energy of the $2(+)$ member of the band is 0.044 Mev above the ground state. Compare your results with Figure 5.6.

7. Np^{237} has levels at 0.033, 0.060, 0.076, 0.103, and 0.159 Mev. Which of these, if any, would you expect to be members of a rotational band whose first member is the $\frac{5}{2}(+)$ ground state of Np^{237}?

8. Calculate the nuclear temperature of an excited nucleus of Bi^{210} which was formed by the capture of a very low (essentially zero) energy neutron in the nucleus Bi^{209}.

9. Assuming that the binding energy of a neutron or a proton is 7 Mev in each case, calculate the depth of the potential well for several nuclei, and draw a graph of well depth vs. mass number.

10. From the shell model, assign spins and parities to: $_{36}Kr^{86}$, $_{37}Rb^{87}$, $_{29}Cu^{64}$.

11. The spin of B^{10} is 3. According to the shell model, what proton and neutron states combine to give this value?

12. What shell model states could be responsible for the $\frac{1}{2}(-)$, $\frac{5}{2}(-)$, and $\frac{13}{2}(+)$ spins of the ground state and first two excited states of Pb^{207}?

CHAPTER 6

Gamma Radiation Processes

A. Introduction

In Chapter 3, we discussed stable and unstable nuclei in terms of the energies available for spontaneous radioactive transformations. In the next three chapters, we will consider each type of decay in more detail. A very common consequence of a radioactive transformation of any type is that the product nucleus is formed in an energetically excited state rather than in its lowest energy (ground) state. Such excited states decay to the ground state usually very rapidly, eliminating their excess energy by the emission either of γ-ray quanta or of electrons which are ejected from the atomic orbits. Since these phenomena are commonly observed as a consequence of any type of radioactive decay, it is convenient to discuss them first.

B. General Theory of γ-ray Emission

The excited states of nuclei are definite quantum states characterized by their energy excess above the ground state, and by their spin and parity. The first objective of the theory of emission of γ-rays from nuclei is then to obtain expressions for the emission probability in terms of the energy available and of the spins and parities of the initial and final levels. The theory falls into two parts, first the investigation of the mechanism of γ-ray emission in general terms, and second, its application to actual nuclei. Only in the second part is it necessary to assume a detailed model of nuclear structure. The models most generally useful, and the only ones that we shall discuss, are the single particle model and the collective model. The choice between these two models in any particular case depends on which of them provides the most accurate description of the initial and final nuclear states.

Since the γ-rays are electromagnetic radiations, their emission by nuclei bears some resemblance to the emission of electromagnetic radio waves from an antenna. In both cases, the emission is due to the oscillation of electric charge. The complex oscillations of electric charge in nuclei may be broken down into the backward and forward motion of charges and into the fluctuation of the electric current flowing in closed loops. The distribution of charge within a nucleus can be given mathematical expression by means of equation (4.10), which introduced the concept of electric multipoles. An analogous expression for the distribution of closed current loops defines the magnetic multipoles. Oscillation of an electric multipole is said to produce electric multipole radiation, and oscillation of a magnetic multipole is said to produce magnetic multipole radiation.

The theory next proceeds to calculate the probability of emission of a photon from an oscillating electric or magnetic multipole. For example, the probability that an electric dipole will emit a photon of frequency ν in unit time is

$$\text{Probability} = \frac{128}{9} \frac{\pi^3 \nu^3}{\hbar c^3} B \tag{6.1}$$

where B is a quantity which remains to be determined. It is called the reduced transition probability.

In the nuclear case, we are concerned with the properties of the initial and final states involved in the transition, and the factor B of equation (6.1) must be evaluated in terms of these properties. It is possible to write an exact expression for B in terms of the wave functions ψ_i and ψ_f of the initial and final states. However, the wave functions cannot be evaluated without the introduction of some simplifying nuclear model. In the second part of the theory, then, the nuclear models are introduced to permit a rough calculation of B and hence of the γ-ray emission probabilities.

Electromagnetic theory of radiation from any oscillating charge or current loop (whether in a nucleus or a radio antenna) shows that the emitted quanta carry away angular momentum as well as energy. For example, the oscillation of an electric dipole causes the emission of one unit of angular momentum ($\hbar$) per emitted quantum. The energy lost per quantum is of course $h\nu$, where ν is the frequency of the radiation.

Further, there may or may not be a change in parity between the initial and final states of the nucleus. The general rules governing the angular momentum l carried away and the presence or absence of a parity change are given by the following relations, in which I_i and I_f and π_i and π_f are the spins and parities of the initial and final states. (The π's are to be equal to $+1$ for even parity, and 0 for odd parity.)

$$
\left.
\begin{aligned}
&\text{1. } I_i + I_f \geq l \geq |I_i - I_f| \\
&\text{2. } \pi_i + \pi_f + l \text{ is odd for radiation by magnetic multipoles.} \\
&\text{3. } \pi_i + \pi_f + l \text{ is even for radiation by electric multipoles.}
\end{aligned}
\right\} \quad (6.2)
$$

These relations are quite general, and independent of any assumptions about nuclear structure.

As an example of the application of equations (6.2), consider the decay of the $\frac{11}{2}(-)$ excited state of Te^{129} to the ground state, whose spin and parity are $\frac{3}{2}(+)$. $I_i + I_f = 7$, and $|I_i - I_f| = 4$. Hence the angular momentum l carried away by the γ-ray could be 4, 5, 6, or 7 units. In practice, the γ-ray nearly always carries away the minimum permitted angular momentum, which is 4 units in this case. (This observation is consistent with calculations of B based on single particle wave functions, and we shall return to this point below.) For $l = 4$, π_i odd (0), and π_f even ($+1$), equation (6.2) shows that the radiation must take place by oscillation of a magnetic multipole.

As a second example, consider Pb^{204}. A state of spin and parity $9(-)$ decays to a lower energy state of spin and parity $4(+)$. The angular momentum carried away must lie between 5 and 13 units, and if it is 5 units, the transition must take place by the oscillation of an electric multipole.

A simple terminology is commonly used to describe the type of transition which is taking place. The letter E or M represents electric or magnetic multipole oscillation, and a number represents the angular momentum carried away. Thus the two examples given above were M4 and E5 radiations respectively. The complete terminology is summarized in Table 6.1.   It must be emphasized that there is no difference between photons which are emitted by the various types of multipoles. Only the processes by which the photons are generated are different.

TABLE 6.1. Terminology of γ-Ray Processes

Radiation type	Name	Angular momentum carried away	Does nuclear parity change?
E1	Electric dipole	1	Yes
M1	Magnetic dipole	1	No
E2	Electric quadrupole	2	No
M2	Magnetic quadrupole	2	Yes
E3	Electric octupole	3	Yes
M3	Magnetic octupole	3	No
E4	Electric 2^4-pole	4	No
M4	Magnetic 2^4-pole	4	Yes
	and so on $\cdots$		

The minimum angular momentum which can be carried away by a γ-ray photon is one unit.   Transitions are therefore absolutely forbidden between two levels which both have spin zero.   The only possible electrical oscillations for such a transition would be caused by alternate expansions and contractions of the nuclear volume.   However, pulsations like this produce no change in the electromagnetic field strength at a distance from the nucleus, and therefore cannot lead to the emission of photons.   Nuclei pulsating in this way can, however, interact with the orbital electrons of the atom, since the wave functions of the electrons are not zero inside the nuclear volume.   Therefore transitions can occur in which the excited state transfers energy to an electron, causing its ejection from the atom.   This process, which is called *internal conversion*, will be described in more detail below.   Its occurrence is not confined to transitions between nuclear states with zero spin, as we shall see.

C. Gamma-Ray Emission and the Single Particle Model

The application of a specific nuclear model permits the calculation of the half life of an excited nuclear state for the emission of a γ-ray. Returning to the example of the $\frac{11}{2}(-)$ state of Te^{129} mentioned above, we may hope to find out why the transition is M4 rather than E5, M6, or E7, which are also permitted by the general rules of equation (6.2). Using the single particle model to describe the nuclear states, Blatt and Weisskopf gave the following equations for the decay constants λ_e and λ_m for electric and magnetic transitions as a function of the angular momentum carried away (l), the γ-ray energy (E, Mev), and the nuclear radius R (in units of 10^{-13} cm):

$$\lambda_e = 10^{21} \frac{4.4(l+1)}{l[(2l+1)!!]^2} \left(\frac{3}{l+3}\right)^2 \left(\frac{E}{197}\right)^{2l+1} R^{2l} \text{ sec}^{-1}$$

$$\lambda_m = 10^{21} \frac{1.9(l+1)}{l[(2l+1)!!]^2} \left(\frac{3}{l+3}\right)^2 \left(\frac{E}{197}\right)^{2l+1} R^{2l-2} \text{ sec}^{-1}$$

(6.3)

The half lives t_e and t_m are of course related to the decay constants by the equations

$$t_e = \frac{\log_e 2}{\lambda_e}$$

$$t_m = \frac{\log_e 2}{\lambda_m}$$

(6.4)

The double factorial symbol !! in equation (6.3) means $(2l+1)(2l-1)$ $(2l-3)\cdots1$. Inspection of equations (6.3) and (6.4) shows that the half life of a transition depends very critically on both the energy E and the angular momentum l. For example in M4 or E4 transitions, the half life is inversely proportional to the ninth power of the energy. An increase in l causes a very great increase in the half life of the transition, and it is for this reason that transitions usually occur by the lowest permitted multipole order. Transitions by higher multipole orders take place, but only an insignificant fraction of all the excited nuclei actually decay this way in most cases.

For any values of E and l, the ratio of the magnetic to electric multipole half lives is, for a nucleus of radius R fermis:

$$\frac{t_m}{t_e} = 2.3R^2$$

In medium-weight elements, where the nuclear radius is about 6×10^{-13} cm, this ratio is approximately 100. Hence electric multipole transitions should be about 100 times faster than magnetic transitions. For this reason, an E2 transition will often compete favorably with a magnetic transition one multipole order lower (M1). For example, the decay of the 0.113 Mev level of Hf^{177} to the ground state takes place by a mixture of 5% M1 and 95% E2 transitions. For higher values of l, successful competition of $E(l+1)$ with $M(l)$ is not observed experimentally.

Nuclear states whose half lives are longer than some very arbitrary amount are frequently referred to as isomeric states or metastable states. The transition to the lower energy state is called an isomeric transition (abbreviation IT). Long-lived isomers occur most frequently in those regions of the periodic system just below the magic numbers. Such groups of isomers are sometimes called "islands of isomerism." A typical example is $_{48}$Cd^{115}. The ground state spin is $\frac{1}{2}(+)$, and the 67th neutron is presumably in the $3s_{1/2}$ level. Just above this level there lies the $1h_{11/2}$ level, and the excitation of the Cd^{115} nucleus by 0.18 Mev raises the 67th neutron into this level, forming an excited state of spin $\frac{11}{2}(-)$. The decay of this state back to the ground state requires an M6 or E5 transition, and by equation (6.3) the calculated half life for the E5 transition is found to be very roughly 5000 years. The M6 transition, of course, would be much slower. In fact, the decay of the excited (metastable) state to the ground state is not observed experimentally, because the excited state decays by β^--decay, for which its half life is only 44 days. As in this example, the existence of the islands of isomerism depends on the depression (by spin-orbit coupling) of high spin states, so that excited states of high spin may lie close in energy above the low spin nuclear ground states. Decay between such pairs of states with a big spin difference and only a small energy difference can take place only slowly.

The interpretation of the half lives of nuclear states by means of the single particle model is fairly successful. The application of a little algebra to equations (6.3) shows that the mean lives τ_e and τ_m for electric and magnetic multipole transitions are given by:

$$\frac{1}{\lambda_e} = \tau_e = (\text{numerical constants}) \times \frac{l[(2l+1)!!]^2}{(l+1)} \left(\frac{l+3}{3}\right)^2 \left(\frac{197}{E}\right)^{2l+1} A^{-\frac{2l}{3}}$$

$$\frac{1}{\lambda_m} = \tau_m = (\text{numerical constants}) \times \frac{l[(2l+1)!!]^2}{(l+1)} \left(\frac{l+3}{3}\right)^2 \left(\frac{197}{E}\right)^{2l+1} \left(\frac{1}{A}\right)^{\frac{2l-2}{3}}$$

$$(6.5)$$

In these equations, the nuclear radius has been replaced by (constant $\times$ $A^{1/3}$).

Inspection of equation (6.5) shows that, for a given value of l, the functions $\tau_e A^{2l/3} E^{2l+1}$ and $\tau_m A^{(2l-2)/3} E^{2l+1}$ should be constant regardless of the energy of the transition or of the mass number A of the decaying nucleus. Figures 6.1 and 6.2 show the values of these functions for a large number of transformations. (The functions are plotted against neutron number N merely to "spread out" the values for display.) The functions (which are called reduced lifetimes) do in fact show a strong tendency to fall into groups corresponding to the different multipole transition types, but within each group there is a variation of several orders of magnitude. The horizontal lines in the figures are theoretical estimates of the reduced lifetimes based on the single particle model of the nucleus. Notice that within each group (except the E2 group), the experimental reduced lifetimes are nearly always longer than the theoretical estimate. In the E2 group, however, many are two orders of magnitude shorter than the theoretical estimate. Most of these fast E2 transitions involve nuclear states which are better described by the collec-

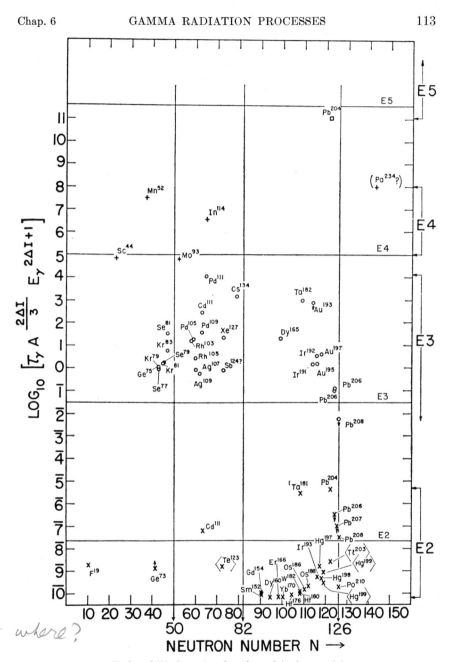

— where?

Fig. 6.1. Reduced lifetimes for electric multipole transitions as a function of neutron number N. (From M. Goldhaber, and J. Weneser, *Annual Reviews of Nuclear Science*, **5**, (1955)

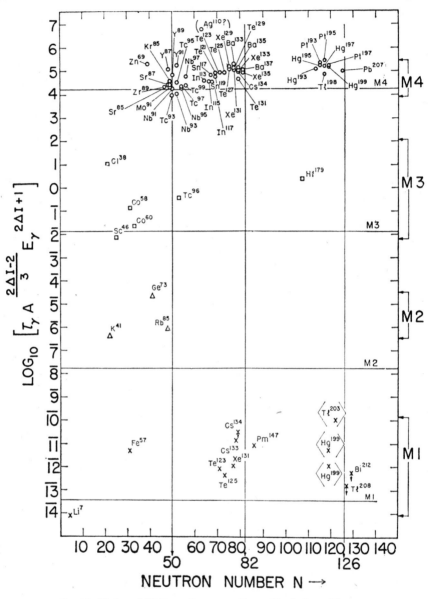

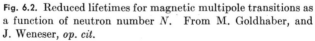

Fig. 6.2. Reduced lifetimes for magnetic multipole transitions as a function of neutron number N. From M. Goldhaber, and J. Weneser, *op. cit.*

tive model than by the single particle model.   They are in fact states in which the excitation energy is stored in the collective motion of large numbers of nucleons rather than in the excitation of a single nucleon to a higher energy level in the nuclear well.

D. Gamma-Ray Emission and the Collective Model

The calculation of the probability of γ-ray emission from a rotational energy level of an excited nucleus again requires the evaluation of the B of equation (6.1).

Many examples are known of rotational bands in even-even nuclei, such as that illustrated in Figure 5.6.   Decay of an excited state at the top of the band is observed experimentally to occur by the stepwise emission of a cascade of γ-rays.   There are no "cross-over" transitions in which a level decays to a lower level two or more steps down.   Decay is by E2 transitions.   The theory of the rotational bands gives the following equation for the decay constant $\lambda(E2)$ for the decay of a level of spin $(I + 2)$ to a state of spin I:

$$\lambda(E2) = \frac{8\pi^6 E^5}{5 c^5 h^5} e^2 Q_0{}^2 \frac{(I + 1)(I + 2)}{(2I + 3)(2I + 5)} \tag{6.6}$$

Q_0 is the "intrinsic electric quadrupole moment," which is closely related to the quadrupole moment discussed in Chapter 4 C.   As we observed in Chapter 5 F, strongly deformed nuclei in the regions where the collective model works best often have very large electric quadrupole moments.   For such nuclei, equation (6.6) shows that the E2 decay constant will be large, or the half life for the transition will be short.

For odd-A nuclei, rotational bands form the sequence of spins $I = K,\ (K + 1),\ (K + 2),\ \cdots,$

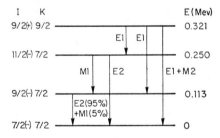

Fig. 6.3. Excited states of the odd-A nucleus Hf^{177} showing rotational band with $K = \frac{7}{2}$

where K is the projection of the total angular momentum on the nuclear symmetry axis (see Fig. 5.8).   For such bands, decays from $I + 1$ to I occur by M1 and E2 transitions (or a mixture of the two).   Crossover transitions from $I + 2$ to I also occur by E2 radiation.   An example of such a rotational band is given in Figure 6.3.   Again, the theory of rotational bands permits calculation of the decay constants for these different transitions.   Equations involving $Q_0{}^2$, similar to equation (6.6), are obtained, but the final term involves the K quantum number as well as I.

When a transition occurs between states which are members of two

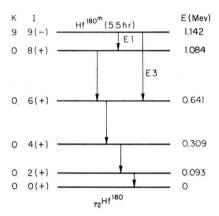

different rotational bands, the multipolarity l of the radiation must be equal to or greater than the difference in the values of the K quantum numbers of the two bands. A transition which violates this rule may still take place, but it will be slowed down. In a few cases, violation of the rule slows down a transition so much that a long-lived isomer results. Figure 6.4 shows the decay scheme of the 5.5 hr isomeric state of Hf^{180}. The two transitions from the isomeric level are E1 and E3, but each of them involves a change of 9 in the K quantum number. As a result, the two transitions are slowed down by factors of about 10^{16} and 10^9 respectively.

Fig. 6.4. K-selection rule for the isomeric state of $_{72}Hf^{180}$

E. Internal Conversion

The interaction of an excited state of a nucleus with the orbital electrons resembles closely the emission of a γ-ray from the nucleus. The reason for this is that both processes are electromagnetic. It was originally thought that the ejection of an atomic electron by internal conversion took place in two steps. The first was the emission of a γ-ray. The second was the interaction of the γ-ray with the atomic electrons, leading to the ejection of one of them by a photoelectric effect. However, this mechanism is definitely incorrect. The simplest argument against it is that internal conversion permits the decay of a state of spin 0 to another state of spin 0, and as we have seen, γ-ray emission is absolutely forbidden in this case.

The ejected electron, which is called a conversion electron, will have kinetic energy E_e which can be readily calculated from the equation

$$E_e = E_\gamma - E_B \qquad (6.7)$$

where E_γ is the energy difference between the initial and final nuclear states, and E_B is the binding energy of the ejected electron to the atom. E_γ is also, of course, the energy of the photon which is emitted when the same transition takes place by the emission of a γ-ray instead of by internal conversion.

The conversion electrons arising from the decay of a particular nuclear state will have an energy spectrum consisting of a series of discrete energy groups. The lowest energy group will contain those electrons which were ejected from the electron shell closest to the nucleus, the K shell, since E_B is greatest for these electrons. The next highest energy group will arise from the L shell, and so on. If the energy difference between the two nuclear states is *less* than the binding energy of the electrons in a particular shell, then obviously no electrons from that shell can be ejected. The line spectrum of conversion electron energies is in marked contrast with the *continuous* spectrum of electron energies arising from the β-decay process.

Decay of a nuclear state by internal conversion takes place in competition with decay by γ-ray emission. To each process there will correspond a partial decay constant and half life, and the overall decay constant for the nuclear state will be equal to the sum of the partial decay constants. The ratio of the number of conversion electrons to the number of γ-ray quanta emitted in the same time is called the conversion coefficient α:

$$\alpha = \frac{\text{Number of conversion electrons}}{\text{Number of } \gamma\text{-ray quanta}} \qquad (6.8)$$

The conversion coefficient may be subdivided according to the electron shells from which the electrons originate. Thus the K shell conversion coefficient α_K, is defined as

$$\alpha_K = \frac{\text{Number of } K \text{ conversion electrons}}{\text{Number of } \gamma\text{-ray quanta}} \qquad (6.9)$$

The total conversion coefficient α will be equal to the sum of all the separate electron shell conversion coefficients:

$$\alpha = \alpha_K + \alpha_L + \alpha_M + \cdots \qquad (6.10)$$

The coefficients for the $L, M \cdots$ shells are further subdivided. Thus α_{L_I} is the coefficient for conversion in the L_I subshell ($2s$ electrons), $\alpha_{L_{II}}$ for the L_{II} subshell ($2p_{1/2}$ electrons) and $\alpha_{L_{III}}$ for the L_{III} subshell ($2p_{3/2}$ electrons).

The partial decay constant λ_{conv} for the internal conversion process may be calculated (approximately) by assuming a suitable nuclear model. However, it is far more useful to tabulate values of the conversion coefficients. Since the conversion coefficients represent *ratios* of the probability of decay by internal conversion to γ-ray emission, the specifically nuclear assumptions vanish from the final results. The calculated conversion coefficients depend almost entirely on the properties of the atomic electron shells, and these are much better understood than nuclear properties. Very extensive tables of conversion coefficients have been published by M. E. Rose (*Internal Conversion Coefficients*, Interscience Publishers, Inc., New York, 1958) and by L. A. Sliv and I. M. Band in the U.S.S.R.

The internal conversion coefficients depend on the atomic number of the atom in which the conversion is occurring, the energy of the nuclear transition, and its multipole order. Therefore by measuring experimentally either one of the conversion coefficients or (which is often easier and more accurate) the ratios of conversion coefficients in two different shells or subshells, it is often possible to determine unambiguously the multipole order of a transition.

As an example of this method, consider the electron-capture decay of Hf^{173} to Lu^{173}. Many levels of Lu^{173} are formed, among them a level with an energy 0.124 Mev above the ground state. This excited level has been assigned spin and parity $\frac{5}{2}(-)$, and it decays to the $\frac{7}{2}(+)$ ground state. The intensities of the various conversion electron lines were measured by Harmatz, Handley, and Mihelich. Table 6.2 shows a comparison of their results with the calculated conversion coefficients of Rose. The results indicate that the transition is E1, since the experimental and calculated ratios agree much better for this assignment than for any other.

TABLE 6.2. Comparison of the Experimental and Calculated Conversion
Coefficient Ratios for Decay of the 0.124 Mev Level of Lu^{173}

	Experimental	Calculated			
		E1	E2	M1	M2
α_K/α_L	4.88	3.6	6×10^{-2}	4.2	1.0
α_{LI}/α_{LII}	3.57	2.3	2.2×10^{-2}	12	11
$\alpha_{LII}/\alpha_{LIII}$	0.87	0.8	0.9	6.5	0.25

For any multipole order, the conversion coefficients always increase with decreasing transition energy. For low energy transitions, they may become very large, and the decay of the excited state then takes place almost entirely by the emission of conversion electrons. In many cases, so few γ-ray quanta are emitted that it becomes impossible to detect them. A few examples of the conversion coefficients calculated by Rose are given in Table 6.3.

TABLE 6.3. Sample of the Internal Conversion Coefficients for $Z = 25$ and $Z = 50$, Calculated by M. E. Rose (*loc. cit.*)

E, Mev	α_K				α_{L_I}			
	E1	E2	M1	M2	E1	E2	M1	M2
				$Z = 25$				
0.05	2.10	6.53(1)	1.21(0)	4.28(1)	1.60(−1)	4.66(0)	1.05(−1)	4.55(0)
0.10	2.70(−1)^a	5.20(0)	1.68(−1)	3.13(0)	2.15(−2)	4.01(−1)	1.46(−2)	3.03(−1)
0.15	7.76(−2)	1.11(0)	5.52(−2)	7.18(−1)	6.33(−3)	8.81(−2)	4.76(−3)	6.65(−2)
0.20	3.19(−2)	3.67(−1)	2.56(−2)	2.58(−1)	2.65(−3)	2.97(−2)	2.21(−3)	2.36(−2)
0.40	3.86(−3)	2.56(−2)	4.31(−3)	2.50(−2)	3.23(−4)	2.14(−3)	3.71(−4)	2.21(−3)
0.60	1.18(−3)	5.72(−3)	1.62(−3)	7.00(−3)	9.93(−5)	4.81(−4)	1.39(−4)	6.09(−4)
0.80	5.31(−4)	2.10(−3)	8.30(−4)	2.97(−3)	4.53(−5)	1.79(−4)	7.16(−5)	2.60(−4)
1.00	2.98(−4)	1.01(−3)	5.04(−4)	1.58(−3)	2.52(−5)	8.57(−5)	4.31(−5)	1.36(−4)
1.50	1.16(−4)	3.05(−4)	2.11(−4)	5.31(−4)	9.93(−6)	2.63(−5)	1.82(−5)	4.61(−5)
2.00	6.48(−5)	1.47(−4)	1.19(−4)	2.61(−4)	5.49(−6)	1.26(−5)	1.01(−5)	2.55(−5)
				$Z = 50$				
0.05	—	—	—	—	5.55(−1)	2.13(0)	3.03(0)	2.12(2)
0.10	9.86(−1)	8.34(0)	3.38(0)	5.66(1)	9.11(−2)	7.16(−1)	3.80(−1)	1.02(1)
0.15	3.31(−1)	2.68(0)	1.05(0)	1.25(1)	3.11(−2)	2.29(−1)	1.17(−1)	1.97(0)
0.20	1.48(−1)	1.07(0)	4.64(−1)	4.36(0)	1.46(−2)	9.63(−2)	5.19(−2)	6.43(−1)
0.40	2.10(−2)	1.05(−1)	6.90(−2)	3.80(−1)	2.16(−3)	1.04(−2)	7.60(−3)	4.98(−2)
0.60	7.04(−3)	2.79(−2)	2.38(−2)	1.00(−1)	7.42(−4)	2.87(−3)	2.64(−3)	1.26(−2)
0.80	3.38(−3)	1.14(−2)	1.14(−2)	4.10(−2)	3.62(−4)	1.20(−3)	1.27(−3)	5.03(−3)
1.00	1.98(−3)	5.96(−3)	6.63(−3)	2.11(−2)	2.11(−4)	6.39(−4)	7.34(−4)	2.55(−3)
1.50	8.10(−4)	2.07(−3)	2.53(−3)	6.75(−3)	8.74(−5)	2.25(−4)	2.81(−4)	7.94(−4)
2.00	4.59(−4)	1.06(−3)	1.31(−3)	3.17(−3)	4.99(−5)	1.17(−4)	1.46(−4)	3.70(−4)

^{a} The numbers in parentheses are the powers of 10. Thus $2.70(−1) = 2.70 \times 10^{-1}$.

F. The Auger Effect

As a result of the emission of a conversion electron, the atom will be left with a vacancy in one of its electron shells. The vacancy is usually filled with an electron from a higher shell. For example, the emission of a K shell electron creates a vacancy in that shell. The vacancy can be filled with an electron from any higher shell. If it comes from the L shell, the atom may emit an X-ray quantum whose energy is equal to the difference in electron binding energy between the K and L shells. Alternatively, the energy may appear as an electron torn from another electron shell. This process, which is analogous to the internal conversion process, is known as the Auger effect, after its discoverer, Pierre Auger. The electrons thus ejected from the atom are called Auger electrons. The Auger electrons will usually be of lower energy than the conversion electrons. The Auger effect creates an additional electron shell vacancy which will lead to further X-ray or Auger electron emission. The complete process of atomic rearrangement may thus be very complex.

The fraction of the vacancies in a given electron shell which, when filled, results in the emission of an Auger electron is called the Auger yield. The fraction which results in the emission of an X-ray is called the

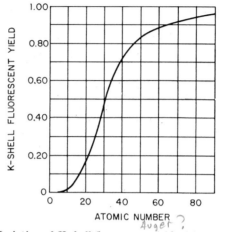

Fig. 6.5. Variation of K-shell fluorescent yield with atomic number. From C. D. Broyles, D. A. Thomas, and S. K. Haynes, *Phys. Rev.*, **89**, 715 (1953)

fluorescent yield. The variation of the K shell fluorescent yield with atomic number is shown in Figure 6.5.

G. Angular Correlations Involving γ-Rays

The emission of radiation of any type from a decaying sample is normally *isotropic*—that is, the radiation intensity is the same in all directions around the sample. The decaying nuclei individually may have a preferred direction for emitting their radiation, but since they are randomly oriented, the radiation will be isotropic unless of course special steps have been taken to destroy the normal random orientation of the nuclei.

Many α- and β-decay processes lead to the formation of excited states of nuclei which often decay very rapidly by the emission of γ-rays. In many cases, there will be a correlation between the direction of emission of an α- or β-ray and the subsequent γ-radiation from the same nucleus. When an excited nuclear state decays by the emission of two γ-ray quanta, there will be a correlation between the direction of emission of the two photons.

These effects may be studied with a pair of suitable counters. The first counter detects the first radiation (α- or β-particle or the first γ-ray of a cascade). This counter is placed in a fixed position relative to the decaying sample. The second counter detects the second radiation, but it only records an event which is virtually simultaneous with an event in the first counter. In practice, "simultaneous" means that the two events must occur within about 10^{-9} sec of each other. By keeping this time interval (the coincidence resolving time) as short as possible, it is possible to ensure that the two events belong to the decay of one and the same nucleus. Then by rotating the second counter around the sample, the angular correlation between the two radiations may be studied.

When the angle between the two counters is θ, the intensity of the radiation measured by the second counter, relative to the intensity when the angle is 90°, is given by the equation

Relative intensity at angle $\theta = 1 + a_2 \cos^2 \theta + a_4 \cos^4 \theta$
$$+ \cdots a_{2L} \cos^{2L} \theta \quad (6.11)$$

The coefficients $a_2, a_4 \cdots a_{2L}$ are functions of the spins of the initial, intermediate, and final levels, and of the multipolarities of the two transitions. The highest power of $\cos \theta$ which occurs in the series is determined by the condition that $2L$ must be equal to or less than $2l_1$, $2l_2$, or $2I_B$, whichever is the smaller.† (l_1 and l_2 are the multipolarities of the two transitions, and I_B is the spin of the intermediate level.) When the smallest of these quantities happens to be $2I_B$, then $2L$ will be equal to the next smallest even number, if $2I_B$ is odd.

As an example of the application of equation (6.11), consider a γ-ray cascade in which a nucleus of spin 0 decays by an E1 transition to a state of spin 1, which in turn decays by an E1 transition to a state of spin 0. In this case, $2l_1$, $2l_2$ and $2I_B$ will all have the value 2. The angular correlation for this case will therefore be

Relative intensity at angle $\theta = 1 + a_2 \cos^2 \theta \quad (6.12)$

There will be no higher powers of $\cos \theta$ in the series. According to this equation, the highest intensity of the second radiation will be found at 0° and 180° relative to the direction of emission of the first radiation.

If the nuclear state responsible for the second radiation has a long enough half life, the nucleus may have time to rotate, with the result that the correlation in direction between the two radiations may partially or completely disappear. The forces responsible for this effect arise from the interaction of the nuclear magnetic moment with intense magnetic fields due to the atomic electrons (in paramagnetic atoms or ions), or to the interaction of the nuclear electric quadrupole moment with intense inhomogeneous electric fields. Such fields may arise from the crystal structure of the sample or from the formation of complex ions. Novey studied the angular correlation between the α-particle emitted by Am[241] and the subsequent γ-radiation from the 0.060 Mev excited state of the daughter nucleus Np[237]. This excited state decays with a half life of 6.3 × 10⁻⁸ sec, which is long enough to permit very considerable attenuation of the angular correlation in solid samples where intense electric fields occur. By using samples of Am[241] dissolved in thin liquid films, Novey was able to obtain much stronger correlations. The correlation was strongest in perchloric acid solutions, and weaker in sulfate and citrate solutions. These observations are consistent with the known order of complexing strength (citrate > sulfate > perchlorate).

Studies of angular correlations can therefore be used to yield information of chemical as well as nuclear interest, and it seems likely that many interesting chemical studies will be made by such methods.

H. Nuclear Resonance Absorption

The emission of a γ-ray causes the emitting nucleus to recoil in the opposite direction in order to conserve linear momentum. For this reason, the energy of the γ-ray is very slightly less than the energy difference between the initial and final nuclear states. The kinetic energy of the recoiling nucleus makes up the difference. When a nucleus of mass M emits a γ-ray of energy E_γ, the kinetic energy of the recoiling nucleus will be

$$E_r = \frac{E_\gamma^2}{2Mc^2} \tag{6.13}$$

For E_γ of 1 Mev, emitted from a nucleus of mass number 50, the recoil kinetic energy is only about 11 electron volts.

If two nuclear states differ in energy by E_0, then it will be possible to raise the lower state to the higher state by the absorption of a γ-ray whose energy is exactly $E_0 + E_r$. The γ-rays emitted by the upper state in its decay to the lower state, however, have energy $E_0 - E_r$, so that they cannot be absorbed to produce the reverse change. For example, the 0.129 Mev γ-ray emitted by an excited state of Ir[191] in its decay to the ground state cannot be reabsorbed by an Ir[191] nucleus to form the excited state again. However, the deficiency in energy is only about 0.8 electron volt. An energy deficiency so small can be made up by moving the Ir[191] absorber rapidly towards the source of the Ir[191] excited state γ-rays. The rapid motion which is required can be obtained, for example, by the use of a high speed centrifuge. If the two samples are approaching each other with sufficient velocity, the energy of the γ-rays will be enough to permit their reabsorption in ground state Ir[191] nuclei, to form the excited state.

The energy of the recoiling nuclei is so low that at temperatures of a few degrees Kelvin, the recoil process is not always able to break the chemical bonds which hold the atoms together in the crystal lattice. Hence an aggregate of atoms will recoil together.   The appropriate value of M to be used in equation (6.13) will then be the mass of the whole aggregate rather than the mass of a single nucleus.   Hence the recoil energy will be even lower.   At low temperatures, many of the γ-rays from the excited state of Ir[191] are emitted with an energy loss so small that they can be reabsorbed in thin foils of stable Ir[191] even when the source

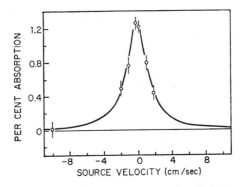

Fig. 6.6. Absorption of 0.129 Mev γ-ray of Ir[191] in iridium metal as a function of the relative velocity of the source and absorber. From L. L. Lee, L. Meyer-Schutzmeister, J. P. Schiffer, and D. Vincent, *Phys. Rev. Letters*, **3**, 223 (1959)

and absorber are not moving towards each other, an effect for whose discovery Mössbauer won a Nobel Prize for 1961.   Relative motion of the two in either direction, in fact, produces a *decrease* in the absorption. The results of an experiment of this type are shown in Figure 6.6.   It was possible to measure the shape of the Ir[191] γ-ray line, even though its width is only 3.5×10^{-6} electron volts.

Such a measurement in fact permits a determination of the half life of the excited state.   We have so far assumed that excited states of nuclei possess a perfectly definite energy above the ground state.   However, this cannot be exactly true for states which decay.   According to the uncertainty principle, there must be a relationship between the half life of a state and the uncertainty in its energy, ΔE.   The relationship is

$$t_{1/2}\Delta E = \hbar \tag{6.14}$$

Hence the shorter the half life, the greater will be the uncertainty in the energy of the state.   Only stable nuclei, with a infinite half life, can have perfectly defined energies.

The width of the γ-ray line from the excited state of Ir[191] arises from the uncertainty in the energy of the excited state itself, since it decays to a stable nucleus. By the use of equation (6.14), the half life of the excited state was found to be 1.3×10^{-10} sec.

REFERENCES

1. Blatt, J. M., and V. F. Weisskopf, *Theoretical Nuclear Physics*, John Wiley & Sons, New York, 1952.

2. Evans, R. D., *The Atomic Nucleus*, McGraw-Hill Book Co., New York, 1955.

3. Orear, J., A. H. Rosenfeld, and R. A. Schluter, *Nuclear Physics (Fermi Lecture Notes)*, University of Chicago Press, Chicago, 1950.

4. Siegbahn, K. (ed.), *Beta- and Gamma-Ray Spectroscopy*, North Holland Publishing Co., Amsterdam, 1955.

5. Nijgh, G. J., A. H. Wapstra, and R. Van Lieshout, *Nuclear Spectroscopy Tables*, North-Holland Publishing Co., Amsterdam, 1959.

6. Rose, M. E., *Internal Conversion Coefficients*, Interscience, New York, 1958.

7. Flügge, S. (ed.), *Handbuch der Physik*, Julius Springer Verlag, Berlin, 1957: Vol. XLII, D. E. Alburger, "Nuclear Isomerism."

8. Rose, M. E., *Multipole Fields*, John Wiley & Sons, New York, 1955.

9. Segrè, E. (ed.), *Experimental Nuclear Physics*, John Wiley & Sons, New York, 1959: Vol. III/10, M. Deutsch and O. Kofoed-Hansen, "Gamma Rays."

10. Elton, L. R. B., *Introductory Nuclear Theory*, Isaac Pitman and Sons Ltd., London, 1959.

PROBLEMS

1. What is the most likely multipole type and order for γ-decay between pairs of nuclei with the following spins and parities?

$$\tfrac{11}{2}(+) \rightarrow \tfrac{7}{2}(-), \quad 2(+) \rightarrow 0(+), \quad \tfrac{1}{2}(-) \rightarrow \tfrac{3}{2}(+), \quad 0(+) \rightarrow 0(+)$$

2. The 0.142 Mev excited state of Tc^{99}, with spin and parity $\tfrac{1}{2}(-)$, decays to $\tfrac{7}{2}(+)$ and $\tfrac{9}{2}(+)$ levels whose energies are 0.140 and 0 Mev respectively. Calculate the partial γ-emission half lives for these two modes of decay.

3. Pb^{204} has two isomeric states above its ground state. The highest state has spin and parity $9(-)$. The lower isomer has spin and parity $4(+)$.

(a) What electric or magnetic multipolarities would be expected for the transition between these two states? *P. 95, 110*

(b) What half life would be expected, the energy difference between the two states being 0.91 Mev? (Ignore internal conversion) *P 111*

4. Derive equation (6.13). What is the kinetic energy of a recoil Br^{80} atom following the emission of a 0.05 Mev γ-ray? Would this energy be sufficient to

break a chemical bond between the Br atom and another atom (for example, carbon)?

5. Consider the following levels of Pt^{195}:

$$\frac{5}{2}(-) \underline{\hspace{2cm}} 0.130 \text{ Mev}$$
$$\frac{3}{2}(-) \underline{\hspace{2cm}} 0.029 \text{ Mev}$$
$$\frac{1}{2}(-) \underline{\hspace{2cm}} 0$$

Will the $\frac{5}{2}(-)$ level decay mainly to the $\frac{3}{2}(-)$ or to the $\frac{1}{2}(-)$ level?

6. Consider the following decay scheme:

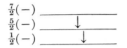

$$\frac{7}{2}(-) \underline{\hspace{2cm}}$$
$$\frac{5}{2}(-) \underline{\hspace{1cm}} \downarrow \underline{\hspace{0.5cm}}$$
$$\frac{1}{2}(-) \underline{\hspace{1cm}} \downarrow \underline{\hspace{0.5cm}}$$

Describe an angular correlation experiment by means of which you could determine whether the $\frac{7}{2}(-)$ to $\frac{5}{2}(-)$ decay occurs by an M1 or an E2 transition.

7. What angular correlation would you expect between two γ-rays in cascade when the spin of the intermediate level is zero? Try to explain your conclusion in simple physical terms.

8. In the heaviest nuclides of even-even type, with $Z > 92$ and $A > 240$, the first excited state is always $2(+)$, and about 40 kev above the ground state. *p. 95*
　(a) What is the spin and parity of the ground state?
　(b) What is the K shell conversion coefficient? The K shell electron binding energy is about 100 kev.
　(c) What is the transition type?

9. U^{238} exhibits a rotational band based upon the $0(+)$ ground state. The energy of the $2(+)$ level is 44.7 kev.
　(a) One of the members of the band is at 525 kev. Calculate the spin of this level.
　(b) What is the highest energy γ-ray that you would expect to see in the de-excitation of the 525 kev level?

10. The first excited state of Th^{232} is the $2(+)$ member of a rotational band based upon the ground state. The energy of the $2(+)$ level is 0.050 Mev, and its half life is 7.8×10^{-10} sec. The conversion coefficient is 340.
　(a) Calculate the partial half life for γ-ray emission.
　(b) Calculate the intrinsic quadrupole moment eQ_0 of Th^{232} (in barns). *p. 115*

11. Ignoring the difference between the intrinsic quadrupole moment calculated in Problem 10 and the electric quadrupole moments discussed in Chapter 5 F, obtain a crude estimate of the number of nucleons involved in collective motion in the Th^{232} rotational band. Assume that the total angular momentum of an odd proton in the region of Th^{232} is $\frac{3}{2}$.

12. What will be the width of the γ-ray line from the decay of the first excited state of Th^{232}? (See Problem 10.) *Hint:* Is the width determined by the total half life of the state, or by the partial γ-ray half life?

CHAPTER 7

Alpha Decay

A. Introduction

The emission of α-particles (helium nuclei) is predominantly a characteristic of the elements heavier than lead. Heavy particles of other types (such as protons, neutrons, or deuterons) are not spontaneously emitted by nuclei in their ground states. Alpha-decay can occur because the helium ion is an unusually stable entity: its total binding energy is 28 Mev. The energy released by the emission of an α-particle must be equal to the binding energy of the α-particle minus the energy cost of removing two protons and two neutrons from the nucleus. Since the first term of this expression is so large, α-emission will be exothermic for many nuclei, and hence can take place spontaneously. In contrast, the binding energy of a deuteron is only about 2 Mev, so that deuteron emission is endothermic for all known nuclear species in their ground states. Of course, emission of any and all kinds of particles can take place from sufficiently highly excited states of nuclei. We shall consider such processes in Chapter 9 (Nuclear Reactions).

The energy spectra of α-particles consist of a series of sharply defined lines corresponding to decay of the initial nucleus to various energy levels of the product nucleus (including of course its ground state). Excited levels of the product nucleus subsequently decay to the ground state by the various γ-processes described in Chapter 6.

The measured half lives of α-emitting nuclei cover an enormous range, the shortest being Po^{212} (3.04×10^{-7} sec) and the longest Nd^{144} (5×10^{15} years). The kinetic energies of the α-particles range from 1.9 Mev (Nd^{144}) to 8.78 Mev (Po^{212}). The association of high particle energy with short half life which is implied in the last sentence is no accident, as we shall see. This relationship was first noticed by Geiger and Nuttall in 1911.

In order to conserve linear momentum, the daughter nucleus formed by an α-decay must recoil in the opposite direction from the α-particle. The recoil nucleus and the α-particle will carry equal and opposite momenta. If their masses and velocities are M_r, M_α, v_r, and v_α respectively, then by conservation of linear momentum,

$$M_r v_r = M_\alpha v_\alpha \tag{7.1}$$

and
$$E_r = E_\alpha \left(\frac{M_\alpha}{M_r} \right) \qquad recoil\ energy \tag{7.2}$$
$$for\ \alpha\text{-}decay$$

where E_r and E_α are the recoil and α-particle kinetic energies respectively. The total energy released in the decay, $E_r + E_\alpha$, is called the decay energy. It is

$$E = E_r + E_\alpha = E_\alpha \left[\frac{M_r + M_\alpha}{M_r} \right] \qquad total\ energy \atop released \tag{7.3}$$

In a typical heavy-element α-decay, with $M_r = 228$ and $E_\alpha = 4$ Mev, the recoil kinetic energy will be only 0.07 Mev. Thus the α-particle, being light, carries most of the kinetic energy.

B. Alpha Decay Theory

The central problem of α-decay theory is to explain how the α-particle can emerge from the nucleus when there exists a potential barrier so high that it should not be possible for the α-particle to escape. The barrier for a typical heavy nucleus which emits 6 Mev α-particles is illustrated in Figure 7.1. The height of the barrier will be about 20 Mev, according to equation (5.1), and yet α-particles of only 6 Mev are observed to escape.

Shortly after the discovery of the Schrödinger wave equation, this problem was solved independently by Gamow and by Gurney and Condon in 1928. These authors considered a simple nuclear model in which the α-particle was supposed to exist as a separate entity retained in the nucleus by the potential barrier. The α-particle was supposed to oscillate

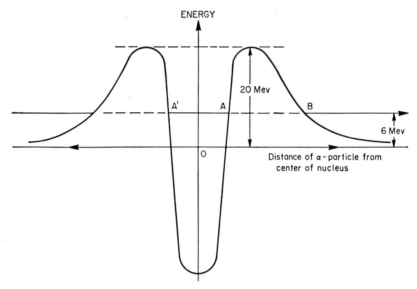

Fig. 7.1. Nuclear potential barrier for α-emission

back and forth inside the barrier, making collisions with the barrier at the points A and A' in Figure 7.1. According to classical mechanics, the particle will never be able to escape from the barrier. However, the solution of the Schrödinger wave equation for this situation shows that ψ^2, the probability of finding the α-particle at any point in space, is in fact not quite zero beyond the barrier. This means that there is a small but not zero probability that the α-particle will be able to escape from the barrier even though it never had enough energy to surmount it. One may think of the particle as escaping through a tunnel in the barrier —the tunnel being the line AB of Figure 7.1. Such a phenomenon would be quite impossible in classical mechanics because the kinetic energy of the particle would be negative in the region AB, and the expression $\frac{1}{2}mv^2$ can never be negative for any real value of the velocity v.

The tunnel effect is not confined to the α-decay phenomenon. It should exist in all cases in which a particle is striking against a barrier. For example, an automobile coasting up a hill with insufficient speed to reach the top might surprise its driver by appearing on the far side of the hill. The probability that this will happen is remarkably small, however. The same effect has been postulated in those chemical reactions which involve the transfer of a hydrogen ion across a potential barrier from one compound to another.

Using a simplified shape for the potential barrier, Gamow arrived at the following expression for the decay constant for α-emission:

$$\lambda = \frac{2^{1/2}\pi^2\hbar^2}{M^{3/2}R^3(B-E)^{1/2}} \exp\left\{-\left(\frac{R}{\hbar}\right)(2MB)^{1/2}\left[\pi\left(\frac{B}{E}\right)^{1/2} - 4\right]\right\} \quad (7.4)$$

M, the so-called reduced mass of the α-particle, equals $M_\alpha M_r/(M_\alpha + M_r)$, where M_α and M_r are the masses of the α-particle and the recoil nucleus respectively. R is the radius of the product nucleus. B is the height of the Coulomb barrier, which is equal to $2Ze^2/R$, where Z is the atomic number of the product nucleus, and E is the decay energy defined above.

Equation (7.4) contains some severe approximations and therefore cannot be expected to yield accurate values of λ. The calculation of λ is extremely sensitive to the choice of the radius R. For this reason, equation (7.4) provides an excellent way of calculating nuclear radii from experimental values of α-decay energies and half lives. Figure 7.2 shows the variation of $\log_{10}\lambda$ calculated for the α-decay of Th^{232} as a function of the assumed radius R. The experimental value of λ corresponds to $R = 9.43 \times 10^{-13}$ cm, which gives a value of $R_0 = 1.43 \times 10^{-13}$ cm in the equation $R = R_0 A^{1/3}$. Observe in Figure 7.2 that a variation in the assumed radius of only about 30% produces a change of about six orders of magnitude in the calculated value of the decay constant.

It is the exponential term in equation (7.4) which is responsible for this great sensitivity. The equation is similarly sensitive to small changes in the decay energy E and the barrier height B. It is for this reason that the half life of Nd^{144} is 5×10^{29} times as long as that of Po^{212}, although the energies of their α-particles are in the ratio of only about 1:5. The exponential term in equation (7.4) represents the probability of penetration of the Coulomb barrier, while the first part of the equation represents approximately the frequency with which the α-particle makes a collision with the barrier. The collision frequency varies much more slowly with change of the parameters.

The most obvious deficiency in this simple α-decay theory is the assumption that the α-particle preexists within the nucleus. There is no reason to believe that this is so, and therefore equation (7.4) should contain an extra term to take into account the probability that two protons and two neutrons within the nucleus will form an α-particle. We should expect this probability to vary considerably from one nucleus to another. As we shall see below, the probability of forming the α-particle is often much less for nuclei containing odd numbers of protons or neutrons than it is for even-even nuclei. For odd nucleon types, therefore, the decay constant may be several orders of magnitude smaller than the value calculated from equation (7.4). It is possible to make an approximate solution of the problem of the formation of the α-particle, and the theory gives good results when applied to the α-decay of odd nucleon nuclei in the region of the 126 neutron magic number.

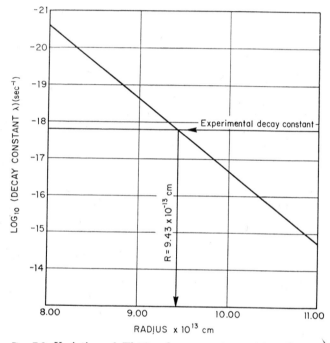

Fig. 7.2. Variation of Th²³² α-decay constant with radius of daughter nucleus

Equation (7.4) contains no reference to the angular momenta of the parent or daughter nuclei. It is, in fact, based on the assumption that no angular momentum is carried away by the α-particle. For the decay of even-even nuclei to the ground states of even-even nuclei, this assumption is of course justified, since both parent and daughter nuclei have spin 0. In many other cases, however, angular momentum will be carried away by the emitted particle. The main effect of this is to raise the effective height of the barrier B, and hence to increase the α-decay half life. The extra part of the barrier is called the centrifugal barrier. The centrifugal barrier is independent of the charge of the emitted particle, and even neutrons must cross such a barrier when they carry angular momentum into or out of a nucleus. The height of the centrifugal barrier is

$$\text{Barrier height} = \frac{l(l+1)}{2MR^2}\hbar^2 \qquad (7.5)$$

where l is the angular momentum which is being carried across the barrier by the particle.

C. Systematics of α-Decay Half Lives and Energies

As we might expect from the discussion above, there exists a particularly simple relationship between the α-decay energy and the half life for the decay of even-even nuclei to the ground states of their daughters.

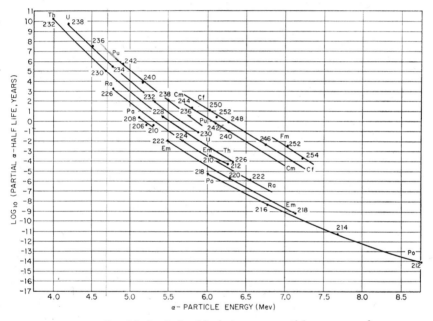

Fig. 7.3. Empirical relationship between α-particle energy and partial half life for the decay of even-even nuclei to the ground states of their daughters

This relationship is shown in Figure 7.3. Each element is represented by a single smooth curve, except Po and Em, which are represented by two curves each. In both cases, one curve contains only the isotopes of the element with $N \leq 126$, while the other curve contains the isotopes with $N > 126$.

The curves of Figure 7.3 may be used to establish, for each element, a "normal" relationship between the α-particle energy and the half life. The half life of any isotope may then be compared with the "normal" value. For example, the α-particle energy of Cm^{245} is 5.45 Mev for the decay to the ground state of Pu^{241}. The appropriate line in Figure 7.3 would require a partial half life of about 2500 years for this decay. The experimental half life is actually about 10^5 years. The ratio of the experimental half life to the "normal" value derived from Figure 7.3 is called the *hindrance factor*. In the case of Cm^{245}, it is about 40. The hindrance factor is a measure of the extent to which α-decay is slowed down relative to the decay of a hypothetical even-even nuclide of the same Z, emitting α-particles of the same energy. To calculate the hindrance factor for odd-Z elements, it is of course necessary to interpolate between the appropriate even-Z lines in Figure 7.3. For example, Bk^{244} emits α-particles of 6.67 Mev. The partial half life is 9 years; the value obtained by interpolation between the lines for Cm and Cf is about 3×10^{-3} years, and the hindrance factor is therefore about 3000.

α-decay of even-even nuclei to excited states of their daughters is usually hindered. Thus in the decay of Cm^{242} to Pu^{238} (whose level scheme is shown in Fig. 5.6), the hindrance factors for decay to the 2(+), 4(+), 6(+), and 8(+) levels are 1.7, 390, 350, and 5100 respectively. These numbers are typical of many other even-even nuclei which decay to the various members of a rotational band in the daughter nucleus.

A further empirical relationship connects the α-decay energies of the heavy nuclides with their mass numbers, as shown in Figure 7.4. The decay energies in the figure are the α-particle plus recoil nucleus kinetic energies for the formation of the ground state of the daughter nucleus. In a few cases, points are included which probably do not represent decay to the ground state of the daughter; they are therefore shown as arrows pointing upwards.

The decay energies of Figure 7.4 are equal in each case to (atomic mass of parent) $-$ (atomic mass of daughter $+$ mass of α-particle). The smooth relationship between decay energy and mass number therefore reflects the not unexpected smooth relationship between atomic mass and mass number which the semiempirical mass equation would predict. The sharp peaks in the vicinity of $A = 214$ are caused by the 126 neutron closed shell. Thus Po^{212} decays to Pb^{208}, which is doubly magic and therefore unusually stable. The decay energy is therefore very large. Po^{211} and Po^{213} decay to Pb^{207} and Pb^{209} respectively, and since neither of these nuclides contains 126 neutrons, the decay energies are less than for Po^{212}. The smaller discontinuity in the region of $A = 252$ is caused by some slight extra stability at a neutron number of 152.

Figure 7.4 may be used to predict the α-decay energies of unknown nuclear species by extrapolation or interpolation on the line of appropriate atomic number. Substitution of the predicted value into Figure 7.3 (after subtraction of the recoil energy) enables the unhindered half life to be predicted.　Such guesses have been very useful in planning experiments to produce and detect new heavy elements and new isotopes of known elements.

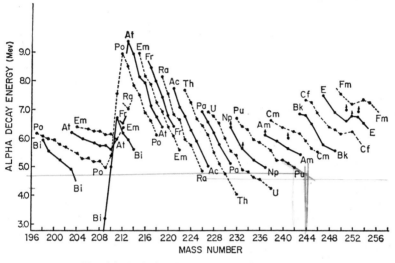

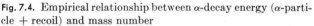

Fig. 7.4.　Empirical relationship between α-decay energy (α-particle + recoil) and mass number

When α-decay energies have been measured, or can be predicted reliably, the values may be used to calculate β-decay energies.　For example, the four nuclides Cm^{242}, Am^{242}, Cf^{246}, and Bk^{246} are related to each other by the α- and β-decay processes shown in Figure 7.5.　The α-decay energy of Cf^{246} is known by experiment to be 6.86 Mev. The β⁻-decay energy of Am^{242} is known by experiment to be 0.59 Mev.　The α-decay energy of Bk^{246} may be predicted from Figure 7.4: it will be about 6.16 Mev.　Application of the principle of conservation of energy then permits calculation of the energy difference between Cf^{246}

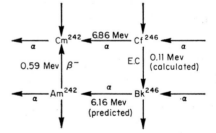

Fig. 7.5.　Decay energy relationship between Am^{242}, Cm^{242}, Bk^{246} and Cf^{246}

and Bk^{246}.　The result is 0.11 Mev, and the difference is in the sense that Cf^{246} must decay to Bk^{246} rather than vice versa.　The decay mode will therefore be electron capture.　(Positron emission requires an energy difference of at least 1.02 Mev, and in any case it is not observed in the heaviest elements.)

This method of closed decay cycles may be extended to include all the heavy nuclides in the manner suggested by the unlabeled arrows in Figure 7.5. Since α-decay causes a change of four in the mass number, and β^--decay and electron capture produce no change at all, there will be four separate diagrams. For example, Cf^{246}, whose mass number may be represented as $(4n + 2)$, where $n = 61$, cannot be related solely by α- and β-processes to Cf^{245}, whose mass number may be represented as $(4n + 3)$. The same is clearly true for the other two diagrams, which will contain nuclides whose mass numbers may be represented as $4n$ and $(4n + 1)$, where the n's are integers. The four series may be related to each other by means of the experimentally measured neutron binding energies. For example, the binding energy of a neutron to Pb^{207} (to form Pb^{208}) is 7.38 Mev (exothermic), and this value serves to relate the whole $(4n + 3)$ series (containing Pb^{207}) to the whole $4n$ series (containing Pb^{208}). In this way, all the α-, β^--, and EC decay energies and the proton and neutron binding energies for the nuclides above Pb^{208} may be calculated.

D. Alpha Particle Energy Spectra

According to equation (7.4), the probability that an α-particle will penetrate a potential barrier depends very critically on the ratio of the barrier height to the energy of the α-particle. We should therefore expect that α-decay will mainly lead to the formation of the ground states of the daughter nuclei, since in this case, the α-particle is emitted with the maximum possible energy. In the decay of even-even nuclei, this expectation is realized. For the other nuclear types, decay to the ground state may sometimes have so large a hindrance factor that decay to an excited state is much more probable. As an example, consider the α-decay of Cm^{243} to the various excited states of Pu^{239}, which is illustrated in Figure 7.6. In this case, the most intense α-group leads to the formation of an excited state which has an energy 0.286 Mev above the ground state. The collective model applies very well to many of the nuclei involved in α-decay (well above the magic numbers 82 and 126), and much of the detail of such complex decay schemes as Figure 7.6 can be explained by the model. The large yield of the 285.7 Kev level of Pu^{239} is due to its having the same nucleon configuration and the same value of the K quantum number as Cm^{243}.

α-decay of even-even nuclides shows a very regular behavior. The low-lying levels of the daughter nuclei often belong to well-defined rotational bands, since the α-emitting heavy nuclei lie in a region of large departure from the spherical shape. The α-decay of Cm^{244} to Pu^{240}, which is illustrated in Figure 7.7, is a typical example. In this case, the most intense α-group leads to the formation of the ground state of the daughter. Higher excited states are indeed formed, but in lower abundance, both because of the lower energy of the α-particles and also because of the greater hindrance factors.

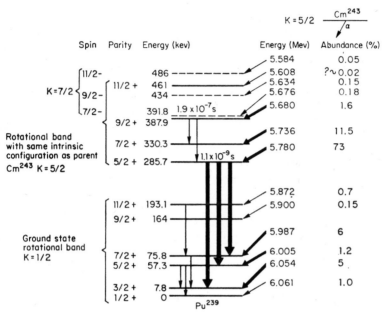

Fig. 7.6. Decay scheme of Cm^{243} including interpretation of Pu^{239} levels as three sets of rotational levels

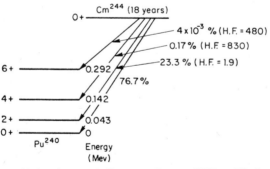

Fig. 7.7. Alpha decay of Cm^{244} to Pu^{240}. H.F. = Hindrance factor

The energy separation between the $0(+)$ ground state and the $2(+)$ first excited state varies in a regular way with changing mass number. Close to the 126 neutron magic number, the separation is large, since nuclei near a magic number are not easily deformed. With increasing neutron number above 126, the spacing decreases to an almost constant value of about 0.04 Mev.   This behavior is illustrated in Figure 7.8.

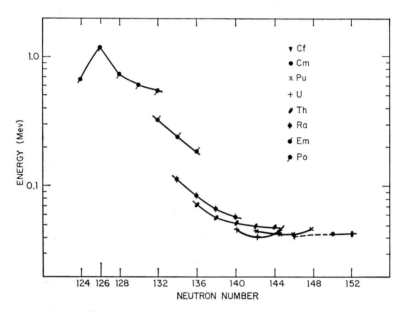

Fig. 7.8. Energies of first excited states of even-even nuclei in the heavy element region

E. Rare Earth-α-Emitters

Although α-decay is energetically possible for elements in the upper half of the periodic table, it will not in fact be observed unless the available decay energies are great enough to permit the decay to take place at an observable rate.   If the α half life is longer than about 10^{17} years, it is very likely that the α-particles will escape detection by even the most sensitive methods.

In the region of the rare earth elements, the presence of the 82 neutron closed shell causes an increase in the energy available for α-decay, just as the 126 neutron closed shell caused the high decay energies in the region of $A = 214$.   Although the decay energies are not very large (about 2–4 Mev), the Coulomb barrier is much lower than in the heavy element region, and therefore observable half lives appear.   The rare earth α-emitters are listed in Table 7.1.

There are in addition a few poorly characterized α-emitters in the region of gold and platinum, as well as several very light elements, such as Be^8, which break up into fragments which include α-particles.

TABLE 7.1. The Rare Earth Alpha-Emitters

Nuclide	α-Particle energy, Mev	Half life
$_{60}Nd^{144}$	1.9	$\sim 5 \times 10^{15}$ years
$_{62}Sm^{146}$	2.55	5×10^{7} years
$_{63}Eu^{147}$	2.9	24 days
$_{64}Gd^{148}$	3.2	~ 130 years
$_{64}Gd^{149}$	3.0	9.3 days
$_{64}Gd^{150}$	2.7	$> 10^{5}$ years
$_{65}Tb^{149}$	3.95	4.1 hr
$_{65}Tb^{151}$	3.4	19 hr
$_{66}Dy^{<153}$ *	4.2	7 min
$_{66}Dy^{<153}$ *	4.1	19 min
$_{66}Dy^{152}$	3.66	2.3 hr
$_{66}Dy^{153}$	3.48	5.0 hr
$_{66}Dy^{154}$	3.37	13 hr
$_{67}Ho^{?}$	4.2	~ 4 min

* The mass number is not known.

REFERENCES

1. Segrè, E. (ed.), *Experimental Nuclear Physics*, John Wiley & Sons, New York, 1959: Vol. III/9, G. C. Hanna, "Alpha-Radioactivity."

2. Flügge, S. (ed.), *Handbuch der Physik*, Julius Springer Verlag, Berlin, 1957: Vol. XLII, I. Perlman and J. O. Rasmussen, "Alpha Decay."

(The review articles listed above give a large number of references to original publications.)

PROBLEMS

1. Calculate the kinetic energy and velocity of the Pu^{240} recoil atoms which are formed by the α-decay of Cm^{244} to the ground state of Pu^{240}.

2. Cf^{250} decays to the ground state of Cm^{246} by the emission of 6.024 Mev α-particles. The atomic mass of Cf^{250} is 250.15441. What is the atomic mass of Cm^{246}?

3. By the method illustrated in Figure 7.2, calculate the nuclear radius of U^{238}.

4. Calculate the hindrance factor for the α-decay of Bk^{245} to the ground state of Am^{241}. The half life of Bk^{245} is 4.98 days, the decay is 99.89% EC and 0.11% α-decay. Thirty-two percent of the α-decays lead to the ground state of Am^{241}. The particle energy is 6.37 Mev.

5. Predict the α-particle energy and partial α half life of Fm^{248}.

6. Using measured α-decay energies where available, and predicted values in other cases, calculate the energy difference between Am^{242} and Pu^{242}. Which way will the decay take place between the two nuclides? The β^--decay energy of Th^{234} is 0.25 Mev.

7. The energy required to remove a neutron from U^{236} is 6.46 Mev. Calculate the energy required to remove a neutron from Cm^{244}.

8. U^{238} decays all the way to Pb^{208} by a series of successive α- and β^--decays.

(a) Why is it that in traveling down this decay chain, one or two successive α-decays are followed by β^--decays, then by more α-decays, and so on? *Hint:* Consider the effect of α- and β^--decays on the position of a nuclide with respect to the β-stability line.

(b) Why are there no positron or electron capture decays in this chain?

9. Explain the following in terms of α-decay theory and any other concepts that may be required:

(a) Th^{226} and Em^{220} have the same α-decay energy, but the half life of Em^{220} is 1 min and that of Th^{226} is 31 min.

(b) U^{235} and U^{236} have nearly the same α-decay energy, but the half life of U^{235} is 7×10^8 years and that of U^{236} is only 2×10^7 years.

(c) In the heavy element region, α-particle energies are not found below 4 Mev, whereas in the rare earth region, they may be as low as 1.9 Mev.

10. About 70% of the α-decays of the even isotopes of curium form the ground state of the plutonium daughter, and about 30% form an excited state about 40 kev above the ground state. Assuming that the ground state transition is unhindered, calculate the hindrance factor for decay to the excited state.

11. Show that α-decay is energetically possible if

$$\frac{\dfrac{E_1}{A_1} - \dfrac{E_2}{A_2}}{A_1 - A_2} < \frac{1}{A_1}\left(7 - \frac{E_2}{A_2}\right)$$

where E_1 and E_2 are the total binding energies of the parent and daughter nuclei, and A_1 and A_2 are their mass numbers. The total binding energy of the α-particle is 28 Mev.

12. (a) Estimate the α-decay half life which U^{235} would have if its decay were unhindered.

(b) If the age of the chemical elements is 4×10^9 years, what fraction of the original U^{235} is still present?

(c) What fraction would still be present if the half life estimated in (a) were the actual half life?

13. Calculate the height of the centrifugal barrier for the emission of α-particles carrying away two units of angular momentum in the decay of Cm^{242}. Assume that the nuclear radius parameter R_0 has the value 1.4×10^{-13} cm. What is the height of the Coulomb barrier for this decay?

CHAPTER 8

Beta Decay

A. Introduction

The term beta-decay includes three processes which involve the interaction of a nucleus with an electron. These processes are the emission
of positive or negative electrons, and the capture by the nucleus of an
orbital atomic electron. In all three processes, the atomic number of the
nucleus becomes one unit greater or smaller, but the mass number
remains the same.

Attempts to analyze the energy spectra of the β^--particles were made
very soon after the discovery of radioactivity. The results were confusing, because it was not realized that many of the electrons which were
observed came from internal conversion processes rather than from
β^--decay. By 1910, however, it was known that in at least two cases,

β^--particles are emitted with a continuous energy and momentum distribution rather than as sharp lines. Superimposed on the continuous distribution, there may be sharp lines due to conversion electrons. It is now known that such a continuous spectrum is characteristic of both the β^-- and β^+-particles. A typical momentum spectrum, showing both the

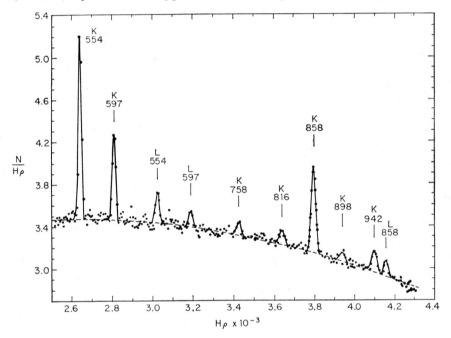

Fig. 8.1. The portion of the U^{240}-Np^{240} β-spectrum between 0.40 and 0.88 Mev, showing a continuous β-spectrum and conversion electron lines. ρ is the radius of the path of a particle in a magnetic field H. $H\rho$ is proportional to momentum. From M. E. Bunker, B. J. Dropesky, J. D. Knight, J. W. Starner, and B. Warren, *Phys. Rev.*, **116**, 143 (1959)

continuous spectrum and some conversion electron lines, is shown in Figure 8.1.

  If identical parent nuclei can decay to identical states of their daughter nuclei by the emission of β-particles of *different* energies, then it would appear that they violate the principle of conservation of energy. There is an equally serious difficulty with the conservation of angular momentum. As we have seen, all even-A nuclei have spins which are integral multiplies of $\hbar$, and all odd-A nuclei have spins which are half-integral multiples. The spin of the positive or negative electron is $\frac{1}{2}$. Since β-processes do not change the odd or even character of A, it would appear that angular momentum cannot be conserved. For example, Na^{24}

(spin 4) decays to Mg^{24} (spin 0). The β^--particle may carry off integral amounts of angular momentum (l) in addition to its spin. However, the equation $4 = 0 + l + (\frac{1}{2})$ cannot be satisfied by any integral value of l.

To avoid these difficulties, Wolfgang Pauli suggested in 1931 that a second particle is emitted simultaneously with the β-particle. The second particle can carry away some of the kinetic energy, but the sum of the kinetic energies of the two particle (plus the very small nuclear recoil energy) must be always equal to the energy difference between the parent and daughter nuclei. Thus the principle of conservation of energy is not violated, even though the β-particles do not all carry the same amount of kinetic energy. Furthermore, angular momentum can be conserved if it is assumed that the new particle has spin $\frac{1}{2}$. The hypothetical particle, which is called the neutrino, must have no electrical charge, and its mass must be small (in fact it is almost certainly zero). In order to escape unobserved, the neutrino must be supposed to interact very weakly with matter. It must not be readily absorbed by nuclei, and being uncharged, it will presumably not interact with the atomic electrons. A particle with these properties would not be detectable with any ordinary type of counter. At first sight, the Pauli neutrino hypothesis seems to be a highly artificial way to save the conservation laws. However, we shall see later that neutrinos have in fact been detected experimentally, and there can be no doubt that they exist.

Because neutrinos interact so weakly with matter, their kinetic energy will escape from laboratory measuring equipment. In 1927, Ellis and Wooster measured calorimetrically the heat liberated in the β^--decay of Bi^{210}. The continuous energy spectrum from Bi^{210} contains β^--particles of energies up to 1.155 Mev, while the average β^--particle energy is about 0.4 Mev. The sample was placed in a lead tube with walls about 0.1 cm thick, and this was sufficient to absorb completely all the β^--particles, converting their kinetic energy into heat. Ellis and Wooster found that the energy absorbed in the calorimeter, per Bi^{210} disintegration, was 0.35 ± 0.04 Mev, which agreed well with the average energy of the β^--particles obtained from the energy spectrum. The difference of about 0.8 Mev between the maximum and average β^--particle energies represents the energy carried away by the neutrinos, all of which escaped from the calorimeter.

The maximum β-particle energy is equal to the energy difference between the parent and daughter nuclei minus the small nuclear recoil energy. This maximum energy is called the end point of the spectrum. Calculation of the β-decay energy from atomic mass differences by means of the equations of Chapter 3, Section E yields the end point of the spectrum (ignoring the recoil energy). Thus the mass difference between Bi^{210} and its daughter, Po^{210}, is 0.00124 atomic mass units, or 1.158 Mev.

B. Beta Decay Theory

The first understanding the β-decay process came as a result of the work of Enrico Fermi in 1934. The Fermi theory adopts the Pauli neutrino hypothesis. Since nuclei do not contain electrons, it is assumed that they, as well as the neutrinos, are created only at the moment of emission. Since the velocities of the particles are large, it is necessary to use relativistic equations.

Fermi assumed that β-decay results from some form of interaction between nucleons, the electron, and the neutrino. This interaction is of a new type, different from the Coulomb, gravitational, or nuclear interactions. It therefore requires a new constant to express its strength, analogous to the constants e and G which express the strengths of the Coulomb and gravitational interactions. The Fermi constant is given the symbol g. Like e and G, g must be measured experimentally—it is not possible to calculate its magnitude from other universal constants. Its value is found to be about 10^{-47} erg cm³, which is roughly 10^6 times smaller than the constant which expresses the strength of the nucleon-nucleon interaction. It is because of the weakness of the interaction that β-decay does not take place almost instantly (in cases where it is energetically possible). Because of the strong interaction between nucleons, α-decay would be virtually instantaneous if it were not for the existence of the Coulomb barrier. There is no barrier having a comparable effect in slowing down β-decay, and yet α- and β-decay half lives have comparable values.

In addition to the constant g, the theory must include some reference to the relationship between the properties of the initial and final nuclei. The relationship is expressed by means of what is called a matrix element, which we shall not describe except to remark that it involves the wave functions of the initial and final nuclear states, and hence their spins and parities and the arrangement of the nucleons. When the initial and final states are very similar, β-decay does not involve a substantial rearrangement of the nucleons, and the transition is easy. In this case, the matrix element, whose symbol is $|M_{if}|^2$, has its maximum value, and the β-decay half life will probably be short. When the two states are very different from one another, $|M_{if}|^2$ becomes smaller, perhaps by many orders of magnitude, and the half life for the transition will probably be long.

The total available energy E_0, which is the energy difference between the initial and final states, can be divided between the electron and the neutrino in a large number of different ways. This affects the shape of the β-spectrum in a manner which will be discussed in more detail below. For the moment, we merely state that the relevant quantity is dn/dE_0, which is the number of ways, per unit of total energy, in which the total energy can be divided up between the electron and the neutrino.

From quantum mechanical theory, we can now write down an equation which gives the probability $P(p_e)$ that in unit time a β-decay will occur, giving rise to an electron whose momentum lies between p_e and $p_e + dp_e$. It is

$$P(p_e) = \frac{4\pi^2}{h} \frac{1}{V^2} |M_{if}|^2 g^2 \frac{dn}{dE_0} \tag{8.1}$$

V is an arbitrary volume which will shortly disappear from the equation. For the β-decay of a particular nucleus, it turns out that the variation of $P(p_e)$ with the energy of the β-particle is mainly determined by the term dn/dE_0 in equation (8.1), so that we shall first discuss this in more detail.

The division of the available energy between the electron and the neutrino has nothing to do with the properties of the decaying nucleus. We start the discussion from the principle that the probability that a certain process will occur is proportional to *the number of different ways in which it can be accomplished.* In the present case, we are interested in the number of different ways in which the total energy E_0 can be divided up. In a rough sort of way, the principle is already very familiar. For example, an operation which must be done in a certain precise way with no leeway for error is likely to be difficult. An easy operation may succeed even if the conditions are allowed to vary in a careless way. In a β-decay process of energy E_0, the electron kinetic energy E_e and the neutrino kinetic energy E_ν are related by the equation

$$E_0 = E_e + E_\nu \tag{8.2}$$

If a particular division of energy can be accomplished so that there are many possible values for the electron momentum lying between p_e and $p_e + dp_e$, then that division will be highly probable. The detailed argument which follows uses the methods of statistical mechanics. It can be avoided by skipping straight to equation (8.11).

Suppose that a β-particle is found at the point (x,y,z) in space, and that its momenta along the three axes are p_x, p_y, and p_z. From the uncertainty principle, we know that the uncertainty Δx in the x coordinate must be related to the uncertainty Δp_x in the corresponding momentum by the equation

$$\Delta x \Delta p_x = h$$

Similarly,

$$\Delta y \Delta p_y = h \quad \text{and} \quad \Delta z \Delta p_z = h$$

Hence

$$\Delta x \Delta y \Delta z \Delta p_x \Delta p_y \Delta p_z = h^3 \tag{8.3}$$

If we try to represent the position and momentum of the particle as the point (x,y,z,p_x,p_y,p_z) in an imaginary six-dimensional space (called phase space), then according to the uncertainty principle we cannot specify the exact point in the space. The best we can say is that the point representing the position and momentum of the particle is somewhere in a volume of size h^3.

This volume is called a unit cell of the phase space. If we specify that a particle is to be found anywhere within a certain volume of ordinary space with a momentum lying between certain limits, then we are in fact

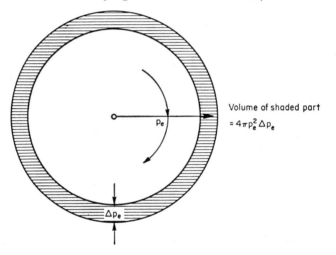

Volume of shaded part

$= 4\pi p_e^2 \Delta p_e$

Fig. 8.2. Cross section of volume in momentum space representing uncertainty in the momentum of an electron

specifying the volume of the phase space corresponding to this situation. The number of different ways in which the specified situation can occur is *equal to the number of unit cells within the specified volume of phase space.*

We are not interested in the direction of motion of the electron but only in its momentum p_e and its uncertainty Δp_e. If we represent p_e as a vector of length p_e pointing in any direction around the nucleus which emitted the electron, then, as shown in Figure 8.2, the term $\Delta p_x \Delta p_y \Delta p_z$ in equation (8.3) becomes $4\pi p_e^2 \Delta p_e$. If we now require that the electron should be somewhere within a volume V, then the corresponding volume in phase space becomes $4\pi p_e^2 \Delta p_e V$. Now the number of different ways in which the electron can have the position and momentum specified by this expression is equal to the number of unit cells within this volume, which is $4\pi p_e^2 \Delta p_e V / h^3$. In other words, the number dN of ways in which the electron may be in volume V with momentum lying between p_e and $p_e + dp_e$ is

$$dN = 4\pi p_e^2 V \frac{dp_e}{h^3} \tag{8.4}$$

The number of ways in which the neutrino can be found in volume V with momentum between p_ν and $p_\nu + dp_\nu$ is given by the same argument:

$$dN = 4\pi p_\nu^2 V \frac{dp_\nu}{h^3} \qquad (8.5)$$

Hence the number of ways, dn, in which a disintegration can lead to the electron having momentum between p_e and $p_e + dp_e$ while the neutrino has momentum between p_ν and $p_\nu + dp_\nu$ is just the product of equations (8.4) and (8.5):

$$dn = \frac{16\pi^2 V^2}{h^6} p_e^2 p_\nu^2 \, dp_e \, dp_\nu \qquad (8.6)$$

The relativistic momentum of a particle of rest mass m and kinetic energy E is

$$p = \frac{1}{c} \sqrt{E(E + 2mc^2)} \qquad (8.7)$$

and hence the momentum of a neutrino of zero rest mass will be

$$p_\nu = \frac{E_\nu}{c} \qquad (8.8)$$

Hence from equation (8.2),

$$p_\nu = \frac{E_0 - E_e}{c} \qquad (8.9)$$

and

$$dp_\nu = \frac{dE_0}{c} \quad \text{(at constant } E_e) \qquad (8.10)$$

Substituting (8.9) and (8.10) into (8.6), we find:

$$dn = \frac{16\pi^2 V^2}{h^6 c^3} (E_0 - E_e)^2 p_e^2 \, dp_e \, dE_0$$

or

$$\frac{dn}{dE_0} = \frac{16\pi^2 V^2}{h^6 c^3} (E_0 - E_e)^2 p_e^2 \, dp_e \qquad (8.11)$$

So far, we have ignored the effect of the nuclear charge on the kinetic energy of the electron. We would expect negative electrons to be slowed down and positive electrons to be accelerated as they leave the vicinity of the positive nuclear charge. Detailed quantum mechanical calculations show that this is indeed what happens. In addition, positrons must cross a Coulomb barrier as they leave the nucleus, and as a result of both these effects, positron spectra are depleted in low energy particles compared with negative electron spectra.   The effect of the Coulomb forces on the energy spectra leads to a rather complex function of the atomic number of the product nucleus and the energy of the escaping electron. We shall not reproduce the function, but merely call it $F(Z,E_e)$, and note that tables of its values have been prepared.

With this additional factor, the value of $P(p_e)$ is given by substitution of dn/dE_0 from equation (8.11) into equation (8.1):

$$P(p_e) = \frac{64\pi^4}{h^7c^3} |M_{if}|^2 g^2 F(Z,E_e)(E_0 - E_e)^2 p_e^2 \, dp_e \qquad (8.12)$$

Equation (8.12) gives the shape of the β-spectrum.   By comparison of the equation with experimentally measured spectra, it is found that $|M_{if}|$ is not a function of the energy with which the β-particle was emitted in the decay of a particular nuclide.   (This statement is only strictly true for the so-called allowed β-transitions, which are discussed below.   We shall not consider the more complicated spectra arising from the forbidden transitions.)   If we may treat $|M_{if}|$ as a constant for the decay of a particular nucleus to a particular state of the daughter, then the spectrum for the β-particles should be given by

$$P(p_e) = (\text{constants})F(Z,E_e)(E_0 - E_e)^2 p_e^2 \, dp_e \qquad (8.13)$$

Equation (8.13) shows that $P(p_e)$ becomes zero when p_e is zero, or when E_e has the maximum possible value E_0.   Between zero and the maximum possible electron energy (the end point of the spectrum), $P(p_e)$ varies smoothly with E_e.   The spectrum looks like that shown in Figure 8.1 (ignoring the conversion electron lines).

Equation (8.13) may be written in the form

$$\left[\frac{P(p_e)}{p_e^2 F(Z,E_e)} \right]^{1/2} = (E_0 - E_e) \qquad (8.14)$$

If the function on the left-hand side of equation (8.14) is plotted as a function of E_e, a straight line should be obtained, making an intercept E_0 on the energy axis.   Such a graph, which is called a Kurie plot, provides a valuable test of the theory and also an accurate way of measuring E_0, the end point of the spectrum.   A Kurie plot of the experimental spectrum of β^--particles from the decay of H^3 is shown in Figure 8.3.

The probability per unit time that a nucleus will emit a β-particle of *any* momentum is obtained by integrating $P(p_e)$ between the limits of zero momentum and the maximum possible momentum (i.e., the momentum of an electron of energy E_0). The integral is then just the decay constant λ. Hence:

$$\lambda = \frac{\log_e 2}{t_{1/2}} = \int_0^{p_e(\max)} P(p_e)\, dp_e$$

$$= (\text{constants})g^2|M_{if}|^2 \int_0^{p_e(\max)} F(Z,E_e)p_e^2(E_0 - E_e)^2\, dp_e \quad (8.15)$$

The matrix element has been omitted from the integration on the assumption that it does not vary with p_e. Equation (8.15) therefore applies only to the allowed types of β-transitions, for which alone this assumption is always valid. The Fermi constant g is not a function of p_e.

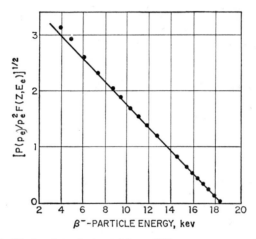

Fig. 8.3. Kurie plot of the tritium (H^3) β^--spectrum. F. T. Porter, *Phys. Rev.*, **115**, 450 (1959)

If we give the integral on the right-hand side of equation (8.15) the symbol f, then

$$\log_e 2 = (\text{constants})g^2|M_{if}|^2 ft_{1/2}$$

or

$$ft_{1/2} = (\text{constants})|M_{if}|^{-2} \quad (8.16)$$

The product $ft_{1/2}$ is now only a function of the matrix element, and hence should be roughly constant for all β-transitions involving the same spin and parity change. $ft_{1/2}$ (which is usually written as ft, or as its logarithm $\log_{10} ft$), is called the comparative half life or ft value for the transitions. Physically, it is the half life corrected for the atomic number Z and the decay energy E_0. Thus all β-transitions are put on a common footing, and comparison of their ft values yields information about the matrix elements.

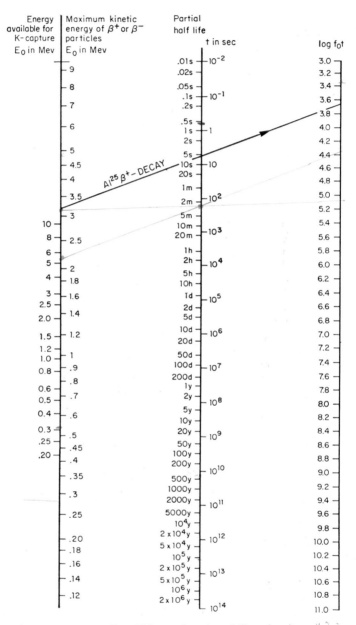

Fig. 8.4. Log $(f_0 t)$ as a function of E_0 and t

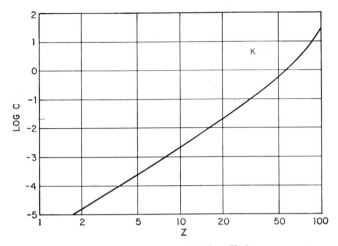

Fig. 8.5. Log (C) as a function of Z for K-electron capture.
$(Z$ = atomic number of initial nucleus)

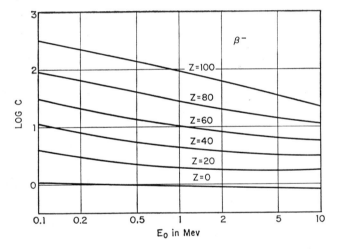

Fig. 8.6. Log (C) as a function of E_0 and Z for β^--emission.
$(Z$ = atomic number of initial nucleus)

Values of log ft may be calculated from the nomograph and curves given in Figures 8.4, 8.5, 8.6, and 8.7, which are due to S. A. Moszkowski.* Observe that log ft values may be calculated for electron capture as well as for β^+- and β^--decay. Log ft is obtained from the figures as a sum of the two terms log (f_0t) and log (C). Obtain log (f_0t) from Figure 8.4 by connecting the appropriate energy and half life with a straight edge and reading the intercept on the log (f_0t) line. Figure 8.4 shows this pro-

* Moszkowski, S. A., *Phys. Rev.*, **82**, 35 (1951).

$$\log ft = \log f_0 t + \log C$$

cedure for the β^+-decay of Al^{25}. The maximum positron energy is 3.24 Mev, and the half life is 7.6 sec, yielding log ($f_0 t$) of 3.7. Interpolation between the appropriate lines in Figures 8.5, 8.6, or 8.7 yields the value of log (C). For Al^{25}, log (C) is found from Figure 8.7 to be -0.2. Hence log ft is 3.5.

The log ft values cover a large range, from about 3 up to more than 20. There is a tendency for the values to fall into groups which can be correlated with the spin difference ΔI between the initial and final nuclei,

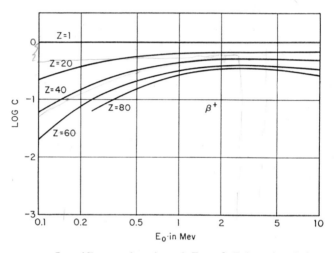

Fig. 8.7. Log (C) as a function of E_0 and Z for β^+-emission. (Z = atomic number of initial nucleus)

and with the presence or absence of a change in parity. The smallest log ft values (corresponding to the shortest half lives for a given decay energy), are found among the so-called mirror nuclei. A pair of nuclei is said to be a mirror pair if the number of neutrons in one member is equal to the number of protons in the other member, and vice versa. Examples of such pairs are $_1H^3$–$_2He^3$, $_8O^{17}$–$_9F^{17}$, $_{11}Na^{23}$–$_{12}Mg^{23}$, and $_{12}Mg^{25}$–$_{13}Al^{25}$. If the internucleon forces are the same for protons as for neutrons, then the binding energies of mirror pairs should be the same except for the extra Coulomb repulsion in the higher Z member of the pair. The difference ΔE in the Coulomb repulsion energy between the mirror nuclei Z^A and $(Z + 1)^A$ is

$$\Delta E = \frac{3e^2(2Z - 1)}{5A^{1/3}R_0} \tag{8.17}$$

where R_0, as usual, is about 1.4×10^{-13} cm.

The proton and neutron themselves comprise a particularly important example of a mirror pair. Neutrons decay by β^--emission to protons; the half life of the transition is about 12 minutes.

In the β-decay of mirror nuclei, the parent nucleus transforms one of its nucleons into a nucleon in the daughter nucleus which must be in the same shell. For example, the odd nucleon in $_9F^{17}$ is a $d_{5/2}$ proton. The odd nucleon in $_8O^{17}$, which is formed by the β^+-decay of F^{17}, is a $d_{5/2}$ neutron. The two relevant nucleons will have very similar wave functions since they belong to identical shell model states. It is this relationship which determines the size of the matrix element $|M_{if}|^2$, and when the matrix element is large, the log ft value will be small, as shown by equation (8.16). For the β-decay of the mirror nuclei to their partners, the log ft values are about 3, which is unusually small. Such transitions are called super-allowed.

TABLE 8.1. Gamow-Teller Selection Rules for β-Decay

Transition type	ΔI	Parity change ?	log ft
Super-allowed	0	No	3
Allowed	0, ± 1; (not $0 \rightarrow 0$)	No	3–6
First forbidden	0, ± 1, ± 2	Yes	6–10
Second forbidden	± 2, ± 3; $0 \rightarrow 0$	No	10–14

"Ordinary" allowed transitions occur when $\Delta I = 0$, ± 1 (except for initial and final nuclear spins both zero), with no parity change. Log ft values lie in the range 3–6. "First forbidden" transitions have $\Delta I = 0$, ± 1, ± 2, with a parity change, and log ft values lie between about 6 and 10. "Second forbidden" transitions have $\Delta I = \pm 2$, ± 3, with no parity change, and log ft will be about 10–14. Thus the spin and parity change will profoundly affect the β-decay half lives.

The rules given in the preceeding paragraph, and summarized in Table 8.1, are called the Gamow-Teller selection rules; they seem to apply to most β-transitions. There is, however, another set of rules known as the Fermi selection rules, and they sometimes apply. For example, O^{14} (spin and parity 0+) decays by β^+-emission to a 0+ excited state of N^{14}. For this decay, log $ft = 3.5$. This is a $0 \rightarrow 0$ transition which is second forbidden by the Gamow-Teller rules but allowed by the Fermi rules. The small log ft value shows that this decay is in fact allowed.

The two sets of rules arise from different assumptions about the relative orientation of the spins of the emitted electron and neutrino. If they are assumed to be parallel, then the Gamow-Teller rules are obtained. If they are antiparallel (spin vectors pointing in opposite directions), then the Fermi rules are obtained. These are the only two relative orientations that are possible for spin $\frac{1}{2}$ particles.

C. Conservation of Parity

In the discussion of parity in Chapter 5 D, we stated that the parity of a system remains constant when the whole system is considered. The parity of a nucleus may change in, for example, a radioactive decay, but the parity of the whole system of nucleus plus emitted particle does not change. It is now known that this last statement need not be true when the decay involves a weak type of interaction such as β-decay.

Conservation of parity in any change requires that the interaction which is causing the change shall be of a certain form which we shall not describe. It appears that the strong interactions between nucleons which are responsible for the emission of nucleons or γ-rays from nuclei are of a form which conserves parity.

Change of the coordinates (x,y,z) of a system into $(-x,-y,-z)$ reverses the sign of all linear momenta within the system. Angular momenta, however, are a product of two vectors, a linear momentum and a position vector, so that they do not change sign. Consider now a nucleus with spin. Suppose that this nucleus emits β-particles only in a direction parallel with the spin. If we now change the sign of all the coordinates of the system, the direction of the vector representing the spin will not change, but the direction of emission of the β-particle will be reversed (since their momenta will change sign). Now, therefore, all the β-particles will be emitted in a direction *opposite* to the spin of the nucleus. This is illustrated in Figure 8.8. The system after reversal of the sign of the coordinates is therefore not the same as the system before the reversal, which is equivalent to saying that parity is not conserved. In order to conserve parity, the emission of the β-particles must take place exactly as often in the direction of the nuclear spin as it does in the opposite direction. Upon reversal of the coordinates, there will then be no change. T. D. Lee and C. N. Yang* suggested in 1956 that parity might not be conserved in weak interactions such as β^--decay, and shortly afterwards, Wu, Ambler, Hayward, Hoppes, and Hudson† found experimentally that this is indeed the case. Their method was to show that, in the β^--decay of Co^{60}, an equal number of particles are *not* emitted parallel and antiparallel to the nuclear spin.

* Lee, T. D., and C. N. Yang, *Phys. Rev.*, **104**, 254 (1956).
† Wu, Ambler, Hayward, Hoppes, and Hudson, *Phys. Rev.*, **105**, 1413 (1957).

At such a low temperature that thermal motion is almost stopped, the ions of Co^{60} contained in a crystal of the paramagnetic substance cerium magnesium nitrate can be "lined up" by a magnetic field so that all the nuclear spins are oriented in the direction of the field. It is then possible to measure the intensity of the β^--radiation in a direction parallel to, or antiparallel to, the direction of the nuclear spins. If parity is to be conserved, there will be no difference. Wu and co-workers found that, at the lowest temperatures, where the Co^{60} nuclei were most completely lined up, about 30% more particles were emitted in a direction opposite

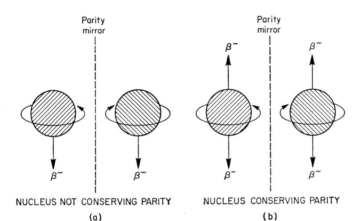

Fig. 8.8. Illustration of parity non-conservation in decay. The mirrors represent the operation of changing the sign of all the coordinates. In (b), the two β-particles coming from each nucleus represent equal probabilities of emission in the up or down directions

to the spin vector than in a direction parallel with that vector. The failure of parity conservation in β-decay was subsequently confirmed in several other investigations.

D. Electron Capture

If the available decay energy is less than $2m_ec^2$ (1.02 Mev), then positron emission is impossible, and a decay from nucleus Z^A to $(Z-1)^A$ must take place by the capture of an orbital electron. When the energy is greater than 1.02 Mev, both electron capture and positron emission may occur. As we have implied, the theory of electron capture is very similar to the theory of β^+- or β^--emission. It involves only one further quantity: the wave function of the atomic electron, which determines the probability of finding the electron within the nuclear volume where the interaction leading to capture can take place.

Among the lighter elements, electron capture and positron emission are about equally probable (when there is sufficient energy for positron emission). With increasing Z, however, the large positive nuclear charge causes the atomic electron shells to become progressively smaller, and hence the probability of electron capture increases. Among the heaviest elements, positron emission is not observed.

Provided that the decay energy is greater than the binding energy of the K shell electrons, then capture of an electron from that shell is more probable than from the L, $M \cdots$ shells. The ratio of the probability of finding a K electron at the nuclear surface to the probability of finding an L_{I} $(2p_{1/2})$ electron there is about 0.05 for $Z = 10$. It increases to about 0.15 for $Z = 80$.

The kinetic energy of the neutrino, E_ν, must be equal to the decay energy E_0 minus the binding energy of the captured electron. Hence the neutrino spectrum must consist of a series of lines at energies $E_0 - E_K$, $E_0 - E_{L_{\mathrm{I}}}$, etc., where E_K, $E_{L_{\mathrm{I}}}$, etc., are the electron binding energies in the different shells. Unfortunately, it is of course not possible to measure the neutrino energy spectra directly. As we shall see (in Section E), the energy spectrum of nuclear recoils following electron capture decay is consistent with the emission of approximately monoenergetic neutrinos, but it is not possible to resolve the different lines in the neutrino energy spectrum.

The capture of an orbital electron produces no primary detectable radiation from the nucleus. There are, however, detectable secondary processes. If the decay proceeds to an excited state of the daughter nucleus, there will of course be γ-rays and perhaps conversion electrons from the decay of this excited state. The primary capture process creates a vacancy in an atomic electron shell, and therefore X-rays and Auger electrons will be emitted just as though the vacancy were created by the internal conversion process. (See Chapter 6 F.) The X-ray and electron energies will naturally be those associated with the daughter nucleus. These secondary radiations permit the detection of the electron capture process with suitable counters.

E. Experimental Detection of the Neutrino

There are many ways in which information may be obtained about the properties of the neutrino. We have already concluded that it must have small or zero mass, zero charge, and spin $\frac{1}{2}$. From a detailed study of the shapes of β-ray spectra, it can be shown that the mass of the neutrino must be less than 1/2000 of the electron mass. The neutrino theory of Lee and Yang, which does not require parity conservation in β-decay, gives the neutrino a rest mass of zero.

The momentum p_ν of a zero rest mass neutrino of kinetic energy E_ν is given by equation (8.8). If monoenergetic neutrinos are emitted in electron capture decay, then the daughter nuclei should all have the same recoil momentum and kinetic energy. By studying the recoil kinetic energy of Cl^{37} atoms formed by the electron capture decay of A^{37}, it has been shown that, in this decay at least, a single neutrino is emitted with a kinetic energy equal to the total decay energy. The rest mass of the neutrino was found to be less than one tenth of the electron mass.

The free neutrino was first detected by Reines and Cowan and coworkers.* They made use of the reaction of the neutrino with a proton:

$$\nu + p \rightarrow e^+ + n$$

The source of the neutrinos was the β^--decay of the fission products inside a large nuclear fission reactor. By shutting down the reactor, the flux of neutrinos through their apparatus could be cut off at will. Since the probability that a neutrino will interact with a proton is extremely small, the experiment required both a high flux of neutrinos and a large number of protons to produce a measurable number of events. The source of the protons was water containing dissolved cadmium chloride. The positrons produced by the neutrino-proton reaction annihilated almost immediately to produce two γ-ray quanta which were detected simultaneously in two large tanks containing terphenyl dissolved in triethylbenzene. This solution produces a small light flash when a γ-ray is absorbed in it. The light flashes were detected by means of 110 photomultiplier tubes placed in each tank.

The neutrons produced in the neutrino-proton reaction were slowed down by collisions with hydrogen nuclei in the water tanks, and after reaching thermal velocities (which takes a few microseconds) they were captured by the nuclei of Cd^{113} in the solution. The neutron binding energy was promptly released as γ-radiation which was also detected by the photomultiplier tubes.

A neutrino-proton interaction therefore produced a characteristic sequence of signals which served to distinguish it from all types of spurious events. In spite of the elaborate nature of the experiment, an average of only 2.88 ± 0.22 neutrino-proton interactions were observed per hour

---

* Reines, F., and C. L. Cowan, *Phys. Rev.*, **92**, 830 (1953).
  Cowan, Reines, Harrison, Kruse, and McGuire, *Science*, **124**, 103 (1956).

while the reactor was in operation. The effective target size which the proton presents to the neutrino was found to be about 10^{-43} cm². This may be compared with the target area presented by a proton to a slow neutron, which is about 0.3×10^{-24} cm.

F. Double β-Decay

There are many nuclei for which simultaneous emission of two β-particles would be energetically possible. For example, U^{238} is stable with respect to the formation of Np^{238} by β^--decay, but could conceivably decay directly to Pu^{238} by simultaneous emission of two β^--particles.

The theoretical half life for the double β-decay process depends on the assumptions which are made about the neutrinos. If two neutrinos are emitted, then half lives of the order of 10^{21} years might be expected. On the other hand, it is possible that no neutrinos are emitted, in which case half lives might be as short as 10^{17} years.

In spite of many attempts, double β-decay has not been definitely observed. In many experiments, half life limits much greater than 10^{17} years were established. For example, Levine, Ghiorso, and Seaborg were able to set a lower limit of 6×10^{18} years for the double β-decay half life of U^{238}. It therefore seems very probable that double β-decay without emission of neutrinos does not occur. Whether it occurs *with* emission of neutrinos is still not firmly established.

REFERENCES

1. Blatt, J. M. and V. F. Weisskopf, *Theoretical Nuclear Physics*, John Wiley & Sons, New York, 1952.

2. Elton, L. R. B., *Introductory Nuclear Theory*, Isaac Pitman and Sons Ltd., London, 1959.

3. Orear, J., A. H. Rosenfeld, and R. A. Schluter, *Nuclear Physics (Fermi Lecture Notes)*, University of Chicago Press, Chicago, 1950.

4. Siegbahn, K. (ed.), *Beta- and Gamma-Ray Spectroscopy*, North Holland Publishing Co., Amsterdam, 1955.

5. Allen, J. S., *The Neutrino*, Princeton University Press, Princeton, 1958.

6. Nijgh, G. J., A. H. Wapstra, and R. Van Lieshout, *Nuclear Spectroscopy Tables*, North Holland Publishing Co., Amsterdam, 1959.

7. Wick, G. C., "Invariance Principles of Nuclear Science," *Ann. Revs. Nuclear Sci.*, **8**, 1 (1958).

8. Segrè, E. (ed.), *Experimental Nuclear Physics*, John Wiley & Sons, New York, 1959: Vol. III/11, M. Deutsch and O. Kofoed-Hansen, *Beta Rays*.

PROBLEMS

1. The following table shows the results of a measurement of the β^--spectrum of Fe^{59}:

E_e = energy of β-particles, Mev	N = Relative number having this energy	$\dfrac{1}{p_e^2 F(Z,E_e)}$
0.086	223	1.075
0.098	217	0.96
0.130	198	0.76
0.165	155	0.62
0.202	109	0.51
0.241	71.2	0.42
0.283	51.2	0.36
0.325	33.1	0.31
0.347	26.6	0.29
0.393	11.5	0.25
0.416	5.3	0.23
0.440	1.0	0.22

In the table, the values of $p_e^2 F(Z,E_e)$ were calculated with the aid of published tables. Make a Kurie plot of these data, and split the resulting curve into the best two straight lines. (Warning: Remember the square root sign. Do not subtract as though for a decay curve.) What are the end points of the two β^--spectra?

2. Given the β-decay scheme of Figure 8.9 for the decay of a pair of isomers to three different excited states A, B, and C of the daughter nucleus, list the spins and parities of the three levels A, B, and C.

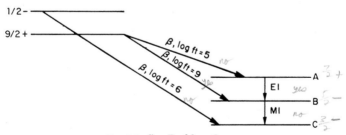

Fig. 8.9. See Problem 2

3. A β-emitter decays primarily to the first excited state of its daughter nucleus, which then de-excites to its ground state by an M1 transition. The ground state has spin and parity $\frac{1}{2}(+)$. The log ft value for the β-transition is 5.3. Draw the decay scheme and indicate the most likely spin and parity assignment for the β-emitter and first excited state of the daughter.

4. Draw a probable decay scheme for a radioactive nuclide exhibiting a one-component positron spectrum with an end point at 0.70 Mev and a 1.10 Mev γ-ray not in coincidence with positrons.

5. A β^--emitter gives a spectrum consisting of a single continuous β^--spectrum with an end point at 0.80 Mev. In addition, four conversion electron groups are observed at 138.0, 158.5, 261.0, and 281.5 kev. The K and L shell electron binding energies of the daughter nuclide are 24.0 and 3.5 kev. What is the most likely decay scheme suggested by this information?

6. Fe^{55} decays to Mn^{55} by K-electron capture with a half life of 2.9 years. The mass difference between Fe^{55} and Mn^{55} is 0.23 Mev.
  (a) What is log ft for this decay?
  (b) From shell theory, is there a parity change?
  (c) Is the transition allowed or first forbidden?

7. K^{40} decays 90% by β^--emission and 10% by electron capture. Its half life is 1.2×10^9 years. The maximum β^--particle energy is 1.4 Mev. Calculate log ft for the β^--decay.

8. In the radioactive decay of a certain nuclide, K and L conversion electrons belonging to a single γ-transition are observed, as well as the γ-ray itself in low abundance. Describe three measurements, involving the examination of these and any other likely radiations, by means of which it would be possible to tell whether the decay was by electron capture or isomeric transition.

9. The β^--decay of Ce^{144} goes according to the scheme shown in Figure 8.10.

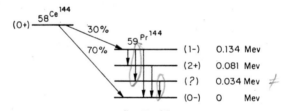

Fig. 8.10. See Problem 9

  (a) What log ft value would you expect for the β^--decay to the $0(-)$ and $1(-)$ states of Pr^{144}?
  (b) Why is there no β^--decay to the $2(+)$ level?
  (c) Construct a table showing the energies of the γ-rays, and the multipolarities of the transitions (for the cases which are determined by the above data).
  (d) What can you say about the spin of the state of Pr^{144} which is marked (?)?
  (e) What spin is predicted by the shell model for the ground state of Pr^{144}?

10. $_{22}Ti^{43}$ has a half life of 0.6 sec. It presumably decays by positron emission to its mirror partner Sc^{43}. Roughly what value would you expect for the end point of the positron spectrum? *Hint:* This problem may be solved by means of Figures 8.4 and 8.7.

11. Am^{244} decays to Cm^{244} by emission of β^--particles. The end point of the spectrum is 1.5 Mev. Which of the two atoms is heavier, and by how much?

12. What is the minimum energy neutron that could be used to bring about the reaction

$$Z^A + \text{neutron} \rightarrow (Z+1)^A + \text{proton}$$

assuming that the nucleus $(Z-1)^A$ emits β^--particles whose spectrum has its end point at 2.10 Mev?

13. Show that the recoil kinetic energy of an atom of atomic mass M due to the emission of a β-ray or conversion electron of energy E Mev is

$$\text{Recoil kinetic energy} = \frac{537E(E-1)}{M} \text{ ev}$$

14. Make use of equation (8.17) to derive an equation for the end point of the β^+-particle spectrum for the decay of a mirror nucleus to its partner. Use the equation to calculate a value for the nuclear radius parameter R_0 from the information that the β^+ end point for Na^{21} is 2.50 Mev.

15. The mass of a neutron is greater than the mass of a proton by 1.30 Mev. These particles are a mirror pair. Calculate:

(a) The maximum kinetic energy of β^--particles from the decay of the neutron, ignoring the small proton recoil energy.

(b) The half life of the neutron.

(c) The kinetic energy of the most energetic proton recoils (see Problem 13).

CHAPTER 9

Nuclear Reactions

A. Introduction

When a layer of some target material is bombarded with a beam of particles, many different phenomena may be observed. If the particles are charged (for example if they are protons or deuterons), the vast majority of them will lose energy by interactions with the atomic electrons of the target material until they either stop or emerge from the rear face of the target layer with reduced energy. Other particles will pass close enough to a nucleus in the target layer to feel the effect of the Coulomb repulsion. These particles will suffer a change of direction (Coulomb scattering) and a small loss of kinetic energy. Other particles will pass close enough to a target nucleus to feel the effect of the short range nuclear forces. Like Coulomb scattering, such interactions cause a change in the direction of motion of the particle, and transfer a small amount of kinetic energy to the target nucleus. The nucleus may be left in an excited state or in its ground state. In the latter case, the total kinetic energy of the system of particle and nucleus remains the same before and after the event. Such particles are said to be elastically scattered. When the target nucleus is left in an excited state, the energy is derived from the kinetic energy of the particle. In such events, the particle is said to be inelastically scattered.

In some cases, the incident particle may undergo a nuclear reaction with the target nucleus. The particle (or a part of it if it is a complex particle such as a deuteron) may be captured by the nucleus, and one or more new particles may be emitted. The different kinds of interactions mentioned above are summarized in Table 9.1.

TABLE 9.1. Summary of Interactions of Charged Particles with Target Atoms and Nuclei

Incident particle interacts with	Type of force	Effect on particle		Effect on nucleus		Name of process
		Direction	Energy	Kinetic energy	Identity	
Atomic electron	Coulomb	Changed slightly	Slight reduction	Slight increase	Same	Atomic ionization and excitation
Nucleus	Coulomb	Changed	Slight reduction	Slight increase	Same	Coulomb or Rutherford scattering
Nucleus	Nuclear	Changed	Slight reduction	Slight increase	Same	Nuclear elastic scattering
Nucleus	Nuclear	Changed	Reduced	Slight increase	Excited state	Nuclear inelastic scattering
Nucleus	Nuclear	Particle transmuted or absorbed		Increased	Transmuted	Nuclear reaction

As a typical example of a nuclear reaction, consider the interaction of high energy, C^{12} nuclei with a target of gold (Au^{197}). Among many other products, At^{204} is formed by a reaction in which the Au^{197} and C^{12} nuclei first amalgamate to form highly excited nuclei of At^{209}. The At^{209} nuclei then emit five neutrons to produce At^{204}. The reaction may be written as an equation:

$$_{79}Au^{197} + {}_6C^{12} = {}_{85}At^{204} + 5 \text{ neutrons} + Q$$

where Q stands for the kinetic energy released or absorbed in the process. (In thermodynamic terms, Q would be called ΔH, the change in heat content.) In a shorter notation, the same reaction may be written $_{79}Au^{197}(_6C^{12},5n)_{85}At^{204}$. The comma separates the initial system on the left from the final system on the right. In this notation, n stands for a neutron, p for a proton, d for a deuteron, α for a helium ion, and t for a triton (H^3 nucleus).

In nuclear reactions induced by low energy (below a few hundred Mev) bombarding particles, the number of protons and neutrons in the initial and final systems separately remain constant. Thus in the reaction $_{83}Bi^{209}(\alpha,2n)_{85}At^{211}$, there are 85 protons and 128 neutrons on each side of the equation. In reactions in which mesons are absorbed or emitted, the total charge and the total number of nucleons must remain constant, but the numbers of protons and neutrons separately may change. For example, in the reaction $_{29}Cu^{63}(p,p\pi^+)_{28}Ni^{63}$, the total charge is 30 units before and after the reaction, but the number of protons decreases by unity and the number of neutrons increases by unity. The total number of nucleons remains the same (since the emitted π^+ meson is not a nucleon).

B. Conservation of Momentum and Energy

Energy and momentum (both linear and angular) must be conserved in a nuclear reaction. The energy release, Q, may be calculated from atomic masses, if they are known, in the manner discussed in Chapter 3. Consider the reaction $C^{12}(\alpha,d)N^{14}$. The target atom C^{12} will be in its normal state, probably in a covalent molecule, while the helium ion will be a bare nucleus with no atomic electrons. The emitted deuteron will undoubtedly be just a bare nucleus, and the N^{14} will probably be partially stripped of its electrons. It is therefore not at all obvious that Q can be calculated from the atomic masses, which include the mass of all the electrons of the atoms.

If we consider only the numbers of electrons and ignore their states of combination (since the electron binding energies are so small by comparison with nuclear energies), we can write the overall reaction as follows:

$(C^{12} + 6$ electrons$) + He^4 = (N^{14} + x$ electrons$)$
$$+ H^2 + (6 - x) \text{ free electrons}$$

The energy released in the reaction is then

$Q = [(\text{mass } C^{12} \text{ nucleus}) + (\text{mass } He^4 \text{ nucleus}) + (\text{mass 6 electrons})]$
$\quad - [(\text{mass } N^{14} \text{ nucleus}) + (\text{mass } H^2 \text{ nucleus}) + (\text{mass 6 electrons})]$ (9.1)

If we add the mass of two extra electrons to each of the terms in square brackets on the right-hand side of equation (9.1), it may be rewritten as follows:

$$Q = [(\text{mass } C^{12} \text{ atom}) + (\text{mass } He^4 \text{ atom})]$$
$$- [(\text{mass } N^{14} \text{ atom}) + (\text{mass } H^2 \text{ atom})]$$

In more general terms,

$$Q = [\text{Sum of atomic masses of reactants}]$$
$$- [\text{Sum of atomic masses of products}] \quad (9.2)$$

If the reactants are heavier than the products, the reaction is exoergic, and Q is positive. If the products weigh more than the reactants, the reaction is endoergic and Q is negative. In other words, some of the kinetic energy of the incident particle has been used to create products of greater mass than the initial system. Such a reaction obviously can take place only if the kinetic energy of the incident particle is at least as great as the amount of energy absorbed in the reaction.

Momentum must be conserved. If a particle of mass m and velocity v strikes a nucleus of mass M, and is absorbed, then the product nucleus, whose mass is $(m + M)$, must move in the same direction as the incident particle and with a velocity V such that

$$mv = (m + M)V \quad (9.3)$$

The kinetic energy T_r of the product nucleus will therefore be

$$T_r = \frac{m}{(m + M)} T_i \quad (9.4)$$

where T_i is the kinetic energy of the incident particle.

Suppose now that we wish to observe an endoergic nuclear reaction in which the reacting system will absorb an amount Q of kinetic energy. It is not enough to bombard the target nuclei with incident particles of kinetic energy Q, because a part of the incident kinetic energy must, according to equation (9.4), end up as kinetic energy of the product nucleus. The minimum required kinetic energy T_m must therefore be greater than Q by the amount T_r:

$$-Q = T_m - T_r = \frac{M}{(M + m)} T_m$$

$$T_m = \frac{-Q(M + m)}{M} \quad (9.5)$$

The negative sign in equation (9.5) arises because Q is a negative quantity in endoergic reactions. The minimum incident kinetic energy T_m which will just enable the reaction to take place is called the threshold for the reaction. Exoergic reactions, of course, have no such threshold. Forgetting for the moment about the existence of the Coulomb and centrifugal barriers, exoergic reactions can be induced by particles of zero kinetic energy.

If in some way the target nucleus could be prevented from moving, then of course the threshold in an endoergic reaction would be equal to $-Q$. In more familiar terms, it is obviously much easier to flatten a ping-pong ball with a hammer when the ball is placed on an anvil than it is if the ball is free to move. According to equation (9.5), in the latter case the kinetic energy of the hammer would need to be greater by the ratio of the mass of the hammer plus ball to the mass of the ball.

The motion of the product nucleus complicates the discussion of nuclear reactions. For example, if we wish to compare the interactions of 50 Mev helium ions with a light nucleus such as Be^9 and a heavy nucleus such as U^{238}, we have to remember that the impact of the helium ions on the Be^9 is "softer" because the target nucleus is much lighter. Such difficulties are overcome by defining a new frame of reference relative to which velocities can be measured. Measurements are usually made by observers and with experimental equipment which are stationary within the laboratory. Such measurements are said to be made in the laboratory system. We can simplify the discussion of nuclear reactions by defining a new reference system which is called the center of mass system. This system, which is in uniform motion relative to the laboratory system, is defined in such a way that the momentum of the incident particle is equal and opposite to that of the target nucleus. The total momentum in this system is therefore zero. Suppose that the velocity of an incident particle of mass m is v in the laboratory system, and that the mass of the target nucleus is M. Let the velocity of a center of mass observer be V relative to the laboratory system. If his velocity is in the same direction as the motion of the incident particle, then he will measure the velocity of the incident particles to be $(v - V)$, and their momentum to be $m(v - V)$. He will observe the target nuclei, which are at rest in the laboratory system, to be moving towards him with velocity V and momentum $-MV$. For the total momentum of the system to be zero, V must be chosen so that

$$m(v - V) - MV = 0$$

$$V = \frac{mv}{(m + M)} \tag{9.6}$$

The total kinetic energy T' of the incident particle plus the target nucleus measured in the center of mass system is

$$T' = \tfrac{1}{2}m(v - V)^2 + \tfrac{1}{2}MV^2$$

$$= \frac{M}{(m + M)} T_i \qquad (9.7)$$

where T_i is the kinetic energy of the incident particles in the laboratory system. Notice that equation (9.7) contains the same factor $M/(m + M)$ as equation (9.5). The center of mass system threshold energy for an endoergic reaction is just equal to $-Q$. We shall observe additional simplifications which arise from the use of the center of mass system.

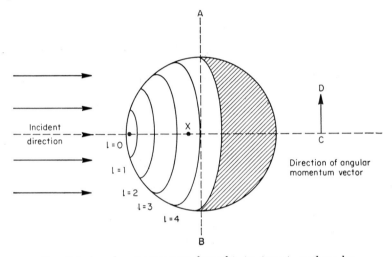

Fig. 9.1. Angular momentum brought to target nucleus by incident particle

As well as conserving linear momentum, a nuclear reaction must conserve angular momentum. As usual, the orbital angular momentum brought to the target nucleus by the incident particle can have only the quantized values $l\hbar$, where l is an integer (which may be zero). In addition, the incident particle may have spin; if it is a proton or neutron with spin $\tfrac{1}{2}$, the total angular momentum which it brings to the target nucleus will be $(l \pm \tfrac{1}{2})\hbar$.

The orbital angular momentum l is equal to $r \times p$, where p is the momentum of the incident particle in the center of mass system, and r is the distance from the center of the nucleus at which it strikes. Since $r \times p$ can only have quantized values, we can think of the target nucleus as divided up into a set of zones as shown in Figure 9.1. For incident particles with a given momentum p, each zone corresponds to a certain value of l. The incident particle can cause the nucleus to rotate only about an axis at right angles to the direction of the incident particle. For example, a particle which strikes the nucleus at the point X will cause rotation about the axis AB. The vector representing this angular momentum will be the line CD, whose length in this case will be $3\hbar$, since X is in the $l = 3$ zone. Wherever the incident particle strikes the nucleus, the vector representing the angular momentum must always be perpendicular to the direction of the incident particle.

The total angular momentum of the system will be the vector sum of the spin of the incident particle, the spin of the target nucleus, and the orbital angular momentum l. As a result of the collision, particles and γ-rays will usually be emitted from the struck nucleus, and they can carry away angular momentum. Where the incident particle has high momentum, for example if it is a heavy particle such as C^{12}, then the angular momentum l may be as large as $100\hbar$. The final product nucleus will have at the most a spin of only a few units, so that the particles and γ-rays emitted in the course of the reaction must carry away a large amount of angular momentum.

C. Reaction Cross Sections

A nucleus of radius R will present a target of projected area πR^2 to an incident particle. For a target of $A = 100$, this area will be approximately $\pi(100^{1/3} \times 1.4 \times 10^{-13})^2$ cm^2, or about 1.3×10^{-24} cm^2 (1.3 barns). The probability that an incident particle will strike the nucleus is proportional to this target area, which of course is equal to the area of a cross section of the nucleus through its center.

Many different kinds of events may follow as a consequence of the collision of a particle and a nucleus. For example, the collision of 24 Mev deuterons with nuclei of Th^{232} may produce, among many others, the following reactions: Th^{232}(d,n)Pa^{233}; Th^{232}(d,2n)Pa^{232}; Th^{232}(d,3n)Pa^{231}; Th^{232}(d,p)Th^{233}; Th^{232}(d,γ)Pa^{234}; Th^{232}(d,fission)Fission products. We may imagine the total cross section of the Th^{232} nucleus to be subdivided into areas corresponding to each of these different reactions, each reaction being assigned an area proportional to the probability that the particular reaction will take place when a 24 Mev deuteron strikes a Th^{232} nucleus. Thus if the total cross section of Th^{232} is 2 barns, and that for the reaction Th^{232}(d,γ)Pa^{234} is 1 millibarn (mb), then for every 2000 deuterons which strike Th^{232} nuclei, only one will lead to the formation of Pa^{234}. These subdivisions are of course mathematical fictions. There is not necessarily any specific area which must be struck in order to produce each reaction.

When the incident particle is of such low energy that its de Broglie wavelength (h/p) is larger than the radius of the target nucleus, then the wavelength of the particle rather than the cross section of the nucleus determines the probability of the interaction. In practice, this happens only when the incident particles are neutrons, since charged particles of sufficiently long wavelength would have too small an energy to penetrate the Coulomb barrier of the target nuclei. The maximum possible cross section σ of a nucleus of radius R for the absorption of $l = 0$ neutrons of wavelength λ is

$$\sigma = \pi \left(R + \frac{\lambda}{2\pi} \right)^2 \tag{9.8}$$

For very low energies, $\lambda \gg R$, and then $\sigma \gg \pi R^2$. For example, the effective cross section for the reaction $Xe^{135}(n,\gamma)Xe^{136}$ is about 3×10^6 barns when the neutron energy is about 0.1 ev.

Experimentally measured values of reaction cross sections are useful for the calculation of yields of products in cyclotron or reactor bombardments. The beam of accelerated ions from a cyclotron (or other type of

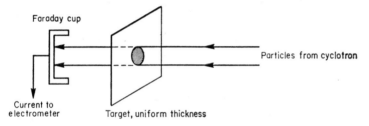

Fig. 9.2. Typical arrangement for bombardment of target in an accelerator

machine) usually falls on a small spot of the target as shown in Figure 9.2. After passing through the target, the beam particles which were not absorbed pass into a Faraday cup which has walls thick enough to stop them completely. The total charge deposited by the beam particles in the Faraday cup is measured with an electrometer. Thus the intensity of the beam is usually expressed in units of electric current; a typical value would be 10 μamp. The total quantity of beam which has passed through the target is usually expressed in μamp-hr. For particles of charge unity, such as protons or deuterons, one μamp-hr of beam corresponds to the passage of 2.26×10^{16} particles. For doubly charged particles, such as helium ions, one μamp-hr will correspond to only half as many particles.

Suppose now that the target of Figure 9.2 consists of a uniform monolayer of atoms with a density of N atoms per cm^2. Let the cross section for some reaction of interest be σ cm^2. Then the fraction of the beam particles which are absorbed to produce this particular reaction will be $N\sigma$. For a beam of intensity I particles per second, the number of reaction produced per second will be $NI\sigma$. Since nuclear reaction cross sections are so small compared with the sizes of atoms, the fraction of the beam absorbed in the monolayer will be very small. Therefore if the target consists of many layers, the beam intensity falling upon each successive layer will still be very nearly equal to I particles per second. If there are T layers, the number or reactions produced per second will be $NI\sigma T$. But NT is the total number of target atoms per square centimeter of target, and therefore

$$\text{(Number of reactions per sec)} = \text{(Number of target atoms per cm}^2\text{)} \times \sigma \times I \quad (9.9)$$

Target thicknesses are usually expressed either in linear units (inches or centimeters) or as weight per unit area. Either of these units can be converted into (number of target atoms per square centimeter) if the atomic weight and density of the target material are known.

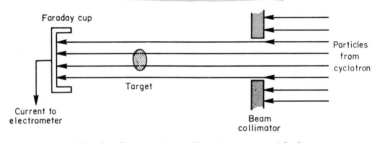

Faraday cup

Particles from cyclotron

Target

Current to electrometer

Beam collimator

Fig. 9.3. Bombardment of small-area target with large-area beam

If the target material is unusually valuable (for example, if it is a separated isotope), then it may be more economical to concentrate all the available material into a small space, and to bombard with a beam which covers a slightly larger area. In this way, all the target material is illuminated by the beam, and none of it is wasted. This situation is illustrated in Figure 9.3. The beam from the accelerator is passed through a collimating hole of known area (usually a hole in a graphite disk), so that the area of the emerging beam is accurately known. The target is placed within the area of the collimated beam. Let the beam intensity be I particles per second, as measured by the Faraday cup, and let the area of the beam be A cm^2. Then the number of beam particles per cm^2 per second is I/A, and let us assume that this beam intensity is constant across the whole area A. Let there be N target atoms placed in the beam. Then

$$\text{Number of reactions per second} = \frac{N\sigma I}{A} \quad (9.10)$$

Observe that here we have used the total number of target atoms rather than the number per square centimeter as in equation (9.9). However, we have used the (number of beam particles per square centimeter) rather than the total beam intensity as in equation (9.9), so that the units remain the same. Dimensional analysis helps to prevent errors in the use of these equations. If the area of the beam is larger than the area of the target material, the N target atoms may be spread out in any convenient way as long as they are all within the area of the beam.

Equations (9.9) and (9.10) give the number of nuclear reactions occurring per second. If the product nuclei are stable, the number present at the end of a bombardment lasting t seconds is just $t \times$ (number of reactions per second). However, if the product is radioactive, with decay constant λ, then some of the product nuclei will decay during the time t. If the bombardment lasts for a very long time, then a state of equilibrium will be reached in which the rate of production is exactly equal to the rate of decay. If the number of product nuclei at equilibrium is P, then

$$P\lambda = N_t \sigma I \qquad (9.11)$$

where N_t is the number of target atoms per square centimeter. (This equation is for the case of a target larger in area than the beam.) Just as in the case of the growth of a short-lived daughter from a long-lived parent, the fraction of the equilibrium amount which will be present after a bombardment for a time t is $(1 - e^{-\lambda t})$. Hence the number of product nuclei present after bombardment for t seconds is

$$P_t = \frac{N_t \sigma I}{\lambda} (1 - e^{-\lambda t}) \qquad (9.12)$$

A bombardment which lasts for one half life of the product will produce 50% of the equilibrium amount, a bombardment for two half lives will produce 75% of the equilibrium amount, and so on. It is usually not worth prolonging a bombardment beyond two half lives of the product nucleus.

Conditions inside a nuclear reactor are different from those described above for charged particle accelerators. The neutrons in a reactor are traveling in all directions, and the quantity which corresponds to the beam intensity in an accelerator must therefore be defined in a different way. The neutron flux, as it is called, is defined as the number of neutrons per second passing in any direction through an area of one square centimeter. Values up to about 10^{15} neutrons per cm^2 per sec are found in some reactors. The situation corresponds to Figure 9.3 (small target area, large beam area), so that the number of reactions per second is given by equation (9.13), where F is the neutron flux, and N is the total number of target nuclei:

$$\text{Number of reactions per second} = N\sigma F \qquad (9.13)$$

The number of product nuclei with decay constant λ remaining at the end of a bombardment of duration t seconds is

$$P_t = \frac{N\sigma F}{\lambda}(1 - e^{-\lambda t}) \qquad (9.14)$$

D. Formation of the Compound Nucleus

As we have seen, many different kinds of events may occur when a beam of particles strikes a target. The different reactions which take place may involve several different kinds of mechanisms. One of the most important types of reaction, particularly when the incident particles are of low energy (less than about 50 Mev), is the capture of the incident particle by the struck nucleus to form what is called a compound nucleus. The theory of reactions of this type was first discussed by Niels Bohr in 1936. Reactions of nuclei with very low energy neutrons, for example, are of this type. The compound nucleus formed by the capture of the incident particle will be in a state of high excitation energy; the excitation will be equal to the binding energy of the captured particle to the nucleus plus the kinetic energy of the captured particle in the center of mass system. For example, a 25 Mev (laboratory system) helium ion incident upon a nucleus of $_{29}Cu^{65}$ will, if it is captured, form an excited nucleus of $_{31}Ga^{69}$. The center of mass kinetic energy of the helium ion will be $(25 \times 65)/69$ or 23.6 Mev. The atomic mass of Ga^{69} is 0.004708 amu. less than the sum of the atomic masses of helium and Cu^{65}, so that the reaction is exoergic, and $Q = 0.004708 \times 931.4$ or 4.385 Mev. The excitation energy of the Ga^{69} nucleus will therefore be $23.6 + 4.4$ or 28.0 Mev.

At excitation energies of many Mev, nuclei must be in a chaotic state. Many nucleons will be excited into energy levels well above their normal ground state levels, and the nucleus may contain a considerable amount of rotational and vibrational energy. There will usually be a very large number of closely spaced energy levels, since according to equation (5.6), the density of the levels increases very rapidly as the excitation energy increases. The levels may be so closely spaced in energy that their widths are greater than the energy separation between levels. It is then no longer possible to recognize discrete energy levels, and the nucleus no longer exists in a single, well-defined quantum state. Its energy and its angular momentum, of course, remain constant, but there may be an enormous number of different nuclear configurations of the same energy and angular momentum, and the nucleus will oscillate very rapidly between all these different possible states.

In these circumstances, we can treat the energy levels statistically. The properties of the excited compound nucleus may therefore be described by means of the level density and the nuclear temperature which were discussed in Chapter 5 E. According to equation (5.6) and Table 5.4, a nucleus of mass number 63 excited to 25 Mev has a level density of about 3.6×10^5 levels per Mev, and a temperature of about 3.5 Mev.

E. Decay of the Compound Nucleus

Immediately after their formation, the highly excited compound nuclei will begin to decay. They are energetically capable, in most cases, of emitting one or more particles such as neutrons, protons, deuterons, and helium ions, or energy may be emitted in the form of γ-radiation. The emission of γ-rays, however, is a slow process by comparison with the emission of particles, so that whenever the nuclear excitation energy exceeds the binding energy of a particle, emission of the particle will nearly always take place in preference to the emission of the energy as a γ-ray. Since there is no Coulomb barrier, emission of neutrons is easier than emission of charged particles, particularly from nuclei of high atomic number. Hence reactions such as $(\alpha,2n)$ usually have larger cross sections than (α,pn) or $(\alpha,2p)$, but there are exceptions.

Using the compound nucleus Ga^{69} mentioned earlier as an example, we may visualize the decay process as follows. The highly chaotic state of the nucleus implies that the 28 Mev of excitation energy is randomly shared among the 69 nucleons. The nucleus passes rapidly from one to another of the vast number of closely spaced energy levels, and any given nucleon has a constantly varying share of the total excitation energy. In order that a nucleon may escape, a quantity of energy at least equal to its binding energy must by chance become concentrated on that nucleon. Such a chance occurs infrequently, since the binding energy (about 7 Mev) is many times greater than the average nucleon excitation energy, which is 28/69, or 0.4 Mev. The escape of a charged particle requires the concentration of not only the binding energy, but also sufficient extra energy to enable the particle to surmount the Coulomb barrier. A neutron needs only enough energy to surmount the centrifugal barrier, and if the neutron is emitted with $l = 0$, even this barrier is zero according to equation (7.5). These emission processes are reminiscent of the evaporation of molecules from the surface of a liquid. The nucleon binding energy is analogous to the latent heat of evaporation.

The time delay required for the concentration of energy on a single nucleon is of the order of 10^{-20} seconds, and although this is very short compared with the time required for the emission of a γ-ray, it is long enough to permit the energy brought in by the incident particle to be randomly distributed through the nucleus. In these circumstances, the direction of emission of the evaporated nucleons need bear no relation to the direction of the incident particle. When many overlapping levels are formed in the compound nuclei, the particles emitted from a large collection of compound nuclei are found experimentally with equal intensity in

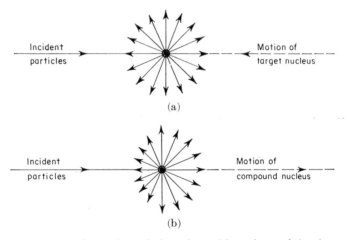

Fig. 9.4 (a). Isotropic emission of particles, observed in the center of mass system. (The arrows, of equal length, represent equal probability of emission in all directions, including directions not in the plane of the page.) (b) Isotropic emission of particles, observed in the laboratory system. (The arrows are longer in the forward direction, representing greater probability of observation in this direction due to the motion of the emitting nucleus)

all directions in the center of mass system. Figure 9.4 (a) shows an isotropic distribution of this type. In the laboratory system, there will be more particles emitted in the forward direction (i.e., the direction of motion of the incident particle), because the decaying compound nuclei are themselves moving in this direction. This phenomenon is illustrated in Figure 9.4 (b).

If the compound nuclei exist in a well-defined quantum state, and if they decay by particle emission to new nuclei which are also in a well-defined state, then the emission of the particles need not be isotropic. However, an argument based on the conservation of parity requires that the probability of emission shall be symmetric about a plane at 90° to the direction of the incident particle, as shown in Figure 9.5.   This argument is exactly the same as that used in the discussion of parity conservation in β-decay in Chapter 8, C.

The difficulty of concentrating a large amount of energy on a single nucleon suggests that the "evaporated" nucleons will be emitted with rather low kinetic energies.   This is found experimentally to be the case. Continuing the analogy with evaporation from a liquid surface, it is not surprising to find that the energy distribution of the emitted particles is a function of the temperature of the excited compound nucleus.   For neutrons, the energy spectrum is approximately of the form

$$P(E) \, = \, Ee^{-E/T} \qquad\qquad (9.15)$$

where $P(E)$ is the probability of emission of a neutron of energy E to leave a residual nucleus at nuclear temperature T.   The shape of this

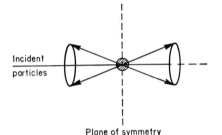

Plane of symmetry

Fig. 9.5. An example of particle emission symmetric about a plane at 90° to direction of the incident particles

spectrum for the typical temperature $T = 2$ Mev is shown in Figure 9.6. The most probable neutron kinetic energy is T Mev.   However, the curve is clearly not symmetrical, and the average neutron energy is $2T$ Mev. The shape of the curve in Figure 9.6 is due to two causes.   The emission of a low energy neutron leaves a residual nucleus with a high excitation energy and hence a high density of levels.   There are therefore more ways available for a low energy neutron to be emitted than for a high energy neutron.   Following the argument of Chapter 8, B, the emission of a low energy neutron should therefore be most probable.   However, the phase space argument of the same chapter favors the emission of high energy neutrons.   Just as in β-decay, the competition between these two opposing effects produces a spectrum with a maximum.

The energy spectrum of evaporated charged particles is given approximately by equation (9.15) multiplied by the appropriate Coulomb barrier penetration probability.   The emission of charged particles with energies below the Coulomb barrier is therefore very improbable.   However, there is some evidence that Coulomb barriers are lower than expected for highly excited compound nuclei, so that rather more than the expected numbers of low energy charged particles may be emitted.

Return once more to the excited Ga^{69} nucleus discussed above. The most probable event is the emission of a neutron of rather low kinetic energy. The excitation energy of the Ga^{68} nucleus thus formed will be $28 -$ (binding energy + kinetic energy of the emitted neutron) Mev, or

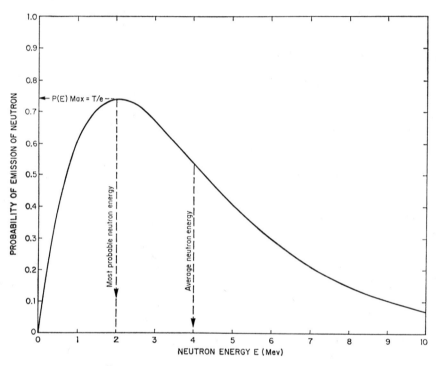

Fig. 9.6. Energy spectrum of evaporated neutrons for nuclear temperature $T = 2$ Mev

about 17 Mev. This is sufficient excitation energy to permit the evaporation of a second particle, and in fact the evaporation process continues until the nuclear excitation energy is less than the binding energy of any particle. The final de-excitation to the ground state can then occur only by the emission of γ-radiation.

F. Cross Sections for Compound Nucleus Reactions

If every incident particle that strikes a nucleus is absorbed to form a compound nucleus, then the total cross section for compound nucleus formation by a nucleus of radius R will be πR^2. Depending on the particular kinetic energies with which they happen to be emitted, the compound nucleus may require the loss of one, or two, or three, evaporated particles to remove all the excitation energy. The total cross section πR^2 will therefore be divided up between reactions such as (p,n), (p,2n), (p,pn), (p,3n), etc., all of which can occur simultaneously in different struck nuclei of the target. The cross sections for these individual

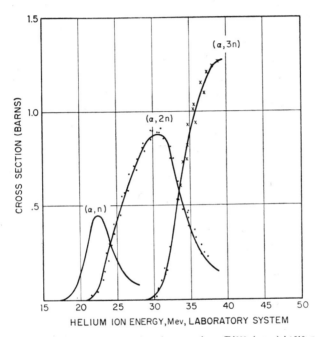

Fig. 9.7. Excitation curves for the reactions Bi^{209} $(\alpha,x\text{n})\text{At}^{213-x}$, for $x = 1,2,3$. The shape of the (α,n) curve is correct, but its vertical scale is arbitrary. (The $(\alpha,2\text{n})$ and $(\alpha,3\text{n})$ results are due to E. L. Kelly; the (α,n) curve is from Jones, Jenkins, Cox, Wood, and McWalters, unpublished)

reactions are found to vary strongly with the energy of the incident particle. Figure 9.7 shows the variation with energy of the (α,n), $(\alpha,2\text{n})$ and $(\alpha,3\text{n})$ reactions from Bi^{209}. Such curves are called excitation functions.

The shape of the $(\alpha,2\text{n})$ curve in Figure 9.7 is very typical of compound nucleus reactions. The reaction is endoergic ($Q = -20.8$ Mev), so that its cross section must be zero for incident helium ion energies below $20.8 \times \frac{213}{209}$ or 21.2 Mev in the laboratory system. Immediately above this energy, the cross section begins to rise. At energies only slightly

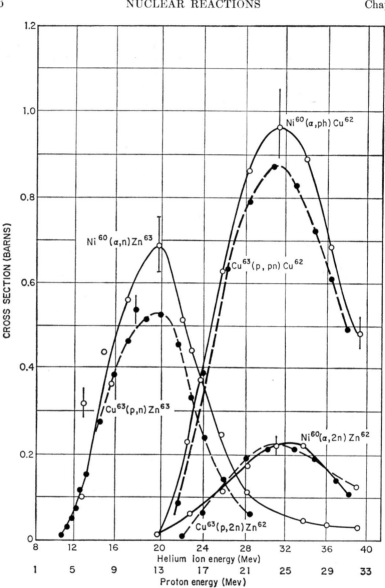

Fig. 9.8. Comparison of decay of compound nucleus Zn^{64} formed by $Ni^{60} + \alpha$ and $Cu^{63} +$ proton. The relative position of the helium ion and proton energy scales is adjusted to give compound nuclei of the same energy. S. N. Ghoshal, *Phys. Rev.*, **80**, 939 (1950)

above threshold, the reaction can take place only if the kinetic energies of the two neutrons are very low, and according to Figure 9.6 the emission of very low energy neutrons is not very probable. Since the average neutron kinetic energy is $2T$ Mev, and T in this example is about 1.4 Mev, the $(\alpha,2n)$ reaction will reach its maximum cross section at a helium ion energy about 5.6 Mev above the energy threshold for the reaction. For higher helium ion energies, the two neutrons will have to carry off an ever increasing amount of energy if they are not to leave enough excitation energy to permit the evaporation of a third neutron. The probability of evaporation of high energy neutrons begins to decrease, so that the $(\alpha,3n)$ reaction becomes more probable as the $(\alpha,2n)$ reaction becomes less probable. The $(\alpha,3n)$ reaction will in turn pass through a maximum, and at yet higher helium ion energies, it will give way to the $(\alpha,4n)$ reaction, and so on. The shape of the excitation curves of Figure 9.7 can in fact be explained rather accurately by means of a neutron evaporation probability given by equation (9.15).

In a few cases, it is possible to form the same compound nucleus by two different reactions. If the assumptions of the compound nucleus theory are correct, then the decay of these compound nuclei formed in different ways should be independent of the method by which they were formed. In the well-known experiment of S. N. Ghoshal, the compound nucleus Zn^{64} was produced by the bombardment of Cu^{63} with protons and Ni^{60} with helium ions. The reaction $Ni^{60}(\alpha,n)Zn^{63}$ was compared with $Cu^{63}(p,n)Zn^{63}$, and so on for other pairs of corresponding reactions. The excitation functions measured by Ghoshal are shown in Figure 9.8. The correspondence between the pairs of reactions is obvious, showing that the mode of decay of the Zn^{64} compound nuclei is indeed independent of the way in which they are formed.

Observe, however, that the cross section for the (α,pn) and (p,pn) reactions is greater than for the $(\alpha,2n)$ and $(p,2n)$ reactions. In this case, the evaporation of a proton is actually more probable than the evaporation of a neutron. The reason for this is not fully understood. The usual explanation is that the product of the (α,pn) and (p,pn) reactions is the odd-odd nucleus Cu^{62}, which is expected to have a higher density of energy levels than the even-even nucleus Zn^{62} which is formed by the $(\alpha,2n)$ and $(p,2n)$ reactions. There are therefore more levels to which proton evaporation can lead, and its probability is favored over neutron emission.

G. Resonance Reactions

If the levels of the compound nucleus are sufficiently well separated, it may be possible to excite them individually by using bombarding particles of just the right energy. The nuclear cross section will then fluctuate violently as the energy of the incident particles is changed. Nuclear reactions of this type are called resonance reactions.

To obtain well-spaced energy levels, the excitation energy of the compound nucleus must be as low as possible, and hence low energy incident

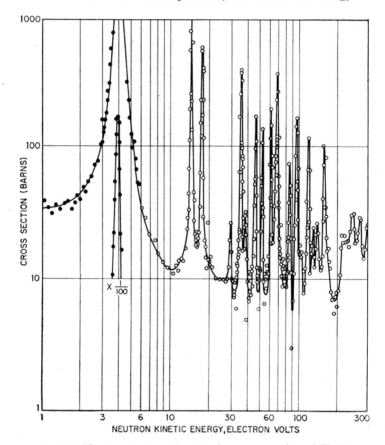

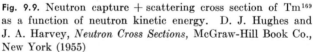

Fig. 9.9. Neutron capture + scattering cross section of Tm[169] as a function of neutron kinetic energy. D. J. Hughes and J. A. Harvey, *Neutron Cross Sections*, McGraw-Hill Book Co., New York (1955)

particles are required. Many experiments have been made with low energy neutrons, since these particles have no Coulomb barrier difficulties at low energies. Figure 9.9 shows the variation of the cross section of Tm[169] for the capture and scattering of neutrons, as a function of the kinetic energy of the incident neutrons. Each of the peaks in the cross section corresponds to the formation of a definite energy level of the compound nucleus Tm^{170}. The neutron binding energy is 6.3 Mev, so that these levels lie at about this energy above the ground state of Tm^{170}. The different energy levels of the compound nucleus will not necessarily decay in the same ways. In particular, the ratios of the probability of particle emission to γ-ray emission will usually differ. Each level will decay with a definite half life, and there will be partial half lives corresponding to each of the possible modes of decay. The energy width Γ of a level is related to the mean life τ by the uncertainty principle:

$$\Gamma = \frac{\hbar}{\tau} \qquad (9.16)$$

(The mean life is equal to the reciprocal of the decay constant, and hence $\tau = t_{1/2}/\log_e 2$.) If the level can decay in several different ways, τ can be split up into a set of partial mean lives, and to each of these there will correspond a partial width, such as Γ_n for neutron emission or Γ_γ for γ-ray emission. By careful analysis of curves such as Figure 9.9, it is often possible to measure these partial widths. For capture of a neutron of wavelength λ by a nucleus of spin J_i to form a single level of the compound nucleus of spin J_c, the variation of the cross section with neutron energy is given by the Breit-Wigner equation:

$$\sigma(n,\gamma) = \frac{\lambda^2}{4\pi}\left[\frac{2J_c + 1}{2(2J_i + 1)}\right]\frac{\Gamma_n\Gamma_\gamma}{(E_n - E_0)^2 + (\Gamma/2)^2} \qquad (9.17)$$

where E_n is the neutron kinetic energy, E_0 is the neutron energy corresponding exactly to the energy of the level of the compound nucleus, Γ is the total width of the level, and Γ_n and Γ_γ are the partial widths defined above. If the level decays only by γ-ray emission or by the re-emission of a neutron (as is often the case, since emission of charged particles is unlikely), then $\Gamma = \Gamma_\gamma + \Gamma_n$. Γ and Γ_γ are approximately independent of the incident neutron energy, but Γ_n is proportional to $(E_n)^{1/2}$. Usually, $\Gamma_\gamma \gg \Gamma_n$. For neutron energies well below E_0, so that $(E_n - E_0)^2 \simeq E_0^2$, equation (9.17) reduces to

$$\sigma(n,\gamma) = \frac{\text{const.}}{v} \qquad (9.18)$$

where v is the neutron velocity. Equation (9.18) is called the "one over v law." The left-hand side of Figure 9.10 shows a $1/v$ dependence for the (n,γ) cross section of Cd^{113}. The maximum is due to a resonance in Cd^{113} with $\Gamma_n = 0.65 \times 10^{-3}$ ev, $\Gamma_\gamma = 0.113$ ev, $E_0 = 0.178$ ev, $J_c = 1$ and $J_i = \frac{1}{2}$.

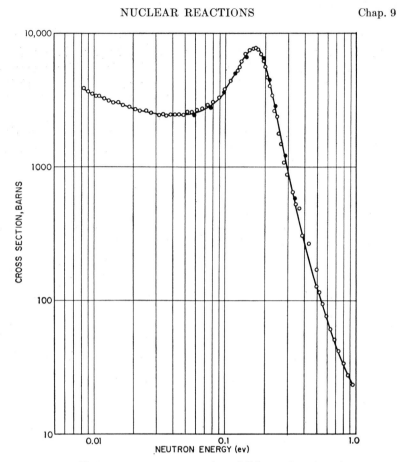

Fig. 9.10. Neutron capture cross section of Cd as a function of neutron energy. The maximum is due to resonance in Cd^{113} $(n,\gamma)Cd^{114}$. Below about 0.03 ev, the curve follows the $1/v$ law. D. J. Hughes and J. A. Harvey, *Neutron Cross Sections,* McGraw-Hill Book Co., New York (1955)

H. High Energy Nuclear Reactions

The assumption that the energy of the incident particle is randomly shared by all the nucleons of the struck nucleus is an approximation which becomes worse as the energy of the incident particle is increased. For energies above about 50 Mev, it is no longer able to explain even the main features of nuclear reactions. Particles are no longer emitted isotropically; rather, they are concentrated into the forward direction. Their energies do not fit the evaporation spectrum of equation (9.15), but are higher. Reaction cross sections vary little with energy; the peaks characteristic of evaporation reactions (Figure 9.7) are not found.

Reactions of this kind are believed to take place by collisions of the incident particle with individual nucleons within the target nucleus. The struck nucleons will quite frequently receive sufficient kinetic energy from the collision to permit them to escape from the nucleus instantaneously, usually in the forward direction. Figure 9.11 gives a crude picture of this type of reaction. An incident proton is shown striking a neutron, and both particles escape from the nucleus, so that the reaction is (p,pn). More complex situations often arise, and both the incident particle and the struck nucleon may make further collisions which can result in the emission of a shower of particles.

Calculations about nuclear reactions of this type are made with the aid of the Fermi gas model (Chapter 5 E). Since the dynamics of the

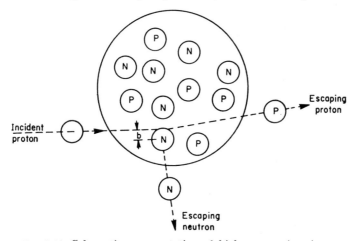

Fig. 9.11. Schematic representation of high energy (p,pn) reaction. The distance *b* is the impact parameter

collision processes are so complex, it is necessary to use a calculation technique known as the Monte Carlo method. The path of a single incident proton through the nucleus is calculated, records being kept of all the collisions which it made, the paths of all the struck nucleons, and their kinetic energies and directions of emission. The calculation is repeated over and over again, using a fast electronic computer, until a reliable picture has been created of what happens when a large number of protons strike a target. The incident protons may strike nuclei at any point on their surfaces. To give all points of impact equal weight, the computing machine picks a number from a collection of random numbers, and this number determines the impact point. Another number from the collection determines the point of impact for the second case, and so on. The use of random numbers in this way is the essence of the Monte Carlo method.

The cross sections for collisions of protons with protons and of protons with neutrons are known from experiments using the free particles. For high energy incident particles, we may treat the protons and neutrons in a nucleus as free particles. From the measured cross sections and the known density of nuclear matter, the computing machine decides, again by the choice of a number, at what point within the nucleus the incident proton makes its first collision, and whether the collision is with a proton or a neutron. In the same way it chooses a value for the impact parameter b (Fig. 9.11), and a value for the velocity and direction of the struck nucleon before the collision. All the information is now available for an exact solution of the directions and energies of the two colliding particles after the collision. The computing machine then follows their paths through the nucleus, decides whether they make further collisions or escape, and so on. When the calculation is complete, it stores all the results in its memory, and starts the calculation over again with a new incident proton. After perhaps 1000 calculations, reliable information will be available about such matters as the relative probabilities of, for example, the (p,pn) reaction and the (p,2p) reaction, the energy spectra of emitted particles, and their probabilities for emission in different directions.

For only one reason is it necessary to remember that the target protons and neutrons are not really free particles. According to the Fermi gas model, all available energy levels of the nucleons are filled as far up as the Fermi energy E_f. If a collision leaves either of the colliding particles with a kinetic energy less than E_f, then the computing machine will ignore the collision, since it is in violation of the Pauli exclusion principle. The incident particle is permitted to continue undisturbed on its path until it either makes another collision or escapes from the nucleus.

After the prompt emission of the shower of particles, the residual nucleus will in most cases be left with some excitation energy. Some nucleons will have been struck, but will fail to escape, and there will also be vacancies in the nuclear structure. At this stage, the nucleus resembles the excited compound nucleus described above, and it will proceed to reduce its energy by the evaporation of low energy particles.

As a result of the two stages of the high energy nuclear reaction, many nucleons may be emitted from the struck target nucleus, so that the final product nucleus may have a much lower A and Z than the target nucleus. Figure 9.12 shows the yields of products, as a function of their mass number A, obtained by the bombardment of copper with 340 Mev and 5700 Mev protons. The lower energy protons can lead to the formation of products with mass numbers as low as about 40, but the 5700 Mev protons give substantial yields of much lighter products. The results of the Monte Carlo calculations agree quite well with experimental results such as those shown in Figure 9.11.   Reactions in which several particles are emitted are often called "spallation," regardless of the mechanism by which they take place.

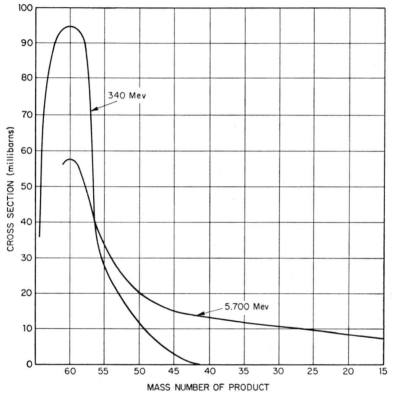

Fig. 9.12. Comparison of the mass yield distribution for the bombardment of copper with 340 and 5,700 Mev protons. B. G. Harvey, *Progress in Nuclear Physics*, Vol. 7, Pergamon Press, London (1959)

The collision of a proton of sufficiently high energy with another proton or a neutron can produce π-mesons by the following reactions:

$$
\begin{aligned}
p + p &= \pi^+ + n + p \\
p + p &= \pi^0 + p + p \\
p + n &= \pi^+ + n + n \\
p + n &= \pi^- + p + p \\
p + n &= \pi^0 + p + n
\end{aligned}
\qquad (9.19)
$$

The kinetic energy of the colliding nucleons must be high enough to be equivalent to the mass of the pion which is created, or about 300 Mev in the laboratory system.

Pions are also produced by the collision of high energy incident protons or neutrons with the nucleons in a target nucleus, and they play an important role in high energy nuclear reactions. The pions may escape from the nucleus, producing reactions such as $(p, p\pi^+)$, or they may interact with pairs of nucleons and be reabsorbed in events which are the reverse of the reactions (9.19) above. In the latter case, the mass and kinetic energy of the pion reappear as kinetic energy of the nucleons. The formation and reabsorption of pions provides an efficient mechanism whereby the kinetic energy of a high energy incident particle may be transferred to other nucleons of the target nucleus.

Beams of pions may be obtained from a high energy accelerator by bombarding a target with high energy protons, and the pions may then be used as projectiles to induce nuclear reactions in other target nuclei. Naturally, the intensity of the pion beam is much less than the intensity of the initial proton beam. The reactions induced by pions are very similar to those induced by high energy protons.

I. Direct Nuclear Reactions

The study of nuclear reactions induced by deuterons led to the discovery of a third nuclear reaction mechanism. The deuteron is a very loosely bound structure. As it approaches a nucleus, the nuclear forces may break off one of the nucleons of the deuteron and cause it to be captured by the target nucleus, while the other nucleon of the deuteron continues on its path almost unaffected by the loss of its partner. The net reaction is therefore (d,p) or (d,n), depending on which part of the deuteron was captured. This reaction mechanism is called stripping. Such reactions may take place with incident deuterons of high or low energy.

The product nucleus may be left in its ground state or in an excited state. In the latter case, the energy of the emitted particle must be reduced, and a study of the energy spectrum of the emitted protons or neutrons can be used to measure the energy of the levels of the product nucleus. Since the process occurs by the capture of a single nucleon, the levels most likely to be formed are those in which only that single nucleon is excited above its normal shell model state. More complex levels, in which several nucleons are in excited states, are much less likely to be formed.

The captured nucleon may bring integral amounts of angular momentum l_c into the target nucleus. The probability that the emitted nucleon will be found at any angle θ relative to the direction of the incident deuteron depends both on θ and on l_c. Therefore a measurement of the angular distribution of the emitted particles may be used to measure l_c, and it is often possible to determine the spins and parities of the various energy levels of the product nucleus. Figure 9.13 shows the angular distribution of the protons emitted in the reaction $Pb^{207}(d,p)Pb^{208}$. The points are experimental, but the solid curve is calculated from stripping reaction theory with the assumption that l_c is 1. A good fit would not be obtained for any other value of l_c.

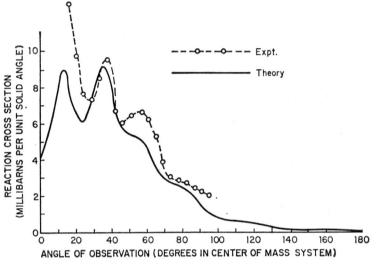

Fig. 9.13. Experimental and theoretical angular distribution of protons from $Pb^{207}(d,p)Pb^{208}$. Points are experimental, and the solid line is theoretical. W. C. Tobocman, *Phys. Rev.*, **115**, 98 (1959)

The conservation of angular momentum leads to the following rule for (d,p) and (d,n) reactions:

$$J_i + J_f + \tfrac{1}{2} \geq l_c \geq |\vec{J_i} + \vec{J_f} + \vec{\tfrac{1}{2}}|_{\min} \qquad (9.20)$$

where J_i and J_f are the spins of the initial and final nuclei. l_c may have any integral value between the upper and lower limits; however, l_c must be even if the parities of the initial and final nuclei are the same, and odd if they are different. The symbol $|\vec{J_i} + \vec{J_f} + \vec{\tfrac{1}{2}}|_{\min}$ means the minimum possible vector sum of the three quantities. Thus in the reaction $C^{12}(d,p)C^{13}$ (ground state), $J_i = 0(+)$, $J_f = \tfrac{1}{2}(-)$. Hence $0 + \tfrac{1}{2} + \tfrac{1}{2} \geq l_c \geq 0 + \tfrac{1}{2} - \tfrac{1}{2}$, so that l_c could be 0 or 1. However, there is a parity change, so that only $l_c = 1$ is allowed. The odd neutron in C^{13} (ground state) is in fact in the $p_{1/2}$ state, with $l = 1$. In the reaction $Cl^{35}(d,p)Cl^{36}$, $J_i = \tfrac{3}{2}(+)$, $J_f = 2(+)$. Hence $\tfrac{3}{2} + 2 + \tfrac{1}{2} \geq l_c \geq -\tfrac{3}{2} + 2 - \tfrac{1}{2}$, and l_c could be 0, 2, or 4. (The odd values 1 and 3 are ruled out because there is no parity change.)   The odd neutron in Cl^{36} is in the $d_{3/2}$ state, and hence $l_c = 2$ should be preferred.   This expectation has been confirmed experimentally.

Stripping reactions have been observed with other incident particles, for example helium ions.   Reactions such as (α,p), with helium ions of about 40 Mev, take place at least in part by this mechanism.   Reactions such as (p,d) or (p,t) are the inverse of stripping, in the sense that the incident particle "picks up" a nucleon instead of losing one.   These reactions, and others, are often called direct reactions, since they involve no formation of an intermediate compound nucleus.

It must be emphasized that both direct and compound nucleus reactions will occur simultaneously in most cases.   Figure 9.14 shows

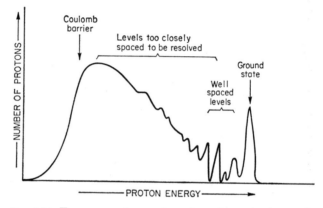

Fig. 9.14. Energy spectrum of protons from (α,p) reaction (schematic)

(schematically) a typical energy spectrum of protons produced by the bombardment of a target with, for example, 40 Mev helium ions.   The protons of highest energy correspond to the reaction (α,p), leaving the product nucleus in its ground state, or in low lying levels above the ground state.   Such protons will be mainly produced by stripping reactions, and they will be concentrated into the forward direction.   The lower energy protons correspond to (α,p) reactions in which the product nucleus is left in a higher state of excitation, and they will mainly be produced by evaporation processes.   The lower energy protons will usually not show distinct energy groups as the high energy protons do, because at the higher excitation energy of the product, the density of energy levels will become so great that the individual proton groups corresponding to the formation of individual levels will not be resolved by the detecting equipment.   In addition to their formation in (α,p) reactions, many of the lower energy protons will result from reactions such as (α,pn) or

(α,p2n), in which neutrons as well as protons are evaporated. The lower energy protons, formed by evaporation from excited compound nuclei, will be emitted more nearly isotropically.

J. Scattering and the Optical Model

In the single particle model, a nucleon is assumed for simplicity to move in a potential well which approximately represents the interaction of that nucleon with all the other nucleons of the nucleus. It should be possible to use this concept to describe the interaction of a target nucleus with an incident particle.

When a beam of particles falls upon a target, some particles will be scattered, while others will be absorbed, bringing about direct or compound nucleus reactions. If the target nucleus is represented as a potential well of depth V Mev, it is found that only scattering will occur, but there will be no absorption. To represent both scattering and absorption, the nucleus must be represented as a potential well having both a real and an imaginary part. Such a potential is written as

$$V = (V_0 + iW_0) \tag{9.21}$$

where i is the imaginary quantity $\sqrt{-1}$. The imaginary part of the potential, W_0, which causes absorption, can be related to the mean free path of the incident particles in the target nucleus. A large value of W_0 corresponds to a short mean free path, and strong absorption. Both V_0 and W_0 vary with the energy of the incident particle; typical values are $V_0 = -50$ Mev and $iW_0 = -5$ Mev. The single particle model, modified by the inclusion of an imaginary part to the potential well, is called the optical model because of a close analogy between the behavior of a nucleus and the behavior of a crystal sphere towards incident light rays. If the crystal sphere is quite clear, it will refract and reflect the rays, but there will be no absorption of light. If the sphere is "cloudy," some of the incident light will be absorbed. The cloudiness therefore corresponds to the imaginary part of the nuclear potential which is responsible for the absorption of incident particles.

The results of scattering experiments are usually expressed in the manner shown in Figure 9.15. The probability for the elastic scattering of incident particles through an angle θ is divided by the probability for Rutherford (Coulomb) scattering through the same angle, and the ratios are plotted as a function of θ. Figure 9.15 shows the results of elastic scattering of helium ions from silver nuclei. The solid line is the result of an optical model calculation using $V_0 = -50$ Mev and $W_0 = -20$ Mev, with a well radius R of 7.5×10^{-13} cm. In order to obtain good agreement with experiment, the simple square well, in which V_0 and W_0 are

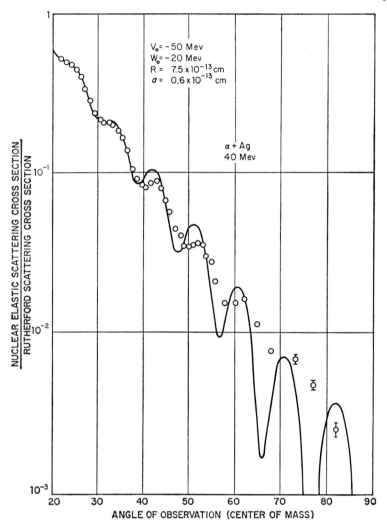

$V_0 = -50$ Mev
$W_0 = -20$ Mev
$R = 7.5 \times 10^{-13}$ cm
$a = 0.6 \times 10^{-13}$ cm

$\alpha + Ag$
40 Mev

NUCLEAR ELASTIC SCATTERING CROSS SECTION / RUTHERFORD SCATTERING CROSS SECTION

ANGLE OF OBSERVATION (CENTER OF MASS)

Fig. 9.15. Elastic scattering of 40 Mev helium ions from silver. A. E. Glassgold, *Progress in Nuclear Physics*, Vol. 7, Pergamon Press, London (1959)

constant up to the nuclear surface and then suddenly zero beyond the surface, must be abandoned in favor of a well with a rounded edge. This is equivalent to the assumption that the density of nuclear matter is lower near the nuclear surface than it is in the center of the nucleus. The variation of V with radius r is often expressed by the equation

$$V = (V_0 + iW_0)[1 + e^{(r-R)/a}]^{-1} \tag{9.22}$$

The quantity a is called the diffuseness parameter. In the example shown in Figure 9.15, $a = 0.6 \times 10^{-13}$ cm. The variation of the factor $[1 + e^{(r-R)/a}]$ with r is shown in Figure 9.16.

The optical model is of increasing importance in the interpretation of experimental results. For example, it may be used to represent the interaction of the nucleus with the outgoing proton in a (d,p) stripping

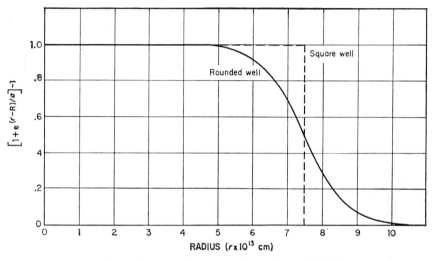

Fig. 9.16. Rounding of nuclear potential for $R = 7.5 \times 10^{-13}$ cm and $a = 0.6 \times 10^{-13}$ cm

reaction. The theoretical curve shown in Figure 9.13 was in fact established in this way.

K. Photonuclear Reactions

Nuclear reactions may be induced by the interaction of photons with target nuclei. The production of suitable beams of high energy photons is usually accomplished by accelerating electrons in some machine, and then allowing them to fall upon a tungsten target. The resulting slowing-down of the electrons causes the emission of photons which are known as "bremsstrahlung" (from the German, meaning "braking radiation"). (The emission of electromagnetic waves by electrons which are traveling in curved paths—i.e., undergoing acceleration—was mentioned in Chapter 1 C.) The bremsstrahlung may be used to induce nuclear reactions in a second target. Such reactions are called photonuclear reactions.

The absorption of photons by nuclei takes place almost exclusively by the electric dipole interaction which is the inverse of the E1 emission of γ-rays discussed in Chapter 6. The spins of the excited states of nuclei formed by dipole absorption will differ by unity from the spin of the initial nucleus, and the parities will be opposite.

The cross section of a nucleus for absorption of a photon is found to show a strong maximum ("giant resonance") for photons whose energies are about $80/A^{1/3}$ Mev for nuclei of A greater than 40, and about 20 Mev (independent of A) for A less than 40. Spheroidal target nuclei may have the resonance split into two parts. Figure 9.17 shows this effect for the target nucleus Ta[181]. At energies below the dipole resonance, there is some photon absorption by quadrupole interaction.

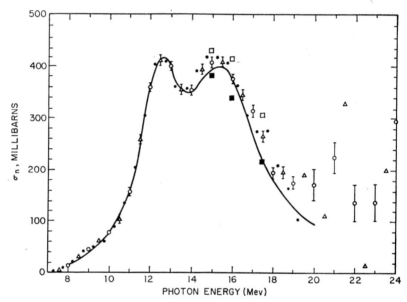

Fig. 9.17. Cross section of Ta[181] for emission of neutrons following absorption of a photon. The cross section includes all neutron-producing reactions such as (γ,n), $(\gamma,2n)$, (γ,pn). E. G. Fuller and M. S. Weiss, *Phys. Rev.*, **112**, 560 (1958)

Two theories have been advanced to explain the dipole absorption resonance. Migdal, Goldhaber, and Teller suggested a "collective" model in which absorption of the photon induces an oscillation of all the protons of the nucleus with respect to all the neutrons. The protons and neutrons may be visualized as two interpenetrating fluids which oscillate back and forth relative to each other. The resonant frequency, and hence the energy, will depend on the nuclear size in the same way that the frequency with which water slops around in a bathtub depends on the size of the tub. The theory provides a natural explanation for the split resonance in spheroidal nuclei, which have different dimensions along two different axes and therefore two slightly different resonant energies.

A theory based on the single particle model was advanced by D. H. Wilkinson. The absorption of a photon leads to the excitation of protons and neutrons mainly from filled shells close to the top of the potential well. The most important transitions are those which require no change in the number of radial nodes in the wave function of the nucleon (see Chapter 5 C), for example $1h_{9/2}$ to $1i_{11/2}$ or $2d_{5/2}$ to $2f_{7/2}$. The single particle model accounts for the photon absorption phenomena about as well as does the collective model, and in fact a more sophisticated analysis shows that the two interpretations are basically the same, even though they seem at first sight to be so different.

Following the absorption of the photon, the excited nucleus can de-excite by (mainly) particle emission, so that reactions such as (γ,n) and (γ,p) are observed. In the language of the collective model, the oscillation of the proton and neutron fluids is damped by their viscosity, so that the oscillation energy is converted into energy of random motion of the nucleons. Evaporation of one or more nucleons then occurs. There is also some direct interaction in which the absorption of the photon leads to immediate emission of a high energy nucleon. The absorption of photons of energy greater than about 100 Mev causes the emission of a relatively large number of proton-neutron pairs. At these energies, the photon absorption process apparently takes place by a mechanism which involves the cooperative action of a proton-neutron pair within the nucleus. The energy of the photon is transferred directly to the members of the pair, causing their immediate emission.

REFERENCES

1. Blatt, J. M., and V. F. Weisskopf, *Theoretical Nuclear Physics*, John Wiley & Sons, New York, 1952.

2. Endt, P. M., and M. Demeur, *Nuclear Reactions*, North Holland Publishing Co., Amsterdam, 1959.

3. Butler, S. T., *Nuclear Stripping Reactions*, John Wiley & Sons, New York, 1957.

4. Mather, K. B., and P. Swan, *Nuclear Scattering*, Cambridge University Press, Cambridge, 1958.

5. Segrè, E. (ed.), *Experimental Nuclear Physics*, Vol. II, John Wiley & Sons, New York, 1953.

6. Frisch, O. R. (ed.), *Progress in Nuclear Physics*, Pergamon Press, London: Vol. 7 (1959), B. G. Harvey, "Spallation"; A. E. Glassgold, "Optical Model for Nuclear Scattering"; Vol. 3 (1953), R. Huby, "Stripping Reactions."

7. Miller, J. M., and J. Hudis, "High Energy Nuclear Reactions," *Ann. Rev. Nuclear Sci.*, **9** (1959); D. H. Wilkinson, "Nuclear Photodisintegration," *ibid*.

8. *Proceedings of the International Conference on the Nuclear Optical Model,* Florida State University, Tallahassee, Florida, (1959).

9. Hughes, D. J., and J. A. Harvey, Neutrons, *American Institute of Physics Handbook,* McGraw-Hill Book Co., New York, 1957. (Tables of neutron cross sections and resonance data.)

10. Flügge, S. (ed.), *Handbuch der Physik,* Julius Springer Verlag, Berlin: Vol. XL (1957), Vol. XLI/1 (1959), Vol. XLII (1957).

11. Ajzenberg-Selove, F. (ed.), *Nuclear Spectroscopy,* Part B, Academic Press, New York, 1960.

12. Eisberg, R. M., and C. E. Porter, "Scattering of Alpha Particles," *Revs. Modern Physics,* **32,** 190 (1961).

13. Tobocman, W., *Theory of Direct Nuclear Reactions,* Oxford University Press, Oxford, 1961.

PROBLEMS

1. Given the following O^{16} physical scale atomic masses, calculate the Q values and thresholds for the reactions $Cm^{244}(\alpha,2n)Cf^{246}$ and $Cm^{244}(\alpha,n)Cf^{247}$.

$$\begin{array}{ll} Cm^{244} & 244.13850 \\ Cf^{246} & 246.14506 \\ Cf^{247} & 247.14762 \end{array}$$

2. The cross section of Na^{23} for the reaction $Na^{23}(n,\gamma)Na^{24}$ is 0.56 barns. How many disintegrations per minute of Na^{24} would be present after the exposure of 1 mg of Na^{23} to a neutron flux of 10^{13} neutrons per cm² per sec for 12 hours?

3. Calculate the maximum number of disintegrations per minute of Po^{210} which could be obtained by leaving 1 gm of Bi^{209} in a neutron flux of 10^{12} neutrons per cm² per sec for a very long time. The reactions are: $Bi^{209}(n,\gamma)Bi^{210}$, $Bi^{210} \rightarrow Po^{210} + \beta^{-}$.

4. A beam of neutrons is incident upon a piece of gold which is 0.1 cm thick. The intensity of the emerging beam is 56% of the intensity of the incident beam. What is the neutron capture cross section of Au^{197}? (The density of gold is 19.3.)

5. Calculate the excitation energy of the compound nucleus P^{31} formed by the bombardment of Al^{27} with 6 Mev (laboratory system) helium ions.

6. The energy liberated in the reaction $Li^{6} + n = He^{4} + H^{3}$ is 4.8 Mev. Calculate the kinetic energy of the H^{3} produced by the bombardment of Li^{6} with very slow (i.e., essentially zero energy) neutrons.

7. The α-decay energy of Pa^{232} is estimated to be 4.47 Mev.

(a) Calculate the α-decay energy of the excited state of Pa^{232} formed by $Pa^{231} + n \rightarrow Pa^{232}$, given the following masses:

$$\begin{array}{ll} Pa^{231} & 231.035936 \\ Pa^{232} & 232.038509 \end{array}$$

(b) Would you expect α-emission from this compound nucleus to compete favorably with de-excitation to the ground state by γ-emission? Show calculations to support your answer.

8. If the threshold for the reaction A(p,n)B is 2.40 Mev, calculate the atomic mass difference between A and B. Which is heavier?

9. The cross section for the reaction $Ni^{60}(\alpha,pn)Cu^{62}$ is 0.9 barn for 32 Mev helium ions. Calculate the number of disintegrations of Cu^{62} per minute at 15 minutes after the end of a 15 minute bombardment of a 0.001-in. thick foil of natural nickel with 10.0 μamp of 32 Mev helium ions.

10. Five μamp of 30 Mev helium ions emerge from a circular collimating hole whose diameter is 0.5 cm, and fall upon a target of 0.1 μgm of Cf^{252}. Calculate the number of disintegrations per minute of the 3.2-hr isotope Fm^{254} which will be present after a 5 hour bombardment. The cross section for the reaction $Cf^{252}(\alpha,2n)Fm^{254}$ is 15 millibarns. Assume that the target is smaller in area than the beam.

11. Calculate the Q value and the threshold (if any) for the reaction

$$Mg^{26}(C^{12},2\alpha p2n)Al^{27}$$

12. Calculate the (n,γ) cross section of Ag^{109} for 0.10 ev neutrons. The resonance for 5.12 ev neutrons has $\Gamma_\gamma = 0.136$ ev and $\Gamma_n = 1.34 \times 10^{-2}$ ev. The spins of Ag^{109} and of the Ag^{110} compound nucleus are $\frac{1}{2}$ and 1 respectively.

13. Prove that equation (9.17) reduces to the $1/v$ law when $E_n \ll E_0$. Remember that $\Gamma_n \sim (E_n)^{1/2}$.

14. What are the most likely values of l_c for the following stripping reactions?

$O^{16}(d,p)O^{17}$ (ground state, $J = \frac{5}{2}(+)$)
$F^{19}(d,n)Ne^{20}$ (ground state)
$Be^9(d,n)B^{10}$ (2(+) level at 3.58 Mev)

15. Show that the flux of neutrons, F, is given by $F = nv$, where n is the number of neutrons per unit volume and v is their velocity.

16. Calculate the maximum orbital angular momentum which could be brought into the nucleus Al^{27} by the capture of a 120 Mev (laboratory system) C^{12} ion.

17. For the reaction A(a,b)B, show that

$$Q = E_b \left(\frac{M_b + M_B}{M_B}\right) - E_a \left(\frac{M_B - M_a}{M_B}\right) - \frac{2\sqrt{M_A M_b}}{M_B} \sqrt{E_A E_b} \cos \theta$$

where the E's and M's are the laboratory system kinetic energies and masses of the particles a, b and the nuclei A, B, and θ is the angle between the directions of the particles a and b.

18. *Monte Carlo Calculation.* Calculate the ratio of the $(\alpha,2n)$ to $(\alpha,3n)$ cross section for a Bi^{209} target with 35 Mev (laboratory system) helium ions by a Monte Carlo method. Proceed in the following way:

(1) Calculate the excitation energy of the At^{213} compound nucleus, using the mass values given in Appendix II.

(2) The probability $P(E)$ of evaporation of a neutron of energy E is $P(E) = Ee^{-E/T}$. Graph this equation for E between 0 and 10 Mev, using a value of 1.4 Mev for the nuclear temperature T.

(3) Choose at random a number between 0 and 10. A suitable procedure is to pick the last two digits from multidigit numbers in a large table such as the list of emission spectra wavelengths in the *Handbook of Chemistry and Physics*. For example, if the last two digits are 73, then call the number 7.3. This number represents the kinetic energy of the first neutron evaporated from At^{213}. Do not use mathematical tables, since these numbers are not supposed to be random. Use any part of the table of numbers once only.

(4) Choose a second number at random by taking the last two digits from the next number in the table. This number must lie between 0 and 1, so if the last two digits are 73, call the number 0.73. If this number is greater than the probability $P(E)$ for the emission of the neutron whose energy was chosen in step (3), reject that neutron. If it is less than $P(E)$, write down the neutron energy. This procedure weights the choice of neutron energies in step (3) according to their probability of evaporation.

(5) Repeat steps (3) and (4) until you have picked at least 20 neutron energies. (100 would be better if you have the time and patience.)

(6) The binding energy of the first neutron to be evaporated is 5.75 Mev. The At^{212} nuclei will therefore have excitation energy equal to the (initial excitation calculated in step (1)) − (neutron kinetic energy + 5.75). Develop a table showing these excitation energies thus:

Initial Excitation Energy of $At^{213} = x$ Mev

Case	Kinetic energy, 1st neutron, Mev	Kinetic energy + 5.75 Mev	At^{212} excitation energy
1	3.8	9.55	$x - 9.55$
2	1.1	6.85	$x - 6.85$
3	4.2	9.95	$x - 9.95$
4	2.2	7.95	$x - 7.95$

If any entries in the last column are negative, then that neutron could not have come out. Erase the line and replace it with a new neutron energy chosen by steps (3) and (4).

(7) The binding energy of the next neutron to evaporate is 5.09 Mev. If any At^{212} nuclei have less than 5.09 Mev excitation energy, then they cannot evaporate the second neutron. Mark such nuclei (α,n). (There may not be any such cases.)

(8) For each of the At²¹² nuclei with more than 5.09 Mev of excitation energy, choose a second neutron energy by steps (3) and (4).   Calculate the residual excitation energy of the At²¹¹ nuclei thus:

Case	At²¹² excitation energy	Kinetic energy 2nd neutron, Mev	Kinetic energy + 5.09 Mev	At²¹¹ excitation energy
1	$x - 9.55$	7.0	12.09	$x - 21.64$
2	$x - 6.85$	0.3	5.39	$x - 12.24$
3	$x - 9.95$	1.6	6.69	$x - 16.64$
4	$x - 7.95$	3.9	8.99	$x - 16.94$

(9) If any of the At²¹¹ nuclei have negative excitation energy, then they could not have evaporated that second neutron.   Pick a new neutron by steps (3) and (4) until a positive excitation energy remains.

(10) The binding energy of the third neutron is 7.73 Mev.   If any of the At²¹¹ nuclei have less than this amount of energy, they cannot evaporate a third neutron.   Mark them $(\alpha,2n)$.   The remaining nuclei can evaporate the third neutron.   Mark them $(\alpha,3n)$.   No nuclei can evaporate a fourth neutron, since 35 Mev helium ions are below the threshold for the $(\alpha,4n)$ reaction.

(11) The ratio of cross sections is just the ratio of the number of $(\alpha,2n)$ cases to the number of $(\alpha,3n)$ cases.   The greater the numbers of cases, the greater the accuracy.   Combine the results of all members of the class to obtain the best result.

CHAPTER 10

Fission

A. Introduction

Fission was discovered in 1938 by O. Hahn and F. Strassman. The bombardment of uranium with neutrons produced several radioactive nuclides which were chemically indistinguishable from elements in the middle of the periodic table, such as barium and lanthanum. These nuclides were at first thought to be isotopes of radium and actinium, but after very careful chemical tests Hahn and Strassman were convinced that the radioactive products were isotopes of much lighter elements formed by the splitting of the uranium nucleus into two parts of comparable size.

Since 1938, the fission process has received more attention than any other nuclear phenomenon, but it is so complicated that it is still poorly understood. No theory exists which can explain more than a small fraction of the experimental observations. The present discussion must therefore consist largely of a description of the observations, with little unifying theory. We shall start by considering the probability that a nucleus will undergo fission (Section B), and then discuss the details of what takes place in the fission act (Sections C and D).

B. Fission Probability

From the atomic mass values of Appendix II, it is easy to show that heavy nuclei are unstable with respect to division into two parts of comparable size. For example, the division of $_{82}Pb^{206}$ into equal parts would produce two nuclei of $_{41}Nb^{103}$. These nuclei are far on the neutron excess side of the stability line, so that they would undergo β^--decay to $_{42}Mo^{103}$ and so on, until they reached the stable nuclide $_{45}Rh^{103}$. The atomic mass of two Rh^{103} atoms is 2×102.904800, or 205.8096 units. The mass of Pb^{206} is 205.974459, so that the energy released in its fission and the subsequent β-decays would be $931.4(205.974459 - 205.8096)$, or about 150 Mev.

In spite of this enormous thermodynamic instability, Pb^{206} is not observed to undergo fission spontaneously, and this is true also for nearly all heavy nuclei which are similarly unstable. The phenomenon of spontaneous fission, however, is observed among the heaviest nuclei. U^{235} decays in this way with a partial half life of 2×10^{17} years, while the spontaneous fission half life of $_{98}Cf^{254}$ is only 55 days. The explanation of these observations closely resembles the theory of α-decay. Although the heavy nuclei are unstable towards spontaneous fission, there is a potential barrier which prevents them from instant decay, and in most cases the half lives are so long that the nuclei appear to be stable. The height of the barrier is found experimentally to be about 6 Mev for nuclei between Th^{232} and Am^{242}. Spontaneous fission involves a tunneling through the barrier in the same manner as in α-decay.

Heavy nuclei which are excited to an energy equal to the barrier height or above can fission almost instantaneously. For example, the capture of slow neutrons by nuclei of U^{235} produces the compound nuclei U^{236} with 6.42 Mev of excitation energy. Some of the excited U^{236} nuclei decay to the ground state by emission of γ-rays, but the majority of them are destroyed by fission before they have had time to emit photons. This observation shows that the partial fission half life of the excited U^{236} nuclei is even shorter than their partial γ-ray emission half life, which is less than 10^{-14} seconds.

In heavy nuclei, charged particle emission is inhibited by the Coulomb barrier, which is about 10 Mev high for protons. The most important modes available for the decay of an excited state are therefore neutron emission, γ-ray emission, or fission. The partial half lives for these modes are usually expressed in terms of partial widths in exactly the manner described in Chapter 9 G. A short partial half life for fission decay corresponds to a large fission width, according to equation (9.16). The fission width Γ_f, the neutron width Γ_n and the γ-ray width Γ_γ are functions of the excitation energy, but their variation is not at all well

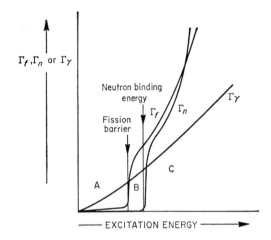

Fig. 10.1. Energy dependence of fission, neutron, and gamma widths. The widths actually increase by many orders of magnitude as the excitation energy increases. The figure is entirely schematic

known. Figure 10.1 shows very schematically what the variation should look like.

At zero excitation energy, the fission width will be very small, but the existence of spontaneous fission will prevent it from being exactly zero. Until the excitation energy reaches the neutron binding energy, Γ_n must be exactly zero, but beyond this point it must increase very rapidly, becoming comparable with Γ_f very shortly above the neutron emission threshold. Figure 10.1 shows the curves for Γ_f and Γ_n crossing at high excitation energy, but it is by no means certain that this actually happens. Γ_γ should increase relatively slowly with increasing excitation energy.

In region A of Figure 10.1, Γ_γ is many orders of magnitude bigger than Γ_f, so that de-excitation is mainly by emission of a γ-ray. Just above the fission threshold, Γ_f and Γ_γ are comparable in size, so that excitation into region B produces fission and γ-ray emission in comparable amounts.   Capture of a slow neutron causes excitation to precisely the boundary between regions B and C, and again Γ_f and Γ_γ are about equal, but early in region C, Γ_f and Γ_n both become much greater than Γ_γ, so that both fission and neutron emission occur, while γ-ray emission becomes unlikely.   The curves of Figure 10.1 are for nuclei such as Pu^{240} or U^{236} whose fission barriers lie below their neutron binding energies.   For lighter nuclei, which have higher fission barriers, or for nuclei whose neutron binding energy is particularly low, the order might be reversed, so that capture of a slow neutron would not cause fission. For example, U^{235} and U^{238} have binding energies for a captured neutron of 6.42 and 4.76 Mev respectively, and since the fission barrier amounts to about 5.5 Mev, U^{235} can be induced to fission by bombardment with low energy neutrons, whereas U^{238} cannot.

The nature of the competition between neutron emission and fission may be illustrated by means of a concrete example.   For target elements light enough for fission to be negligible, bombardment with helium ions gives rise to (α, xn) reactions for which typical excitation curves are shown in Figure 9.7.   The $(\alpha, 4n)$ cross section has a maximum value of about 1 barn for a heavy nucleus like Bi^{209} for which the fission barrier is about 20 Mev.   For the target U^{235}, however, the maximum value achieved by the $(\alpha, 4n)$ cross section is only 7.5 mb, or about 0.6% of the value for a nonfissioning nucleus.   This drastic reduction is due to the decay of about 99.4% of the Pu^{239} compound nuclei by fission rather than neutron emission.   In this system, most of the compound nuclei fission before they have had time to emit even a single neutron; the fission barrier height is only about 6 Mev.   In a few cases, however, a neutron is emitted first, and the excited nuclei of Pu^{238} which are thus formed then fission, or very occasionally emit a second neutron.   Only very rarely are four neutrons emitted, but when this happens, the excitation energy which remains may be so low that Γ_γ is much greater than Γ_f and Γ_n.   The nucleus can then finally de-excite to the ground state of Pu^{235} by emitting γ-rays.

Instability with respect to spontaneous fission is due to the large Coulomb repulsion term in the semiempirical binding energy equation (3.6).   Since the size of this term is proportional to $Z^2/A^{1/3}$, there should be some connection between this parameter and the spontaneous fission half lives.   It is usual to plot the logarithm of the half life as a function of Z^2/A rather than $Z^2/A^{1/3}$.   Figure 10.2 shows such a plot for the even-even nuclei.   The half lives of the other nuclear types are several orders of magnitude longer than those of the adjacent even-even nuclei. We shall consider an explanation for this phenomenon in Section F.

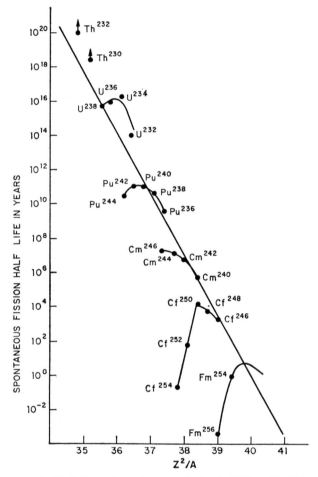

Fig. 10.2. Variation of spontaneous fission half life with Z^2/A. E. K. Hyde, unpublished

C. Fission Products and Fission Yields

The products of the fission of heavy nuclei at low excitation energy are light nuclei lying between approximately zinc and terbium ($Z = 30$ to 65). In addition, a few neutrons are emitted, typically between two and three per fission on the average. The neutron to proton ratio N/Z of a heavy nucleus lying near the β-stability line is much greater than the ratio for a stable, medium weight nucleus. For example, N/Z for U^{236} is $\frac{144}{92}$ or 1.57, whereas for the stable nucleus $_{57}La^{138}$ it is only 1.42. If the fission of a U^{236} compound nucleus produced a nucleus of lanthanum with the same neutron to proton ratio as U^{236}, it would have to be $_{57}La^{147}$, which is very far on the neutron excess side of the line of β-stability. Even allowing for the escape of two or three neutrons, it is clear that the products of fission must be neutron-rich, and therefore will for the most part be *unstable to β^--decay.*

The fissioning nuclei in a given system do not all divide in the same way. For example, a compound nucleus $_{94}Pu^{240}$ formed by the bombardment of Pu^{239} with slow neutrons might divide into $_{36}Kr^{94} + {}_{58}Ce^{144} +$ 2 neutrons, or it might divide into two nuclei of $_{47}Ag^{118} + 4$ neutrons. In all cases, the total numbers of protons and neutrons are unchanged before and after the division, but the division may take place in a large number of different ways. It has required a great amount of skillful radiochemical work to measure the yields of each of the many different fission products for each of a large number of different initial fissioning systems, and this work still continues.

In practice, it is not often possible to determine the atomic numbers of the two primary fragments, because their β^--decays are usually extremely rapid. Ag^{118} mentioned above would surely have a β^- half life of only a few seconds, so that it would be very difficult to separate it by chemical means from the dozens of other fission products formed in the same bombardment in time to measure its radiation. The Ag^{118} would decay to Cd^{118}, whose half life is 50 minutes. However, Cd^{118} is presumably also formed in fission, so that a measurement of its radiation will give the sum of the amounts of Ag^{118} and Cd^{118} formed in fission (plus the amounts of any other nuclides with $A = 118$ which decay rapidly to Ag^{118} and thence to Cd^{118}). A series of products with the same mass number A is called a fission product chain, and instead of obtaining the yields of the separate nuclides, it has been the aim of most radiochemical experiments to measure the cumulative chain fission yield, $Y(A)$. This quantity is defined by the equation

$$Y(A) = \frac{(\text{Number of product nuclei of mass number } A) \times 100\%}{(\text{Number of fissioned nuclei})} \quad (10.1)$$

Obviously the chain yield $Y(A)$ is equal to the sum of all the independent yields of the various members of the chain. Since each fission act produces two fragments, the sum of all the chain yields must be 200%, not 100%. A plot of chain fission yield against A is called a fission yield curve; a typical example of the curve for the fission of a nucleus at fairly low excitation is shown in Figure 10.3.

The most striking feature of Figure 10.3 is the presence of the two large maxima with a very deep minimum between them. The minimum falls at an A value corresponding to division of the U^{236} fissioning nucleus into two fragments of equal size, and the low fission yields in the region of $A = 117$ show that this symmetrical division is very unlikely to occur.

The most probable division, as the positions of the maxima show, is into fragments with masses 95 and 138. No theory of fission has so far been able to give any entirely convincing explanation for the very high probability of this asymmetric division.

The fission yield curve of Figure 10.3 is very nearly symmetrical about the minimum, as of course it should be, since the yield of any mass

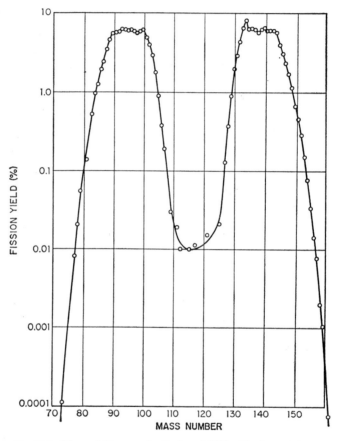

Fig. 10.3. Mass yield curve for fission of U^{235} with slow neutrons. E. K. Hyde, unpublished

number must be the same as the yield of the complementary fragment on the other side of the curve. However, the sum of the masses of a fragment and its partner is about 233 rather than 236, because on the average 2.47 neutrons are emitted in the fission of U^{235} induced by slow neutrons.

The two small spikes near the maxima of the fission yield curve are associated with mass numbers 100 and 134. Their high yields may be due to shell model effects, but they are not fully understood. The primary fragments with 82 neutrons should have mass numbers in the vicinity of 134 and because of the extra stability associated with the 82 neutron magic number, they might be formed in the initial fission process in high yield. The complementary fragments of mass about 100 would therefore also be formed in high yield. In addition, the binding energy of the 83rd neutron is unusually low (Chapter 5 C), and if in many cases fragments with this neutron number lose a neutron by evaporation, then fragments of mass 135 will end up in the mass 134 chain, so that the yield of mass 134 will be enhanced at the expense of the yield of mass 135.

The depth of the central valley in the mass yield curve is a function both of the excitation energy and the mass number of the fissioning nucleus. As the excitation energy is increased, the depth of the valley decreases until finally no valley remains, and the most probable division is into two fragments of equal mass. Figure 10.4 illustrates the effect of energy on the fission of Pu^{239} under bombardment with deuterons of various energies. In the zero excitation energy (spontaneous) fission of Cm^{242} and Cf^{252}, for which fission yield curves have been measured, the valley is so deep that the yields of the products corresponding to symmetrical division are too low to permit measurement.

In the fission of somewhat lighter elements, for example the fission of Bi^{209} under bombardment with 22 Mev deuterons, only a single narrow peak appears, corresponding to a high relative probability of symmetric fission. In the intermediate nucleus Ra^{226}, bombardment with 11 Mev protons was found by Jensen and Fairhall to give a fission yield curve with *three* peaks, so that both the symmetric and asymmetric fission modes occur together. This phenomenon is illustrated in Figure 10.5. It seems likely that symmetric and asymmetric fission are quite separate and distinct processes. On this view, the filling-in of the valley (Fig. 10.4) with increasing energy is not due to a gradual change in the nature of the fission process, but rather to an increase in the amount of the symmetric fission relative to the asymmetric process.

In a few cases, it is possible to measure the independent yield of a single nuclide rather than a cumulative chain yield. If the nuclide Z^A is β-stable, or at least has a long β^--half life, then its decay may contribute so little to the amount of the nuclide $(Z + 1)^A$ that the actual yield of $(Z + 1)^A$ in the fission process can be measured. $(Z + 1)^A$ is called a shielded nuclide if Z^A is β-stable. Because of their special chemical properties (or lack of them), the inert gases krypton and xenon can be separated very rapidly from a mixture of fission products, so that it is possible to measure the independent yields of some of their isotopes.

From such independent yield measurements it is possible to form a picture of the way in which the fissioning nucleus divides the available protons and neutrons. Thus when a fragment of mass 140 is formed, it might be Cs^{140}, Ba^{140}, La^{140}, Ce^{140}, etc. The atomic number which is formed in highest yield for a given mass A is given the symbol $Z_p(A)$. Products with atomic numbers greater or less than Z_p are formed in

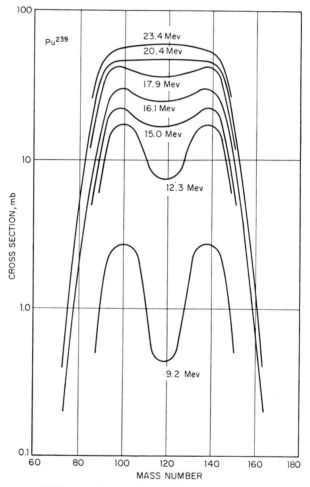

Fig. 10.4. Fission yield for fission of Pu^{239} induced by bombardment with deuterons of various energies.

lower yields. The experimental results for low energy fission may be represented by the Gaussian equation

$$P(Z,A) = 0.565e^{-[Z-Z_p(A)]^2} \qquad (10.2)$$

$P(Z,A)$ is the independent fission yield of the product of atomic number

Z and mass A, divided by the total chain yield for mass A. A graph of equation (10.2) is shown in Figure 10.6.

The value of Z_p for any given A can be calculated from the hypothesis of *equal charge displacement*, which states that the most probable charges Z_p and Z_{p*} for a given mass number A and its complement A^* will be equally displaced from the most β-stable charges for those masses. Thus

$$Z_A - Z_p(A) = Z_{A*} - Z_p(A^*) \tag{10.3}$$

Z_A and Z_{A*} are the most stable charges for mass numbers A and A^*. The masses A and A^* must be related to the mass number A_f of the

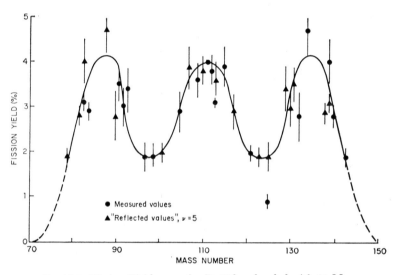

Fig. 10.5. Fission Yield curve for Ra^{226} bombarded with 11 Mev protons. R. C. Jensen and A. W. Fairhall, *Phys. Rev.*, **109**, 942 (1958)

fissioning nucleus and $\bar{\nu}$, the average number of neutrons emitted, as follows:

$$A + A^* = A_f + \bar{\nu} \tag{10.4}$$

The conservation of charge requires that:

$$Z_p(A) + Z_p(A^*) = Z_f \tag{10.5}$$

where Z_f is the charge of the fissioning nucleus. From equations (10.3) and (10.5), it follows by elimination of $Z_p(A^*)$ that:

$$Z_p(A) = \tfrac{1}{2}(Z_A - Z_{A*} + Z_f) \tag{10.6}$$

For a fission product of given mass A, the complementary mass A^* can be obtained from equation (10.4), and then in principle, Z_A and Z_{A*} can be calculated or obtained from a study of β-stability by the methods described in Chapter 3 I.   Insertion of these values into equation (10.6) then gives $Z_p(A)$, and the independent yield for any nuclide of mass A can then be obtained from equation (10.2) as a fraction of the cumulative chain yield for the mass A chain.

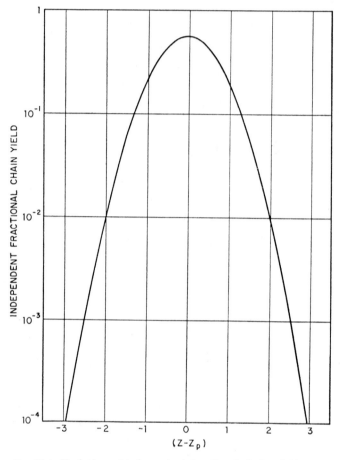

Fig. 10.6. Variation of independent fractional chain yield with $(Z - Z_p)$

As an example of the calculations described above, we can obtain the fraction of the total mass 91 chain yield which belongs to Rb[91] formed in the fission of U[235] with low energy neutrons.   For $A = 91$, equation (3.9) yields $Z_A = 39.5$.   The complementary mass A^* will be 143, and hence $Z_{A^*} = 59.4$.   From equation (10.6), therefore, $Z_p(91)$, the most probable charge for mass 91, is 36.05.   Hence the fraction of the chain yield to be expected for $_{37}\text{Rb}^{91}$ is $0.565e^{-(37-36.05)^2}$, or 0.23.   The value found experimentally is 0.35.

Calculations such as these help in correlating the experimental information about fission yields, but unfortunately they cannot as yet be related to any theory of the fission process.

In cases where the fission process is very fast, it seems reasonable to expect that the two fragments will retain the same neutron-proton ratio as the fissioning nucleus, since there might not be time for the rearrangement of the nucleus which would be needed to satisfy the requirements of equal charge displacement.   In the fission of Bi^{209} by bombardment with 190 Mev deuterons, this fast process does appear to take place.   For the slow neutron fission of U^{235}, a constant neutron-proton ratio would require that the most probable charge for mass 91 would be 35.5, whereas we found above that the equal displacement hypothesis gave $Z_p = 36.05$. The difference is therefore not large.

D. Energy Release in Fission

The large amount of energy released is the reason for the great importance of fission as a source of power: it amounts to approximately 200 Mev per fissioning nucleus.   The combined mass of the fission fragments must be less than the mass of the fissioning nucleus by an amount corresponding to about 200 Mev.   The released energy appears as kinetic energy of the fragments and neutrons, and partly as γ-radiation.   The subsequent β-decay of the fission products produces a further energy release in the form of β-particles and γ-rays.   By far the biggest part of the energy appears as the kinetic energy of the two fragments, one light and the other heavy, which separate from each other with equal and opposite momenta.   If the masses of the two fragments are M_L and M_H respectively, and their velocities are v_L and v_H, then by the conservation of momentum

$$M_L v_L = M_H v_H \qquad (10.7)$$

It follows from equation (10.7) that the kinetic energies E_L and E_H of the fragments are:

$$\frac{E_L}{E_H} = \frac{M_H}{M_L} \qquad (10.8)$$

Thus the kinetic energy and velocity of the light fragment in an asymmetric division is greater than that of the heavy fragment.   The velocities can be measured by timing the flight of the fragments down an evacuated pipe, and the kinetic energies can be measured in any one of several kinds of counters.   Results of a velocity measurement are shown in Figure 10.7. As might be expected from the simple relationships between the masses and the velocities and kinetic energies, the measurements shown in Figure 10.7 reflect the two-peaked shape of the fission yield curve of Figure 10.3. The total kinetic energy of the two fragments

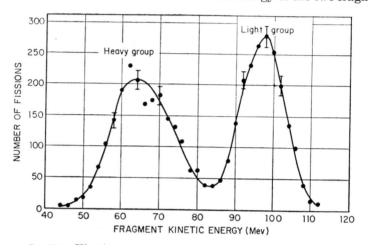

Fig. 10.7. Kinetic energy spectrum of fragments from slow neutron fission of U^{233}, obtained by velocity measurements. W. E. Stein, *Phys. Rev.*, **108**, 94 (1957)

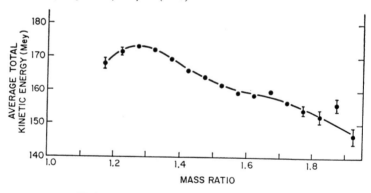

Fig. 10.8. Variation of average total fragment kinetic energy with mass ratio in the slow neutron fission of U^{235}. W. E. Stein, *Phys. Rev.*, **108**, 94 (1957)

depends on the ratio of their masses. Figure 10.8 shows this variation for the fission of U^{235} with thermal neutrons.

The fragment kinetic energies arise from the Coulomb repulsion between their nuclear charges. A rough estimate of the total kinetic energy may be made by assuming that the two fragments (immediately after fission) can be represented as two charged spheres in contact. For two spheres of equal size and charge, the Coulomb potential energy E is

$$E = \frac{0.151Z^2}{A^{1/3}} \text{ Mev} \qquad (10.9)$$

where Z and A are the atomic numbers and mass numbers of the original fissioning nucleus. For U^{236}, equation (10.9) gives a total kinetic energy of about 206 Mev, which is in rough agreement with the values shown in Figure 10.8. If fission is induced by higher energy incident particles, the kinetic energy of the fragments remains almost unchanged. The Coulomb repulsion is not affected, and the extra energy appears as extra excitation energy of the fragment nuclei which produces an increase in the average number of neutrons which are emitted.

Approximately ten γ-ray photons whose energies add to a total of about 7 Mev are released on the average within 10^{-8} seconds of the fission act. Further γ-radiation arises from the β-decay of the fission products. It is clear that the two fragments are highly excited, but it is strange that so much of the excitation energy is emitted as γ-radiation instead of being used in the evaporation of neutrons.

On the average, about 2.5 neutrons are emitted per fission in the fission of U^{233}, U^{235}, and Pu^{239} induced by slow neutrons. The number of neutrons emitted in an individual event may differ widely from the average—for example, it might be as low as zero or as high as eight. The neutrons are emitted with equal probability in all directions around the moving fragments. The energy spectrum is very similar to the evaporation spectrum shown in Figure 9.6, with a nuclear temperature of about 1.3 Mev.

The β-decay of a fission product produces, in many cases, excited states of the daughter nucleus. In a few cases, the excitation energy exceeds the binding energy of a neutron. As a result of this process, neutrons are emitted at a measurable time after the fission act. For example, Br^{87} (half life 50 sec) decays to a neutron-emitting excited state of Kr^{87}. Since the neutron emission follows immediately after the formation of the Kr^{87}, the neutron intensity will decay with the 50 second half life of the Br^{87} parent. Six groups of such delayed neutrons have been discovered; they decay with half lives ranging from 0.1 to 54 seconds. Altogether, these delayed neutron groups are only about 1% as abundant as the prompt neutrons. However, as we shall see later, they are of great importance in the operation of fission reactors, since they greatly simplify the problem of controlling the rate of the chain reaction.

E. The Liquid Drop Model of Fission

Although it does not yet provide a complete theory of fission, the liquid drop model throws some light on the nature of the fission process.

According to this point of view, a nucleus tends to assume a spherical shape (just like a water drop), under the influence of a surface tension. As we saw in Chapter 3 H, this surface tension arises because nucleons in the nuclear surface have fewer close neighbors than nucleons in the center, and are therefore less strongly bound. The surface tension causes a loss of total binding energy which is proportional to the surface area. In any liquid drop, the surface energy is just the product of the surface tension and the surface area, so that work must be done to cause an increase in surface area.

However, in the case of an electrically charged drop, such as a nucleus, the Coulomb repulsion is greatest for the very compact spherical shape. Thus the Coulomb repulsion tries to make the drop assume a nonspherical shape, while the surface tension tries to keep it spherical.

In light nuclei, the Coulomb repulsion is small, and hence a nearly spherical shape is preferred. For the very heavy nuclei, however, the

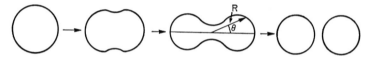

Fig. 10.9. Shapes of a nucleus undergoing fission, according to the liquid drop model. The nuclear volume is the same at each stage

repulsion is much stronger; at the least provocation it can overcome the surface tension and the nucleus will divide, or fission. The surface area, and hence the surface energy, is greater after the nucleus has divided, but the Coulomb energy is very much lower, so that the fission is accompanied by a net drop in the potential energy.

These ideas can be made quantitative by assuming that a nucleus which is in the process of fissioning passes through a sequence of shapes such as those shown in Figure 10.9. It is possible to calculate the surface and Coulomb energies as a function of the nuclear shape, and thus to obtain the total potential energy change as the nucleus distorts away from the spherical shape. In mathematical terms, the shape of a nucleus is described by means of the equation

$$R = \frac{R_0}{\lambda}\left[1 + \alpha_2\left(\frac{3}{2}\cos^2\theta - \frac{1}{2}\right) + \alpha_4\left(\frac{35}{6}\cos^4\theta - \frac{15}{4}\cos^2\theta + \frac{3}{8}\right)\right]$$
$$(10.10)$$

In this equation, R is the radius measured at the angle θ as shown in Figure 10.9, R_0 is the radius of the undistorted spherical nucleus, λ is a number which is adjusted in order to make the nuclear volume equal to $4\pi R_0^3/3$, and α_2 and α_4 are two coefficients whose values determine the

nuclear shape.   The sequence of shapes shown in Figure 10.9 can be
represented by a series of values of α_2 and α_4.   Figure 10.10 (a) shows the
variation of the potential energy as a function of α_2 and α_4.   The energy
is plotted as a contour map in which the lines join points of equal energy.
The spherical nucleus ($\alpha_2 = \alpha_4 = 0$) lies in a "hole" or minimum in the

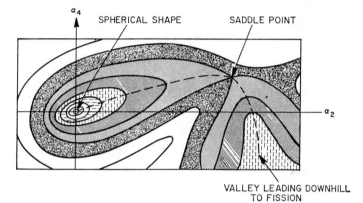

Fig. 10.10a. Schematic contour map of nuclear potential energy
as a function of the deformation parameters α_2 and α_4.   Darker
shading represents higher potential energy

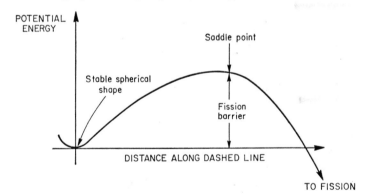
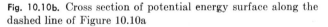

Fig. 10.10b. Cross section of potential energy surface along the
dashed line of Figure 10.10a

potential energy surface.   If the nucleus is given enough energy, however,
it can escape from the hole, and the dashed line in Figure 10.10 (a) shows
a distortion path which leads over a "pass" or saddle point in the energy
surface and into a descending valley leading to fission.   The sequence of
shapes along this path is that shown in Figure 10.9.   Figure 10.10 (b)
shows a cross section of the potential energy surface taken along the
dashed line.   The height of the pass corresponds to the fission barrier.

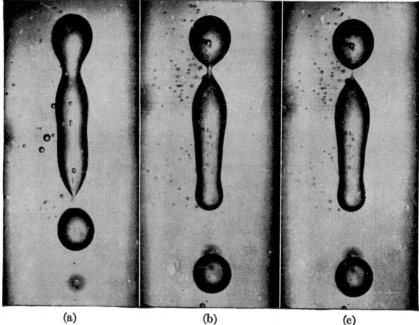

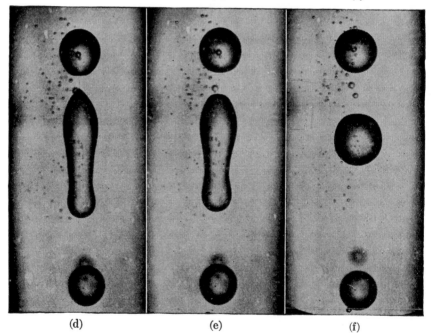

Fig. 10.11. Successive stages in the division of an electrically charged water drop into three pieces. In (a), the first division is just complete and a "neck" is forming at the point where the second division will occur. S. G. Thompson, R. L. Martin, W. J. Swiatecki and H. R. Bowman, private communication (1961)

It is this barrier which prevents the heavy nuclei from instantaneous decay by spontaneous fission. The barrier height is found experimentally to be about 6 Mev for nuclei between Th^{232} and Pu^{239}; the values calculated from the liquid drop model range from 15 Mev down to about 9 Mev.

It was at first thought that the liquid drop model predicted fission to be always symmetric. However, later work showed that the potential energy surface is really much more complex than had been thought. Although the model seems at first sight to be so simple, it is surprisingly difficult to work out all its consequences and it is still not clear whether the model is consistent with the high probability of asymmetric fission.

A charged water drop suspended in oil divides by electrostatic repulsion in a way which is much like the fission of a nucleus. The sequence of photographs in Figure 10.11 shows the last stages in the division of a water drop into three parts.

F. Fission and the Collective Model

The collective nuclear model throws some light on several fission phenomena which cannot be understood in terms of the liquid drop model. In low energy fission, the nucleus must contain very little internal excitation energy by the time it reaches the saddle point. All the available excitation energy will have been converted into the deformation potential energy required to produce the saddle point shape. It may be, therefore, that the energy levels available to the distorted nucleus will be similar to those near the ground state of a spheroidal nucleus. For an even-even nucleus, these low-lying levels are the $0(+), 2(+), 4(+) \cdots$ members of a rotational band, but in addition there is usually a $1(-)$ level which corresponds to a vibration of the nucleus (see, for example, Fig. 5.6). A negative parity level must belong to a nucleus which is not symmetric about a plane at right angles to its symmetry axis; such a nucleus may be visualized as pear-shaped. A nucleus in this shape is obviously well placed to undergo asymmetric fission. When fission takes place at higher energies, the nucleus will still contain a considerable amount of internal excitation energy at the saddle point, so that the level structure will be completely different. The increasing probability of symmetric fission may be due to the decreasing importance of the $1(-)$ vibrational levels.

The quantum number Ω (see Fig. 5.8) may have an important effect in lengthening the spontaneous fission half lives of nuclei containing one or two unpaired nucleons. (Ω is the projection of the unpaired particle angular momentum j on the nuclear symmetry axis.) For even-even nuclei, $\Omega = 0$. For an unpaired nucleon, the energy associated with a given value of Ω increases as the deformation of the nucleus is increased, so that the nucleon must become more and more excited in order to be able to maintain its Ω value. This excitation energy will increase the height of the fission barrier for even-odd, odd-even, and odd-odd nuclei, with a resulting increase in their spontaneous fission half lives. The effect has been evaluated quantitatively, and is in approximate agreement with the experimentally observed spontaneous fission half lives.

REFERENCES

1. Halpern, I., "Fission," *Ann. Revs. Nuclear Sci.*, **9** (1959).

2. Hyde, E. K., *A Review of Nuclear Fission*, University of California Radiation Laboratory Reports UCRL-9036 (low energy) and UCRL-9065 (high energy), 1960. To be published by Prentice-Hall.

3. *Proceedings of the Symposium on the Physics of Fission*, Atomic Energy of Canada Ltd., Chalk River, Ontario, Report CRP 642 A (1956).

4. Bradley, J. E. S., *Physics of Nuclear Fission*, Pergamon Press, London, 1958.

5. Walton, G. N., "Nuclear Fission," *Quart. Revs.*, **XV,** 71 (1961).

6. "Chalk River Symposium on Nuclear Chemistry," *Canadian J. Chem.*, **39,** 601 (1961).

PROBLEMS

1. Show from mass values that Te^{130} should be unstable with respect to symmetric fission. What should be the energy release?

2. What would you expect to be the main reactions induced in Th^{23e} by neutrons of zero energy, 2 Mev, and 10 Mev? The fission barrier is about 6.5 Mev, and the binding energies of the last neutrons in Th^{232} and Th^{233} are 6.40 and 4.93 Mev respectively.

3. Calculate the independent fractional chain yield—$P(Z,A)$ of equation (10.2)—for Sr^{91} and Y^{91} formed in the fission of U^{235} induced by slow neutrons.

4. Draw accurately a distorted nucleus for which $\alpha_2 = 1.20$, $\alpha_4 = 0.20$. Assume that $\lambda = 1$.

5. On the assumption that all the transitions are E1 direct to the ground state, what equation should connect Γ_γ and the excitation energy of a nucleus?

6. From the semiempirical mass equation, calculate the change in Coulomb energy and surface energy in the fission of U^{236} into (a) two equal fragments (b) two fragments whose mass ratio is 1.5. Assume $\bar{\nu} = 2$ in each case.

7. How many curies of Ba^{140} would you expect to find 14 days after the end of a 30 day irradiation of 1 gm of natural uranium in a slow neutron flux of

2×10^{13} neutrons per cm² per sec?   The fission cross section of U^{235} is 580 barns, the cumulative chain yield of mass 140 is 6.44% and the fractional chain yield of Ba^{140} is 0.07.

8. In the (d,p) reaction, the target nucleus captures a neutron whose kinetic energy may be positive or negative.   What energy proton is emitted from the bombardment of U^{235} with 12 Mev deuterons when the captured neutron has just enough energy to induce fission?   The binding energy of the deuteron is 2 Mev, the fission barrier is 5.5 Mev, and the binding energy of a neutron in U^{236} is 6.42 Mev.   Since the target is such a heavy nucleus, the difference between laboratory and center of mass systems may be ignored.

9. Using Figure 10.8, calculate the velocity of the light and heavy fragments whose mass ratio is 1.6, in the slow neutron fission of U^{235}.

10. From a study of Figure 10.2, predict the spontaneous fission half life of the mass 258 isotope of element 102.

CHAPTER 11

The Interaction of Radiation
with Matter

A. Introduction

We now leave the study of the properties of the nucleus, and consider the ultimate fate of the various types of radiation as they move away from their point of origin. In a perfect vacuum, all forms of radiation will continue to move indefinitely, unless the particle is unstable. In solid, liquid, or gaseous media, however, all forms of radiation lose energy or are absorbed through a variety of different mechanisms. We shall divide the discussion into several parts, depending on the mass and charge of the particular radiation.

B. Interaction of Heavy Charged Particles with Matter

Particles such as protons, deuterons, or helium ions interact, by virtue of their electric charge, with the atomic electrons of the medium through which they are passing. In comparatively rare events, the charged particle will interact with a nucleus, but since atoms are much bigger than nuclei, collision with electrons is far more probable. If the charged particle is much heavier than an electron, its direction will not be appreciably altered by the interaction. Therefore particles which are much heavier than electrons travel through matter in almost straight lines. The result of interaction with an electron is that a part of the kinetic energy of the moving particle is transferred to the electron, and the velocity of the moving particle is slightly decreased. Eventually, the particle will be stopped, but a very large number of collisions will be required.

The struck electron will sometimes be knocked out of the atom to which it belonged, so that a free electron and a positive ion are produced. This ionization is frequently used as a means of detection of charged particles, for example in ion chambers and proportional counters, which are discussed in Chapter 12. In many collisions, however, the electron is merely raised to a higher potential energy state while remaining in the same atom or molecule. Both ionization and excitation of molecules may lead to the rupture of chemical bonds. New chemical species may be formed; in many cases they are free radicals. The study of these chemical changes constitutes the subject of radiation chemistry, which is closely allied to photochemistry. The electrons which are liberated in ionizing collisions may themselves have sufficient kinetic energy to induce further ionization or excitation in atoms along their paths.

Because heavy charged particles move in almost straight lines and lose energy in a large number of small steps (so that fluctuations in the energy loss have a chance to "average out"), they have definite *ranges*. The range of a particle is a function of its initial energy, its mass and charge, and of the properties of the stopping medium. The rate at which a particle loses energy along its path, $-dE/dx$, was calculated by Bethe:

$$ -\frac{dE}{dx} = \frac{4\pi e^4 z^2}{mv^2} NZ \left[\log_e \frac{2mv^2}{I} - \log_e (1 - \beta^2) - \beta^2 \right] \quad (11.1) $$

z is the charge of the moving particle whose velocity is v, m and e are the mass and charge of an electron, N is the number of stopping atoms per cm³, and Z is their atomic number. β, as usual, is the ratio v/c, where c is the velocity of light. I is the *average* energy required to excite or ionize the atoms of the stopping material.

For particles whose velocities are much smaller than c, the terms containing β may be ignored. Since the term $\log_e 2mv^2/I$ will vary rather slowly with v, equation (11.1) may be written in an approximate form which is often useful:

$$-\frac{dE}{dx} \propto \frac{Mz^2}{E} \tag{11.2}$$

where M and E are the mass and energy of the moving particle.

According to equation (11.2), the rate of energy loss *increases* as the particle slows down, so that the density of ionization along the path

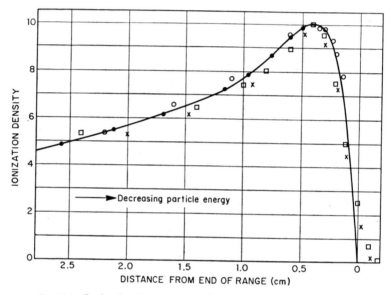

Fig. 11.1. Ionization density along the path of an α-particle moving in air (the Bragg curve). M. G. Holloway and M. S. Livingston, *Phys. Rev.*, **54**, 29 (1938)

will increase. However, when the velocity of the particle is very low, it can capture an electron from an atom of the stopping medium. Further along its path, it may lose the electron again, but the average value of the charge z will decrease near the end of the particle's range. Hence $-dE/dx$ decreases, and the ionization becomes *less* dense. Figure 11.1, which is called a Bragg curve, shows the changes in the density of ionization along the path of an α-particle moving in air.

At very high velocities, $-dE/dx$ becomes very small, but the terms containing β in equation (11.1) cause a slow rise in $-dE/dx$ as v approaches c. This effect is illustrated in Fig. 11.2. $-dE/dx$ reaches a minimum value of about 2.3×10^{-3} Mev per cm of path for a proton of about 2000 Mev moving in air.   By contrast, the rate is about 0.12 Mev per cm for 3 Mev protons.

The ranges of particles can be calculated by integration of equation (11.1), but the result will be slightly in error because of the reduction in the average charge of the particles near the end of their range.   Furthermore, the value of the average excitation energy I must be experimentally determined.   For elements heavier than aluminum, a rough value of I may be obtained from the empirical equation

$$I \text{ (ev)} = 9Z \qquad (11.3)$$

where Z is the atomic number of the element.

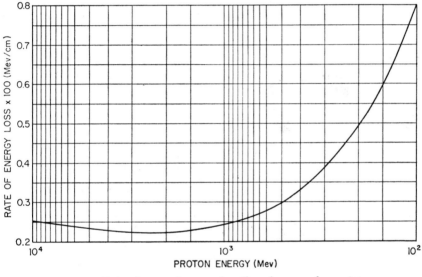

Fig. 11.2. Rate of energy loss as a function of energy, for protons moving in air. Aron, Hoffman, and Williams, University of California Report AECU 663 (1949)

The ranges of charged particles have been measured very carefully as a function of their initial energy.   Figures 11.3 (a) and (b) show the range–energy curves for protons and helium ions respectively in aluminum metal.   The ranges are expressed in milligrams of aluminum per cm^2 rather than in length units.

Range–energy curves may be used to determine the energy of a particle from a measurement of its range.   They are useful in calculations of the thickness of shielding which would be required to protect people or equipment against incident radiation.   Absorbers are frequently placed in beams of particles from accelerators to reduce the energy of the particles to some desired value for a particular experiment.

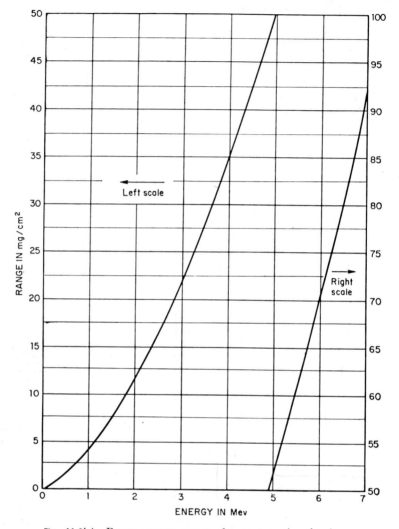

Fig. 11.3(a). Range-energy curves for protons in aluminum metal. H. Bichsel, R. F. Mozley, and W. A. Aron, *Phys. Rev.*, **105,** 1788 (1957).

As an example of this, consider the thickness of aluminum foil which would be required to reduce the energy of helium ions from 40 Mev to 20 Mev. The range of 40 Mev helium ions (Fig. 11.3) is 170.3 mg/cm². After passing through t mg/cm² of aluminum, they will emerge with a residual range of (170.3 − t) mg/cm². But if the emergent energy is to be 20 Mev, the range must be 51.9 mg/cm², and hence (170.3 − t)

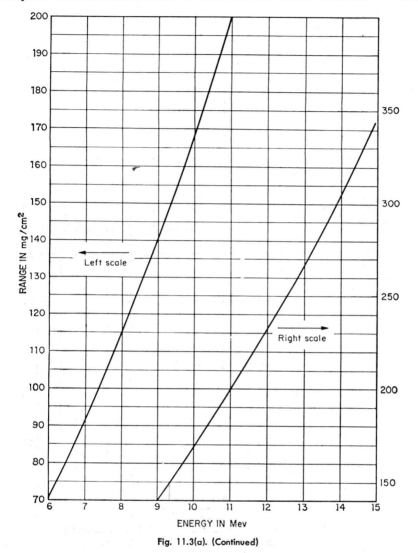

Fig. 11.3(a). (Continued)

$= 51.9$, or $t = 118.4$ mg/cm^2. By a similar calculation, it is easy to find the energy of the emerging particles if the absorber thickness is known.

If the range of protons in a particular stopping medium is known, then the range of another particle of different mass and charge can readily be calculated. According to equation (11.1), the rate of energy loss of a proton of velocity v ($\ll c$) in a given medium is

$$- \left(\frac{dE}{dx} \right)_p = \frac{a}{v^2} \ln bv^2$$

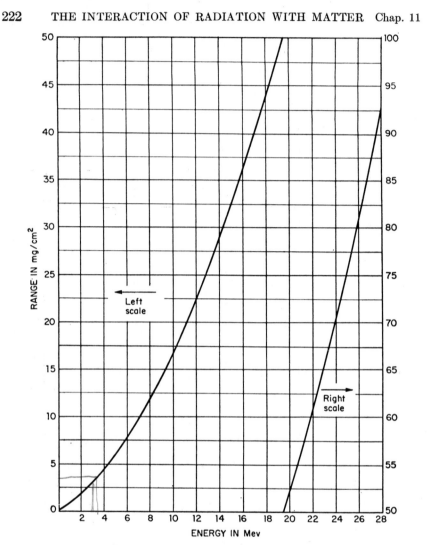

Fig. 11.3(b). Range-energy curves for helium ions in aluminum
metal, calculated from proton ranges by H. E. Conzett.

where a and b are constants.   The rate of energy loss for a particle of
mass M, charge Z, and velocity v is

$$ - \left(\frac{dE}{dx}\right)_{M,Z} = \frac{aZ^2}{v^2} \ln bv^2 $$

$$ \therefore \quad \frac{\left(\dfrac{dE}{dx}\right)_{M,Z}}{\left(\dfrac{dE}{dx}\right)_{p}} = Z^2 $$

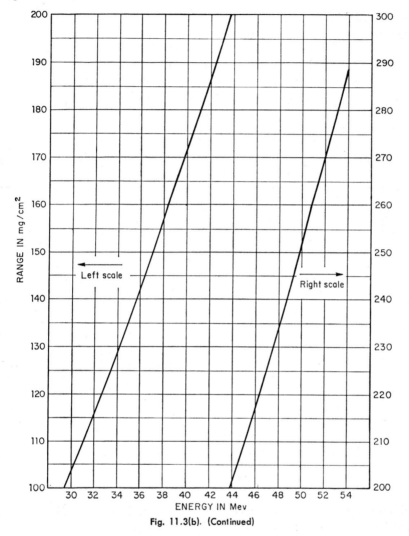

Fig. 11.3(b). (Continued)

Hence the mass M, charge Z particle loses energy Z^2 times as fast as a proton of the *same velocity*. However, its energy (for the same velocity) is M times as great, and hence its range will be M/Z^2 times that of a proton. In other words, its range will be M/Z^2 times as great as that of a proton with $1/M$ times as much energy:

$$R_{M,Z}(E) = \frac{M}{Z^2} R_p \left(\frac{E}{M} \right) \qquad (11.4)$$

Thus the range of a helium ion is equal to the range of a proton with one quarter the energy. This relation is not quite accurate because of the slight differences at the end of the range due to the electron pickup process. For the comparison of proton, deuteron, and triton ranges, however, there is no error, since the electron pickup effect should be the same for these isotopic particles.

We have so far assumed that all particles of the same type and energy have identical ranges. Because of the statistical nature of the energy loss processes, there will be slight fluctuations in range; some particles will travel a slightly greater or lesser distance than the average before coming to rest. This phenomenon is called range straggling. If the intensity of a beam of particles is measured while absorbers of

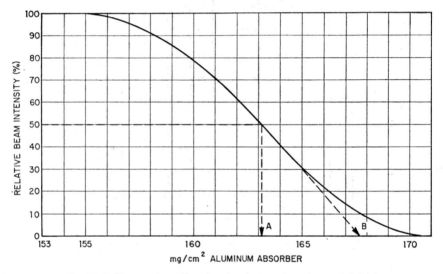

Fig. 11.4. Range straggling in aluminum of protons of initial energy 9.8 Mev. Point A represents the mean range, point B, the extrapolated range

different thicknesses are placed in the beam, it will remain constant until the absorber thickness is such that a few of the particles, which by chance have lost a larger than average amount of energy, fail to emerge. A typical result of such a measurement is shown in Figure 11.4. The thickness required to reduce the beam intensity to one half of its initial value is called the *mean* range. In older work the *extrapolated* range, defined by B in Figure 11.4, was often used. The curves of Figure 11.3 are the mean ranges.

For many purposes, especially in understanding the operation of counters, it is important to know how many electrons and positive ions are set free in the stopping of a particle. The average excitation energy given to an atom in an interaction is the quantity I of equation

(11.3). In many interactions, however, an electron will be liberated with enough energy to cause further ionization. As a result of a rather fortuitous balancing of various effects, the final result is that one electron-positive ion pair is formed on the average for every 30 ev of energy lost by the particle. Surprisingly, the average energy lost by a particle for each ion pair is almost the same for all kinds of particles (including electrons), all stopping elements, and all particle energies. Thus a 6 Mev α-particle stopping in argon will produce $(6 \times 10^6)/30$ or 2×10^5 electrons, and as many positive ions. About the same number of electrons will be produced by *any* 6 Mev particle stopping in *any* medium. (In certain semiconductor materials, such as germanium and silicon, these statements are not true. This effect is discussed in Chapter 12 C.)

C. Interaction of Electrons with Matter

Electrons induce excitation and ionization in stopping media in just the same way as heavy charged particles. However, an electron can

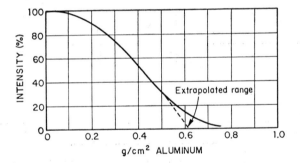

Fig. 11.5. Absorption of 1.4 Mev electrons in aluminum. J. S. Marshall and A. G. Ward, *Canadian J. Res.* **A 15,** 39 (1937)

lose up to one half of its energy in a single encounter, and it may suffer a considerable deflection. The paths of electrons are therefore not good straight lines. A beam of initially monoenergetic electrons will be far from monoenergetic after passing through an absorber. The range of electrons is therefore a quantity which is not as well defined as the range of heavier particles. Figure 11.5 shows the range straggling of initially 1.4 Mev electrons in aluminum. Even with an absorber thickness which is only about one third of the extrapolated range, about 10% of the particles have been removed from the incident beam.

In spite of the severe range straggling, electron kinetic energies can be measured approximately by means of an extrapolated range determination. Figure 11.6 shows the extrapolated range–energy relationship for initially monoenergetic electrons of various energies. Observe that the range of an electron is much greater than the range of a proton of the same energy.

In Chapter 1 B, we mentioned that, according to the theories of nineteenth century physics, an electron traveling in an orbit around a nucleus should continuously radiate electromagnetic waves. We saw that, when the electron is in a Bohr orbit, it does *not* radiate. However, when a free electron passes close to an atomic nucleus, it experiences an attractive force which deflects it, and this deflection of course corresponds to an acceleration. Such an event can lead to the emission of a

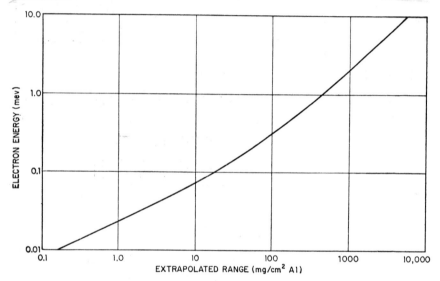

Fig. 11.6. Extrapolated range in aluminum as a function of electron energy. L. Katz and A. S. Penfold, *Revs. Modern Phys.*, **24,** 28 (1952)

photon, with a corresponding decrease in the kinetic energy of the electron. The emitted bremsstrahlung radiation becomes an important source of energy loss in a medium of atomic number Z by electrons of kinetic energy greater than a critical energy E_c, where

$$E_c \approx \frac{800}{Z} \text{ Mev} \tag{11.5}$$

At very high energies, bremsstrahlung radiation becomes the main cause of energy loss. It is unimportant for heavier particles because their greater masses reduce the magnitudes of the accelerations which they can receive in the Coulomb field of a nucleus.

The energy spectrum of electrons emitted in β-decay is continuous. Even when the maximum energy is high, the spectrum contains electrons of nearly zero energy which will be stopped by even very thin layers of absorbing material. If the counter C of Figure 11.7 is used to detect the β-particles emitted at a steady rate from the source S, then even a very thin absorber A will cause a reduction in the counting rate. It is important to remember that this would not be so if the source emitted monoenergetic heavy particles such as α-particles. In such a case, the counting rate would be virtually unaffected until the absorber thickness became almost as large as the range of the particles.

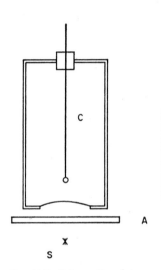

Fig. 11.7. Schematic picture of source, absorber and counter arrangement for measuring absorption curve for a β-emitter. C is the counter, A the absorber and S the source

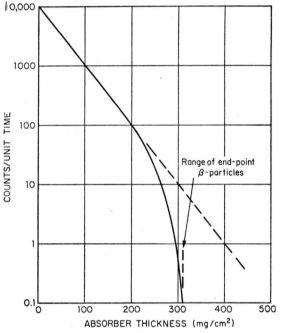

Fig. 11.8. Schematic absorption curve for a continuous β-spectrum of end point 310 mg/cm²

For an arrangement such as that shown in Figure 11.7, the counting rate is found to vary with absorber thickness in an approximately exponential way, as shown in the semilogarithmic plot in Figure 11.8. At high absorber thicknesses, the absorption curve departs from the exponential (straight line) and becomes asymptotic towards an absorber thickness corresponding to the range of the highest energy particles in the spectrum. From such curves, an approximate value can be obtained for the end point energy of the spectrum. The absorber thickness corresponding to absorption of half the particles can also be used as a rough measure of the spectrum end point.

If spectra with two radiations of different type or energy are emitted from the source, then absorption curves similar to Figure 11.9 are obtained. In this case, both β^--particles and X-rays were present. X-rays and γ-rays produce a curve with a flat "tail," since they are harder to absorb than electrons (v. infra). Composite absorption curves of this type may be resolved into the individual components in just the

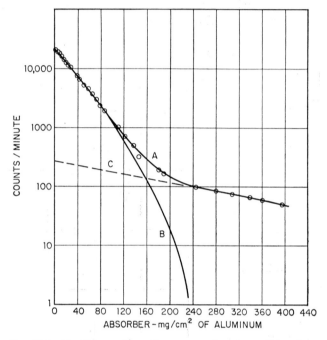

Fig. 11.9. Aluminum absorption curve for β^--particles from Am²⁴². A: Experimental curve, C: Component due to X-rays. B: (Curve A minus curve C). Curve B is due to the β-particles alone. J. M. Grunlund, B. G. Harvey, N. Moss and L. Yaffe, *Phys. Rev.*, **78**, 69 (1950)

same way as composite decay curves. In the past, absorption curves were frequently used to measure the end points of β-spectra, but the method has become of diminishing importance since the invention of β-particle scintillation spectrometers (Chapter 12).

D. Interaction of Gamma Rays with Matter

The absorption of γ-rays in matter occurs by mechanisms which are completely different from the absorption of charged particles. The interaction is mainly with the atomic electrons, but the γ-ray can lose a large fraction of its energy, or all of it, in a single encounter. There is, therefore, no quantity corresponding to a range.   The rays are absorbed according to an exponential law which is characterized by a half thickness and an absorption coefficient μ.   If I_0 is the initial intensity of a beam of γ-rays, then the intensity I of rays of the initial energy after passing through x cm of absorber will be

$$I = I_0 e^{-\mu x}$$ (11.6)

The linear absorption coefficient μ is a function of the energy of the γ-rays and of the absorbing medium.   The half thickness X is the thickness of absorber required to absorb one half of the incident photons. It is related to μ by the equation

$$X = \frac{(\log_e 2)}{\mu} = \frac{0.693}{\mu}$$ (11.7)

If the absorber thickness is expressed in terms of gm/cm², then the absorption coefficient μ of equation (11.6) will have a different numerical value.   It is then called the mass absorption coefficient:

$$\mu \text{ (mass absorption)} = \frac{\mu \text{ (linear)}}{D} \frac{\text{cm}^2}{\text{gm}}$$ (11.8)

where D is the density of the absorbing material.

The absorption of low energy γ-rays is mainly due to the *photoelectric effect*.   In this interaction, an atomic electron is ejected from its orbit, while the absorbed photon vanishes.   The kinetic energy of the electron is therefore equal to the energy of the incident photon minus the binding energy of the electron in the atom from which it was ejected.   The electron most probably comes from the K shell, provided that the γ-ray has sufficient energy to supply the K shell binding energy.

The absorption due to the photoelectric effect decreases sharply with increasing γ-ray energy, but increases very rapidly with increasing absorber atomic number.   Very roughly, the photoelectric absorption follows the equation

$$\text{Probability of photoelectric absorption} \propto \frac{Z^5}{E_\gamma^{7/2}}$$

Hence it is most important for the absorption of low energy γ-rays in heavy elements.

When the γ-ray energy is below the binding energy of the electrons in a particular shell, it cannot eject them from the atom, and those electrons contribute nothing to the absorption of the photons.   The graph of absorption coefficient versus γ-ray energy therefore shows sharp discontinuities when the photon energy is just sufficient to eject electrons from an additional shell.   Figure 11.10 shows the mass absorption coefficients of photons in iron, copper, and nickel.   Superimposed on the smoothly falling absorption coefficients, there are sharp discontinuities at photon energies exactly equal to the K shell binding energies.   These sharp absorption edges may be used to measure γ- or X-ray energies. Thus if a particular radiation is absorbed strongly in nickel but only weakly in the next lighter element copper, then its energy must lie

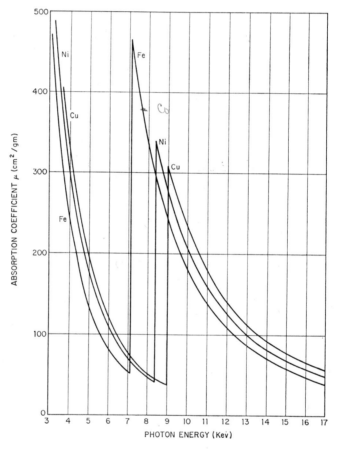

Fig. 11.10. Absorption coefficients for Fe, Ni, and Cu, data from *Handbook of Chemistry and Physics*, 41st. Edition, Chemical Rubber Publishing Co., Cleveland, Ohio

between 8.35 and 9.02 kev, as Figure 11.10 shows.   Nickel is said to be a *critical absorber* for the radiation.

For medium energy photons, the most important energy loss mechanism is *Compton scattering*.   The photon transfers part of its energy to an electron, but there still remains a photon of lower energy which may then undergo a further photoelectric or Compton interaction.

The Compton effect is illustrated in Figure 11.11. Energy and momentum must be conserved, so that

$$E_I = E_c + E_e$$

$$\frac{E_I}{c} = \frac{E_c \cos \theta}{c} + p \cos \phi \tag{11.9}$$

$$\frac{E_c \sin \theta}{c} = p \sin \phi$$

The first equation follows from the conservation of energy, assuming that the binding energy of the electron is small enough to be neglected. The second equation represents the conservation of momentum along

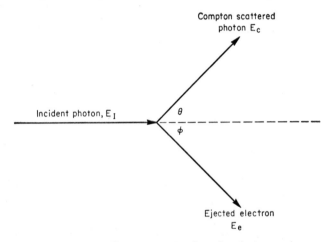

Fig. 11.11. Compton scattering of a photon

the direction of the incident photon; the momentum of the electron is p, and the momentum of a photon of energy E is E/c. The third equation expresses the conservation of momentum at 90° to the direction of the incident photon. The momentum of the electron is related to its kinetic energy E_e by the relativistic equation

$$p^2 = \frac{1}{c^2} [E_e(E_e + 2mc^2)]$$

where m is the mass of an electron at rest.

The equation above, with equations (11.9), may be used to eliminate p, E_e, and ϕ, with the result

$$\lambda_c - \lambda_I = \frac{h}{mc} (1 - \cos \theta) \tag{11.10}$$

where λ_I and λ_c are the wave lengths of the incident and Compton scattered photons. Thus the change in wave length depends only on the angle θ of the scattered photon and not on its initial energy. However, the *fractional* change in energy is proportional to the incident energy:

$$\frac{E_I - E_c}{E_c} = \frac{E_I}{mc^2} (1 - \cos \theta)$$

$$= \frac{E_I}{0.51} (1 - \cos \theta) \qquad (11.11)$$

For $E_I = 10$ kev, the fractional energy change when the photon is scattered at $90°$ is only $\frac{10}{510}$ or about 2%, whereas for $E_I = 5$ Mev, it is $5/0.51$ or about a tenfold change. Compton scattering is an important energy loss mechanism for photons between about 0.1 and 10 Mev. The mass absorption coefficient due to Compton scattering varies very little with the atomic number of the absorber. Although the fractional energy loss is much greater for high energy photons, the probability that a photon will be Compton scattered at all decreases about linearly with increasing energy. Therefore Compton scattering makes only a small contribution to the absorption of high energy photons.

Photons of energy greater than 2×0.51 Mev may be absorbed by a third mechanism, *pair production*. The photon vanishes, to be replaced by an electron-positron pair whose kinetic energies E_e and E_p are related to the incident photon energy E_I by the equation

$$E_I = E_e + E_p + 2mc^2 \qquad (11.12)$$

The $2mc^2$ (1.02 Mev) represents the mass energy which must be supplied to create the particles. The process is not exactly the reverse of the electron-positron annihilation, because in that process *two* photons are emitted, whereas in pair production only *one* is absorbed.

In order simultaneously to conserve momentum and energy in pair production, a third body (usually a nucleus) must be present. In the annihilation process, energy and momentum are conserved simultaneously by the emission of *two* photons. The importance of pair production increases slowly for photon energies above 1.02 Mev, and increases about as the square of the atomic number of the absorbing material. In heavy elements and at high photon energies, it is much more important than the photoelectric and Compton effects.

The mass absorption coefficient is the sum of the partial mass absorption coefficients due to the photoelectric, Compton, and pair production effects. Its variation with γ-ray energy in several absorbing materials is shown in Figure 11.12. Because of the sharp discontinuities at low energies due to the onset of the photoelectric effect in the K and L shells, and because pair production causes a slow rise in μ for silver and lead at high energies, a given value of μ may correspond to two γ-ray energies. It is possible to distinguish between the two values by measuring μ in a different element. For example, if the mass absorption coefficient is found by experiment to be 136 cm²/gm in lead, the γ-ray energy might be 0.0175 or 0.0100 Mev. If a measurement in silver gives 27.5 cm²/gm

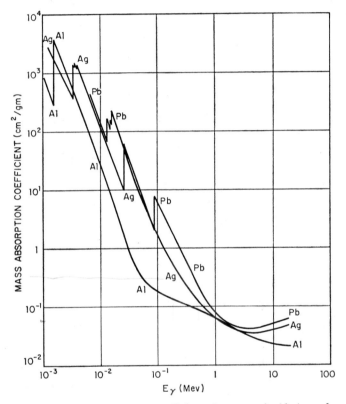

Fig. 11.12. Mass absorption coefficients for γ-rays in Al, Ag and Pb. Data from *Handbook of Chemistry and Physics*, 41st. Edition, Chemical Rubber Publishing Co., Cleveland, Ohio

then the energy must be 0.0175 Mev. Measurement of γ-ray energies by determination of absorption coefficients is of diminishing importance since the invention of scintillation spectrometers (see Chapter 12).

E. Interaction of Neutrons with Matter

Being uncharged, neutrons behave in a manner quite different from protons. They interact only very weakly with the atomic electrons (the interaction being due to the magnetic moments of the two particles).

The slowing down of fast neutrons as they travel through matter is due almost entirely to collision of the neutrons with the atomic nuclei. If the sum of the kinetic energies of the neutron and the nucleus following collision is equal to the sum of these quantities before collision, then the collision is called elastic. If part of the initial kinetic energy is converted into excitation energy of the struck nucleus, then the collision is called inelastic. If a neutron of kinetic energy E_0 is deflected through an angle θ by an elastic collision with a stationary nucleus of mass A, then its kinetic energy E will be:

$$E = \frac{E_0[(A + 1)^2 - 2A(1 - \cos \phi)]}{(A + 1)^2} \tag{11.13}$$

where ϕ (the center of mass scattering angle) is given by

$$\cos \theta = \frac{A \cos \phi + 1}{[(A + 1)^2 - 2A(1 - \cos \phi)]^{1/2}}$$

The value of E is least for $\phi = 180°$:

$$E_{\min} = \frac{E_0[(A + 1)^2 - 4A]}{(A + 1)^2}$$

$$= E_0 \left(\frac{A - 1}{A + 1}\right)^2 \tag{11.14}$$

For very heavy nuclei, $E_{\min} \approx E_0$, and the neutron loses very little energy per collision. However, in a collision with a hydrogen nucleus ($A = 1$), equation (11.14) shows that $E_{\min} = 0$. Hence neutrons are most rapidly slowed down by materials such as paraffin wax or water, which contain a large proportion of hydrogen atoms.

In addition to being slowed down by elastic and inelastic collisions, neutrons may be captured by nuclei in the stopping medium. This will be particularly probable if there exists some neutron energy for which the neutron capture cross section of the medium is very large (i.e. a neutron resonance). For example, fast neutrons are rapidly slowed down by collision with hydrogen nuclei in passing through an aqueous solution of $CdCl_2$. When the neutron energy is in the neighborhood of 0.178 ev, resonance capture by Cd^{113} becomes very probable because the Cd^{113} (n,γ) cross section for neutrons of this energy is about 8000 barns.

In the absence of substances with large neutron capture cross sections, the kinetic energy of an initially fast neutron continues to decrease until it becomes comparable with the thermal agitation energy of the stopping nuclei. The neutron is then as likely to gain energy in a collision as to lose it. It will continue to diffuse through the medium until it is eventually captured in an (n,γ) reaction.

Neutrons which have slowed down to thermal equilibrium with their surroundings are called thermal neutrons. They have a roughly Maxwellian distribution of velocities, just like molecules in a gas. At room temperature, the most probable kinetic energy is about $\frac{1}{40}$ ev, which corresponds to a neutron velocity of only 2,187 m/sec.

The neutrons themselves produce virtually no ionization while slowing down. However, nuclei which they strike will usually be knocked out of the molecule to which they belonged, and will themselves produce some ionization as they slow down. This effect is particularly noticeable when neutrons slow down in a hydrogenous medium, because many of the recoil protons will have large energies (as high as the energy of the incident neutrons). Finally, the absorption of the γ-rays following capture of a neutron will produce some ionization.

F. Stopping of Heavy Ions in Matter

The stopping of heavy, relatively slow-moving ions (such as recoil ions produced by α-decay, nuclear reactions, or fission) has been studied both theoretically and experimentally. By collision with the atoms of the stopping medium, the moving ions become stripped of all those electrons whose orbital velocities are slower than the velocity of the ion. As it slows down, the ion picks up electrons again; its charge is therefore greater at the beginning of its track than it is at the end. The charge Z^* is given very roughly by

$$Z^* = \frac{Z^{1/3}V\hbar^2}{e^2} \tag{11.15}$$

where V is the velocity of the particle and Z is its atomic number. For fission fragments near the beginning of their range, Z^* is about $+20$.

For velocities greater than about 2×10^8 cm per sec, the moving ion loses energy mainly by causing ionization and excitation of the surrounding medium. The range is very roughly proportional to the initial energy of the particle. The ranges of ions in the fission product mass region are fairly well represented by the equations

$$R = 0.19E^{2/3} \text{ mg per cm}^2 \text{ aluminum}$$
$$R = 0.14E^{2/3} \text{ mg per cm}^2 \text{ air} \tag{11.16}$$

where E is the initial energy in Mev.

As the ion slows down, becoming less highly charged, energy loss by elastic collisions (i.e. without causing ionization or excitation of the medium) becomes relatively more important, and for ions whose velocities are below about 2×10^8 cm per sec, it becomes the main energy loss mechanism. In this low velocity region, the behavior of the ion is largely determined by the ratio of its mass M_1 to the mass of the atoms of the stopping medium, M_2. If M_1/M_2 is large, then the average energy lost per collision will be small and the ions will travel in nearly straight lines. If M_1/M_2 is unity or less, the paths will be far from

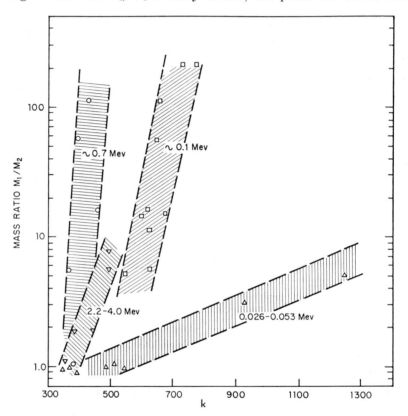

Fig. 11.13. Variation of k (Equation 11.17) with mass ratio M_1/M_2 in the elastic stopping region. B. G. Harvey, *Annual Reviews of Nuclear Science*, **10** (1960)

straight, and if M_1/M_2 is near unity, the ion may lose a large fraction of its energy in a single encounter so that it becomes meaningless to talk about a range.

N. Bohr gave an expression for the range of ions which have an initial velocity below about 2×10^8 cm per sec:

$$R_0 = kE \frac{M_2(M_1 + M_2)}{M_1} \frac{(Z_1^{2/3} + Z_2^{2/3})^{1/2}}{Z_1 Z_2} \qquad (11.17)$$

where E is the initial energy of an ion of mass and atomic number M_1

and Z_1 moving in a medium of mass and atomic number M_2 and Z_2. R_0 will be obtained in μg per cm^2 when E is in Mev and the constant k has the value 602. Thus in the elastic collision region, the range is proportional to the energy. Unfortunately, the constant k is a function not only of the mass ratio M_1/M_2 (as might be expected from the discussion above) but also of the initial energy E. Figure 11.13 shows some experimental values of k; except for the lowest energies, the values are not far from the theoretical value of 602.

Measurements of ranges can be used to determine the kinetic energies of the heavy ions, but the results are much less accurate than for protons or electrons because the range energy relationships are less well established. Further, there is considerable range straggling; all ions of a given initial energy do not stop after precisely the same distance. The probability $W(R)$ that an ion of initial velocity less than 2×10^8 cm per sec will have a range R is given by the Gaussian expression

$$W(R) = \frac{1}{(2\pi)^{1/2}\rho R_0} \exp\left[- \frac{(R_0 - R)^2}{2\rho^2 R_0^2} \right] \tag{11.18}$$

where R_0 is the mean range and ρ is the range straggling parameter given by

$$\rho^2 = \frac{2M_1M_2}{3(M_1 + M_2)^2} \tag{11.19}$$

The range straggling is least when $M_1 \gg M_2$, but the width of the range distribution at half its maximum height can never be less than about $0.1R_0$ even for a very heavy element ion stopping in hydrogen. Nevertheless, range measurements of recoil ions are sometimes a valuable method in the study of nuclear reaction mechanisms, since the momenta of the recoils are related to the momenta imparted to the target nuclei by the incident particle and the emitted particles.

REFERENCES

1. *Handbook of Chemistry and Physics*, Chemical Rubber Publishing Co., Cleveland, Ohio. (Tables of mass absorption coefficients for γ-rays.)

2. *American Institute of Physics Handbook*, McGraw-Hill Book Co., New York, 1957: Section 8c, "Passage of Particles Through Matter," and Section 8f, "Gamma Rays."

3. Segrè, E. (ed.), *Experimental Nucelar Physics*, Vol. I/2, John Wiley & Sons, New York, 1953.

4. Uehling, E. A. (ed.), *Penetration of Charged Particles in Matter*, Publication 752, National Academy of Science–National Research Council, Washington, D. C., 1960.

5. Compton, A. H., and S. K. Allison, *X-rays in Theory and Experiment*, D. Van Nostrand, New York, 1935.

6. Aron, W. A., B. G. Hoffman, and F. C. Williams, *Range–Energy Curves*, USAEC Document AECU-663 (1951).

7. Hubbard, E. L., *Range–Energy Relations for Heavy Ions in Metals*, University of California Radiation Laboratory Document UCRL-9053 (1960).

8. Millburn, G. P., and L. Schecter, *Graphs of RMS Multiple Scattering Angle and Range Straggling for High Energy Charged Particles*, University of California Radiation Laboratory Document UCRL-2234 (Rev.) (1954).

9. Segrè, E. (ed.), *Experimental Nuclear Physics*, John Wiley & Sons, New York, 1953: Vol. II/7, B. T. Feld, "The Neutron."

10. Siegbahn, K. (ed.), *Beta- and Gamma-Ray Spectroscopy*, North Holland Publishing Co., Amsterdam, 1955.

11. Harvey, B. G., "Recoil Techniques in Nuclear Reaction and Fission Studies," *Ann. Revs. Nuclear Sci.*, **10**, 235 (1960).

PROBLEMS

1. Calculate the thickness of aluminum required to reduce initially 47.6 Mev helium ions to 25 Mev.

2. What is the energy of a 12 Mev proton after passing through a layer of aluminum which is 0.025 inches thick?

3. Calculate the ranges in aluminum of the following particles:

$$He^3, \quad 25 \text{ Mev}$$
$$C^{12}, \quad 120 \text{ Mev}$$
$$H^3, \quad 15 \text{ Mev}$$

Discuss any sources of error in your results.   Assume in each case that all atomic electrons are removed from the moving particle.

4. Consider the mechanisms by which γ-rays are absorbed, and explain the following relations shown in Figure 11.12:

(a) The absorption coefficient (cm^2/gm) in lead is considerably greater than in aluminum for 0.2 Mev γ-rays.

(b) They are roughly the same for 1.5 Mev γ-rays.

(c) The curves for silver and lead show a minimum, and rise again at high energies.

5. When an absorber is used to reduce the energy of a cyclotron beam, most of the energy lost by the particles ends up as heat in the absorber.   Assuming that it *all* ends up in this way, calculate the heat dissipated in a 100 mg/cm^2 aluminum foil placed in a beam of 10 μamps of 48 Mev helium ions.

6. The energy liberated in the reaction:

$$Li^6 + neutron = He^4 + He^3$$

is 4.8 Mev.   Calculate the ranges in aluminum of the He^3 and He^4 ions when the neutron has very low (i.e. essentially zero) energy.

7. Derive equations (11.10) and (11.11).

8. Prove from energy and momentum conservation that pair production requires the presence of a third body.

9. Using tabulated data (e.g. the mass absorption coefficients, X-ray spectra, and absorption edges tabulated in the *Handbook of Chemistry and Physics*), determine which element would make a critical absorber for the K X-rays from electron capture decay of Mn^{54}.

10. Calculate the range of 10 Mev protons in lead.

11. Calculate the ionization density (i.e., the number of ion pairs per cm) for a 4 Mev helium ion moving in argon gas at 25°C and 76 cm Hg pressure.

12. Assuming that you have counters which can measure simultaneously the energy E of particles and their rate of energy loss $-dE/dx$, devise a method whereby you could distinguish between protons and deuterons.

13. Devise a method whereby you could use a counter to detect a few **protons** in the presence of a large number of 40 Mev helium ions.   The counter is equally sensitive to both types of particles.   What would be the lowest energy **proton** that you could detect in this way?

CHAPTER 12

Counters

A. Introduction

All types of counters that are used in the detection and measurement of radiation depend on the ionization and excitation effects discussed in the previous chapter. Ionization chambers, proportional counters, and Geiger counters are devices in which the electric charge of the ion pairs is collected, and amplified electronically. In certain organic and inorganic materials, the passage of a particle or γ-ray produces excited atomic states which decay by the emission of light in or near the visible part of the spectrum. In the family of scintillation counters, this light is converted into electrical pulses by means of which the incident particles are counted.

Counters and circuits of great complexity are often used for special measurements, for example in the identification of new types of particles. In most cases, however, these systems are built up from the few counter types already mentioned, and we shall restrict the discussion to these basic types.   In Section G, the properties of the various counter types are summarized in tabular form.

B. Ionization Chambers

In the simplest type of ionization chamber, the electrons and positive ions liberated in a gas by the passage of charged particles are collected by means of an electric field between two electrodes.   In the arrangement of Figure 12.1, the electrons would be collected on the upper (positive) charged plate, and the negative ions on the lower.   Almost any gas would be suitable.   If each of N particles per second lost E Mev in passing through the chamber, then the total charge Q (positive and negative) liberated per second would be:

$$Q = \frac{2NEe \times 10^6}{30} \text{ e.s.u./sec} \quad (12.1)$$

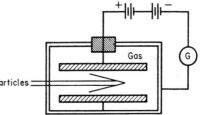
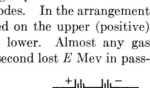
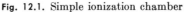

Fig. 12.1. Simple ionization chamber

The charge per ion pair is $2e$, and each ion pair, on the average, corresponds to an energy loss of 30 ev. If the strength of the electric field is sufficient, it is possible to collect all the electrons and positive ions, so that the current flowing in the circuit becomes equal to Q. Usually a few hundred volts are sufficient to collect all the charge.

If a meter is used to measure the current, as shown in Figure 12.1, the device is not properly a counter.   A meter is too slow and insensitive to respond noticeably to the arrival of individual particles.   Instead it integrates the effect of many particles, giving a reading which is proportional to the number of particles arriving per second and to their energy loss in the gas.   Such a detector is sometimes useful for measuring rather large particle fluxes.   It may be used for measuring neutron fluxes if its walls are coated with a layer of boron.   (The cross section of B^{10} for the reaction $B^{10}(n,\alpha)Li^7$ is very large for low energy neutrons, and the ionization produced by the α- and Li^7 particles is easily detected and measured.)

If the ionization chamber of Figure 12.1 is connected to the circuit shown in Figure 12.2, it may be used to detect the arrival of individual particles.   The free electrons are collected by the positive plate in about 10^{-6} seconds, but the positive ions, which move quite sluggishly, require about 10^{-3} seconds to reach the negative plate.   Collection of the charge causes a pulse of current to flow in the resistor R. Since the voltage drop across R is proportional to the current flowing, the voltage will increase rapidly and then decrease again as the current pulse dies away. R is usually a very large resistance— about 10^9 ohms—so that even a very small current produces an easily measurable voltage pulse. This pulse is amplified, and is finally recorded by an electronic counting circuit.

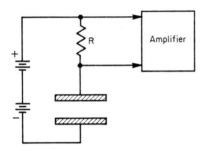

Fig. 12.2. Ionization chamber and circuit for detection of individual particles

The behavior of pulses in an amplifier containing a capacity C and a resistance R is largely determined by the value of the product RC, whose dimensions are time (if R is expressed in units of 10^6 ohms, C in units of 10^{-6} farads, then the time will be in seconds). If the time constant RC is made substantially longer than the time required to collect both the electrons and the positive ions then the amplified pulse will vary with time roughly as shown in Figure 12.3 (a). The fast rise at A is due to collection of electrons, the slow rise at B to the collection of positive ions, and the slow exponential fall F is due to discharge through R of the charge stored in the capacity C. The "mean life" for the exponential fall is just the time constant of the circuit, RC. The disadvantage of such an arrangement is that the time which must elapse before the

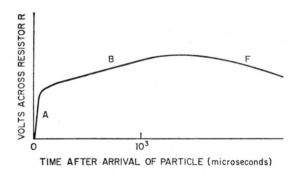

Fig. 12.3a. Signal from ionization chamber with $RC \gg 10^{-3}$ sec.

chamber is ready to detect another particle (the resolving time), is several milliseconds. Therefore only low counting rates can be measured.

If RC is made of the order of a few microseconds, then the output pulse resembles that shown in Figure 12.3 (b). A small value of C does not permit storage of much charge, and a small value of R allows the stored charge to leak away rapidly. If RC is substantially less than the time required to collect the positive ions ($\sim 10^{-3}$ sec), then only the fast part of the pulse, due to electron collection, appears. The ionization chamber and amplifier are rapidly restored to a condition in which a

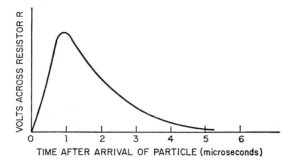

Fig. 12.3b. Signal from ionization chamber with $RC \approx 10^{-6}$ sec.

second pulse can be detected. If the counter is to detect only the collection of the electrons, then clearly the electrons must remain free to move. In some gases, for example oxygen and water vapor, the electrons rapidly become attached to neutral molecules to form slow-moving negative ions. These gases must therefore be carefully excluded from the chamber. The gas most commonly used is argon, usually mixed with about 10% of methane or carbon dioxide for reasons which will be discussed below.

The ionization chamber and circuit of Figure 12.2 is reasonably satisfactory for the *detection* of charged particles. Often, however, it is convenient to use the detector for measurement of the *energy* of the particles too, and the arrangement is not satisfactory for this purpose. The commonest application is in measurement of the energies of α-particles from a source which is placed on the negative electrode.

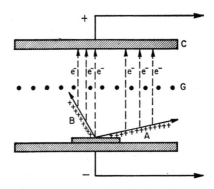

Fig. 12.4. Operation of ionization chamber with grid

The particles are emitted into the gas in all directions, as shown in Figure 12.4 (lines A and B). The electrons are immediately removed from the tracks and travel rapidly towards the collecting electrode C. The positive ions remain behind, and they induce a small charge on C whose magnitude depends on the distance between C and the "center of gravity" of the positive ion track. This distance is clearly less for track B than for track A.   Hence the pulse produced by particle B will be less than that due to A, even if each particle initially produced the same number of ion pairs.   To minimize this effect, the grid G is placed as an electrostatic shield between the positive ions and the collector.   It is operated at a potential just sufficiently negative to prevent electrons from being

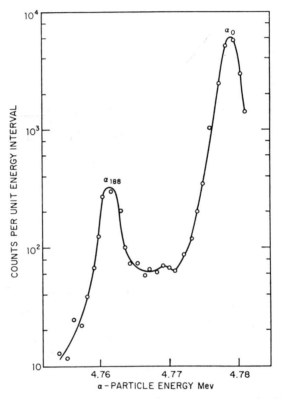

Fig. 12.5. Spectrum of α-particles from Ra^{226} measured with a grid ionization chamber.   The α_0 peak (4.7790 Mev particles) has a width, at half its maximum height, of 27 kev, corresponding to an energy resolution of 0.57%.   B. G. Harvey, H. G. Jackson, G. C. Hanna, and T. A. Eastwood, *Canadian Journ. Phys.*, **35** 268 (1957)

attracted to it, but since it consists of very fine wires (0.005 in. diameter) spaced well apart (0.03 in.), the electrons can readily pass through it. Such a gridded ionization chamber gives an output pulse proportional to the number of ion pairs produced by the α-particle, and thus to its energy, regardless of the orientation of the track in the chamber.   The spectrum of pulse sizes produced by a sample of Ra^{226} is shown in Figure 12.5.   The peaks marked α_0 and α_{188} are the α-particle groups leading to the ground state and 188 kev excited state of Em^{222} respectively. The center peak is due to simultaneous detection by the chamber of an α-particle from the α_{188} group and a K conversion electron from the decay of the Em^{222} excited state.

The time required for collection of the electrons depends on their velocity of drift through the gas towards the collector. The initially fast electrons are slowed down by collisions with the gas atoms, but argon is a poor stopping gas for low energy electrons. It is a tightly bound atom with a large ionization potential, so that there are no low energy states which can be formed in inelastic collisions with the electrons (the lowest excited state of argon is at 11.5 ev). A quantum mechanical phenomenon called the Ramsauer effect produces a very large increase in the average distance between collisions with argon atoms for electrons with kinetic energies below 10 ev, but in pure argon, it is not easy for electrons to slow down to energies as low as this. The velocity v with which electrons drift through a gas of pressure p under the influence of an applied electric field of E volts per cm is

$$v = \frac{eE\lambda}{p \sqrt{2m\epsilon}} \tag{12.2}$$

where m is the electron mass, ϵ is their average kinetic energy, and λ is the mean free path between collisions.

If a few percent of carbon dioxide or methane is added to argon, inelastic collisions become more probable because these molecules have many low-energy vibrational and rotational states which can take up energy in collisions with electrons. The average energy ϵ of the electrons is therefore only one tenth as great in argon containing these molecules as it is in pure argon. Hence, because of the Ramsauer effect, λ becomes much larger, and both the reduction in ϵ and the increase in λ cause v to increase. Thus the addition of about 10% of CO_2 or CH_4 decreases the time required for collection of electrons in an argon-filled ionization chamber, and gives a corresponding decrease in the resolving time.

C. Diffused Junction Silicon Detector

A variety of very useful detectors make use of semiconductor phenomena in solids, and are therefore sometimes known by the rather unsatisfactory name "solid state" detectors. We shall discuss only one type, the diffused junction silicon diode.

The isolated silicon atom has four valence electrons. In a silicon crystal, they are all used in chemical bond formation, so that very few of them are free to move about in the silicon lattice. The pure material is therefore a poor conductor of electricity at room temperature. The

normal energy levels of the isolated silicon atom are considerably dis-
turbed by the presence of neighboring atoms in the crystalline material.
At an excitation energy of 1.1 ev above the energy of the valence electrons,
there is a broad band of levels in which the electrons are not bound to any
specific silicon atom, but are free to move. Normally, this upper band
is almost completely empty, so that silicon is only a poor conductor.
However, thermal agitation keeps a few electrons in the band, and the

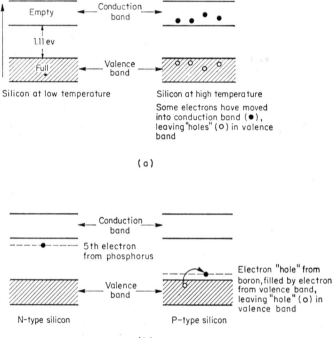

Fig. 12.6. Electron bands in silicon under various conditions

number increases rapidly as the temperature is raised, as shown in Figure
12.6 (a).

    If an atom of phosphorus, which has five valence electrons, is intro-
duced into a silicon crystal, four of the electrons are used in bond formation, but the fifth goes into a level which lies only slightly below the upper
band (the conduction band). This situation is illustrated in Figure
12.6 (b). Silicon containing a trace of phosphorus is called N-type (for
negative, since there is an extra electron).

    If an atom of boron, which has three valence electrons, is intro-
duced into a silicon crystal, there is one electron missing at the site of
the boron atom. This "hole" can be filled with an electron from the

valence band, and this electron then occupies an energy level just above the top of the valence band.   Silicon in this condition is called P-type (for positive, since there is one electron missing).   Phosphorus and boron are called donors and acceptors respectively, for obvious reasons.

Since the electrons from a donor lie close in energy to the conduction band, and can readily enter it, N-type silicon will conduct electricity. Similarly, P-type silicon conducts because the "hole" in the valence band can be passed along from one silicon atom to another.

If a piece of P-type silicon is brought into contact with a piece of N-type material, a contact potential is established between them, just as it is between any two dissimilar substances.   The P material acquires a negative potential with respect to the N material.   As a result, the relative energies of the bands are shifted, so that they look like Figure 12.7.   To move an electron from the N to the P region would require work against the negative charge of the P region; hence the energies of the P bands must be higher.   The contact potential arises because the electrons from the donors in the N region can move down in energy and fill the vacancies due to the acceptors in the P region. Therefore, the P region becomes negative.

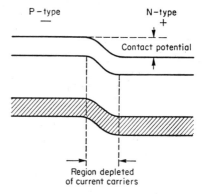

Fig. 12.7. Bands in p- and n-type silicon in contact

In the region of the junction, all the spare electrons from the donors have traveled into the N region and neutralized all the acceptors, so that the silicon on each side of the junction becomes nonconducting.   If an external voltage is applied across the junction, the N side being made more positive than it already is, the only effect is to cause a further small flow of electrons from the donors to the acceptors, and to increase the thickness of the nonconducting region around the junction.

If now an ionizing particle passes through the nonconducting layer (which is called the depletion layer), free electrons and positive ions ("holes") will be formed.   The electrons immediately migrate towards the positive (N) side, and the holes toward the negative (P) side, so that a pulse of current flows.   The collection takes place very fast, in less than 10^{-8} sec.   The positive ions of silicon do not move, since they are fixed in a crystal lattice.   Instead, they carry their share of the current by capturing electrons.   If a positive ion captures an electron from a neutral atom on its right, then that atom becomes a positive ion.   Thus the hole has moved to the right, while an electron has moved to the left.

By this mechanism, the positive ions in silicon can carry current much faster than positive ions in a gas like argon where the mechanism involves the bodily motion of the ions.

A practical PN junction counter is made by diffusing phosphorus to a depth of about 10^{-3} mm into silicon containing a very small concentration of P-type impurity, as shown in Figure 12.8. The junction is established just below the surface, where the concentration of phosphorus (an N impurity) exactly cancels the concentration of the P impurity. A conducting layer of aluminum is alloyed on to the back surface, and electrical contacts are installed. The front of the disk is maintained with a battery at a positive potential with respect to the back to establish

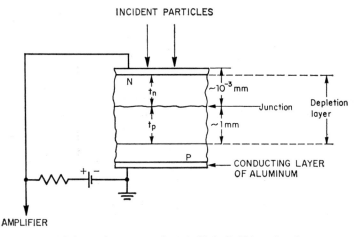

Fig. 12.8. Schematic cross section of silicon P-N junction detector

the layer depleted in donors and acceptors, and to collect the ionization caused by charged particles.

The thickness of the depleted layer increases as the applied voltage is increased, according to the equations

$$t_n = \left(\frac{\epsilon V}{2\pi e N_n}\right)^{1/2}$$

$$t_p = \left(\frac{\epsilon V}{2\pi e N_p}\right)^{1/2}$$

(12.3)

where t_n and t_p are defined in Figure 12.8, ϵ is the dielectric constant of silicon, V is the applied voltage, e is the electron charge, and N_n and N_p are the numbers of N- and P-type impurity atoms per unit volume. Because a rather large amount of phosphorus is diffused into the surface, N_n is high and therefore t_n is small. The greatest part of the depleted layer, which is the only region sensitive for the detection of radiation, is t_p.

Thus to obtain large depths for the sensitive layer, N_p should be very small, which means that silicon of fantastic purity is required. Such material is readily available, because it is required for making rectifiers, diodes, transistors, and other electronic devices.

Silicon (and also germanium) are exceptions to the rule that the average energy lost by a particle is about 30 ev for each ion pair formed. Because the energy separation between the valence electrons and the conduction band is only 1.1 ev in silicon, the average energy loss is low, about 3.6 ev per ion pair. This does not mean that the ranges of particles are unusually long in silicon. The primary events by which a particle loses energy are presumably about the same in silicon as in any other medium, but a much bigger fraction of the absorbed energy ends up as ionization in secondary events. The energy resolution which can be obtained from a counter depends, among other things, on the statistical fluctuation in the numbers of ion pairs produced by the incident radiation. In a perfect counter, the resolution R will be

$$R = \frac{100}{\sqrt{N}} = \frac{100\sqrt{\epsilon}}{\sqrt{E}} \% \qquad (12.4)$$

where N is the average number of ion pairs produced by a particle of energy E, and ϵ is the average energy loss per ion pair. Thus for 6 Mev helium ions, the best resolution that could be obtained in a grid ionization chamber ($\epsilon = 30$ ev) is 0.22%, but in a silicon counter it is 0.077%. Such a resolution figure has never been achieved in practice; the best results which have been claimed are about 0.4% for grid chambers and about 0.25% for silicon counters. Although the silicon counter is inherently very fast, the design of the amplifier restricts the resolving time to about a microsecond when high energy resolution is required.

In addition to the high speed and energy resolution which can be obtained, diffused junction silicon detectors have the important property that the pulse size is proportional to the energy deposited by a particle in the depletion layer, regardless of the mass and charge of the particle. Thus the pulse produced by a 50 Mev helium ion is exactly 5 times that produced by a 10 Mev proton. This is not true for any other counter type; highly ionizing particles such as helium ions usually give a smaller pulse than less highly ionizing particles of the same energy because at high ionization densities, some electrons and positive ions recombine before they can be separated.

Counters with a depleted layer as much as 2 gm per cm² in thickness have been made by using lithium as the donor element instead of phosphorus. By heating the diode to 125°C, the lithium can be made to drift into the P-type region in precisely the right amount to compensate the acceptor element. Thus N_p [equation (12.3)] becomes extremely small, and thick depletion layers are obtained with even a small bias potential.

D. Proportional Counters

One disadvantage of the counters described above is the small size of the pulses—a few millivolts. High gain amplifiers of careful design are required. The proportional counter avoids this difficulty.

If the electron-collecting electrode in a gas-filled counter is made of thin wire (typically 0.001 in. diameter), the electric field close to the

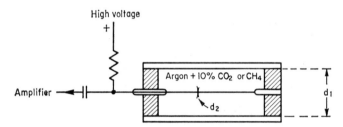

Fig. 12.9. Proportional counter (schematic)

wire will be very strong. If the counter has the form shown in Figure 12.9, the electric field strength E at a distance r from the wire is

$$E = \frac{V}{r \ln \left(\dfrac{d_1}{d_2} \right)} \quad \frac{\text{volts}}{\text{cm}} \tag{12.5}$$

V is the (positive) voltage of the central wire relative to the outer cylinder and d_1 and d_2 are the counter and wire diameters. Large values of E are obtained at small distances r, but the smallest possible value of r is limited by the wire radius. Hence the field strength is greatest just outside a thin wire, even though thick wires give greater values of E *for a fixed value of r.*

In a proportional counter, the field strength near the wire is so great that electrons traveling towards the wire receive sufficient acceleration between collisions to permit them to ionize gas molecules. An avalanche of ionization can thus be initiated by even a single electron, as shown schematically in Figure 12.10. Most of the avalanche occurs very close to the wire, where the electric field gradient is high: the process is called gas multiplication. The size of the output pulse is proportional to the number of primary electrons (and hence to the energy lost by the particle), and to the gas multiplication factor. The last quantity depends on V, the high voltage on the wire, as shown in Figure 12.11. If the energy of a particle is to be measured in a proportional counter, a very

stable high voltage supply is required in order to keep the gas multiplication constant. Energy resolution of about 1% can be achieved.

Proportional counters are often used for the detection and counting
of radiations from α, β^-, β^+, and EC decays when measurement of the

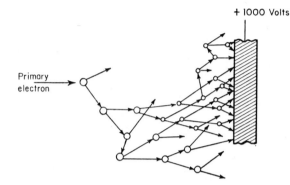

Fig. 12.10. Schematic picture of ionization avalanche near
proportional counter wire

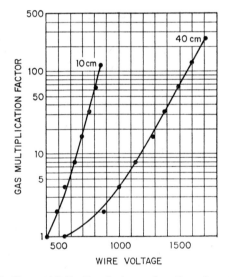

Fig. 12.11. Gas multiplication factor as function of applied voltage for argon pressures of 10 cm Hg and 40 cm Hg in counter of
diameter 0.87″, wire diameter 0.01″.   From B. B. Rossi and
H. H. Staub, *Ionization Chambers and Counters*, McGraw-Hill
Book Co., New York, 1949

energy of the particles is not required.   The sample is placed inside the
counter and air is removed by means of a continuous flow of gas, usually
methane or even natural gas.   A typical arrangement is shown in
Figure 12.12.   The circuitry which is used is shown as a block diagram in

Figure 12.13. The discriminator rejects pulses unless they exceed a certain voltage, which can be adjusted. In this way, very small pulses due to "noise" in the amplifier are rejected. The scaler and register record the number of pulses which arrive. Since the counter can detect as many as 10^5 particles per second, an electronic rather than mechanical register must be used, since mechanical systems are far too slow. A

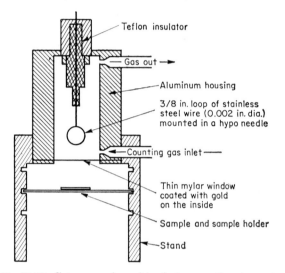

Teflon insulator

Gas out →

Aluminum housing

3/8 in. loop of stainless steel wire (0.002 in. dia.) mounted in a hypo needle

Counting gas inlet

Thin mylar window coated with gold on the inside

Sample and sample holder

Stand

Fig. 12.12. Cut-away view of typical proportional counter

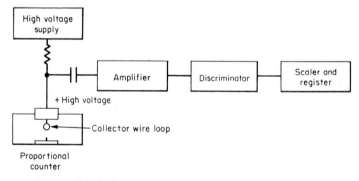

High voltage supply

Amplifier

Discriminator

Scaler and register

+ High voltage

Collector wire loop

Proportional counter

Fig. 12.13. Block diagram of typical circuit used with a proportional counter

typical electronic register (scaler) records up to 999 pulses. On arrival of the 1000th pulse, it returns to zero and sends out a pulse to the mechanical register which records the number of thousands which have arrived.

For a fixed setting of the discriminator, the counting rate from a given source depends on the high voltage and amplifier gain. If these are set at low values, the counter may produce no pulses large enough to pass the discriminator. For a fixed discriminator setting and fixed amplifier gain, the counting rate changes as the high voltage is increased, as shown in Figure 12.14. In the region marked "plateau," the counting rate is independent of the high voltage value, because every particle entering the counter is now making a pulse large enough to pass the discriminator.

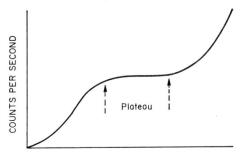

Fig. 12.14. Counting rate vs. high voltage in proportional counter

At even higher values of the voltage, the counting rate goes up again because of various effects which produce spurious counts.

E. Geiger Counters

The Geiger counter is one of the oldest counting devices, and about the least satisfactory. In many ways, it resembles a proportional counter, but the electric field near the wire is operated at such a high value that the avalanche of electrons and positive ions spreads all along the wire, producing a pulse which is usually in the range 20–100 volts.

Special precautions are required to stop the avalanche from turning into a continuous discharge. When the positive ions recombine with electrons, which they must eventually do, photons are emitted which may strike the counter walls and eject photoelectrons which initiate the avalanche anew. This effect is reduced by adding a polyatomic gas or vapor to the argon. Common mixtures are 90% A + 10% ethyl alcohol, or argon with 0.2 mm pressure of chlorine. The positive argon ions become neutralized by removing electrons from the alcohol molecules. The alcohol ions then drift relatively slowly away from the wire towards the counter wall, but their energy of recombination with electrons from the counter wall goes into decomposing the alcohol rather than into emission of new electrons. In this way the avalanche is prevented from becoming self-sustaining.

The disadvantage of the Geiger counter is that, compared with the proportional counter, it is very slow. Following the detection of a particle, the entire length of the wire is surrounded by a dense sheath of positive ions which reduce the electric field strength. The counter may fail to respond if a second particle arrives before the positive ions have drifted away from the wire, and this requires almost 10^{-3} seconds. A further disadvantage is that it is inconvenient to place the radiation source inside the counter; the particles usually enter through a thin window as shown in Figure 12.15. The stand provides a series of shelves which support the source and any absorbers that may be required.

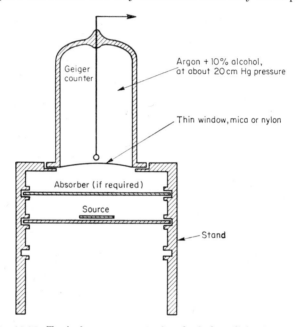

Fig. 12.15. Typical arrangement of end-window Geiger counter

The advantage of the Geiger counter is that it produces a large pulse requiring little further amplification, and the pulse size is independent of the nature of the incident radiation. Geiger counters are cheap and simple. They find their main use as portable instruments in surveying laboratories for radioactive contamination, and in mineral prospecting.

F. Scintillation Counters

Gas-filled counters are not very sensitive to X-rays and γ-rays because the probability that an energetic photon will produce an electron within the counter volume is very low. Thus a Geiger counter typically detects only 1% of the γ-rays which pass through it. In order to obtain a higher efficiency, a higher density stopping medium, preferably containing heavy elements, is required.   The sodium iodide scintillation counter detects γ-rays with much higher efficiency.

The counter consists of a single crystal of NaI grown from the molten salt.   It may be as large as 5 in. in diameter and 5 in. long, but smaller crystals are more common.   The NaI contains about 0.5 mole percent of thallium iodide as an activator.   Any type of ionizing radiation causes the emission of a short flash of light in the wavelength range 3300–5000 Å. The light flash is detected by means of a photomultiplier tube, whose output is an electrical pulse of several volts amplitude.   The arrangement is shown in Figure 12.16.   Because NaI is very hygroscopic, it must be sealed in an airtight can with a thin entrance window (0.001 in. aluminum foil).   The light escapes through a transparent window behind the

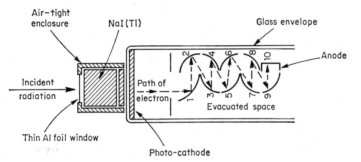

Fig. 12.16. Schematic view of NaI(Tl) crystal and photomultiplier assembly

crystal.   The inside of the can is coated with a thin layer of magnesium oxide which serves as a light reflector.   The crystal assembly is pressed against the front surface of the photomultiplier tube with a thin layer of transparent oil or grease to make a good optical contact and reduce internal reflections.

The photocathode surface of the photomultiplier is a semitransparent layer of a cesium-antimony alloy, which emits photoelectrons with high efficiency when struck by photons from the NaI crystal.   These electrons are accelerated towards the positively charged electrode (dynode) labeled 1.   The surface of this electrode (as well as the others) is made either of a cesium-antimony or a silver-magnesium alloy.   These substances emit several low energy electrons for every incident electron. The secondary electrons are accelerated towards the second dynode, which is at a higher positive potential, and the process is repeated.   Thus the number of electrons reaching the last electrode (the anode) is enormously greater than the initial number.   If the number emitted at each dynode is n times greater than the number incident, then in a nine stage tube, the multiplication is n^9, and for $n = 4$, this quantity is about 2.6×10^5. The photomultiplier therefore acts as a very high gain amplifier. The gain is very sensitive to the voltage applied to the dynodes because little or no multiplication occurs if the electrons are not sufficiently accelerated from one stage to the next. Operation with an overall high voltage of about 2000 volts can give rise to output pulses of several volts which require little further amplification.

The size of the output pulse is nearly proportional to the energy lost by the incident particle, so that NaI (Tl) crystals can be used for energy measurements as well as for detection of particles. Very high counting rates (10^5 per second) are possible, because the light flash is completed at a very short time after the arrival of the radiation.

The most important function of the NaI (Tl) counter is in γ-ray spectroscopy, where its high stopping power is valuable. γ-rays interact with the crystal, by the mechanisms described in Chapter 11, to produce fast electrons. If the crystal is sufficiently large, these electrons are absorbed and a flash of light is produced. If the primary interaction is the formation of a photoelectron, then the full energy of the γ-ray is absorbed. However, if the primary electron is produced in a Compton scattering, it will not have the full energy of the γ-ray. Often, the Compton scattered γ-ray will escape from the crystal, and since only a part of the incident energy has been absorbed by the crystal, the output pulse will be smaller. The spectrum of pulses produced by the γ-rays of Cs^{137} is shown in Figure 12.17. The largest pulses are produced by the photoelectric absorption, and this peak is used for measurements of γ-ray energies. Compton events produce a flat distribution on which is superimposed a small peak due to γ-rays which scattered from the lead shielding surrounding the counter. At the lowest pulse size, a peak appears which is due to the K X-rays of Ba, the daughter of the Cs^{137}. The photopeak is relatively larger in a bigger crystal, since a Compton scattered γ-ray has a better chance of interacting a second time and losing the rest of its energy before its escapes. The energy resolution (width of the photopeak at half its maximum height) is inversely proportional to the square root of the γ-ray energy. About 8% resolution may be obtained with 1 Mev γ-rays.

Because their light flashes are of even shorter duration than those of NaI (Tl), various organic crystals such as stilbene and anthracene are used for particle detection and counting when high rates of counting are required. The duration of the light flash is only about 10^{-8} seconds in these substances. Being composed of light elements, they offer no advantage in γ-ray energy measurements. The light output is proportional to the energy lost by an ionizing particle provided that the ionization density is sufficiently low. Organic crystals are used for the detection of particles in experiments where fast response rather than good energy resolution is important. Their usefulness for total energy measurements of heavy particles is limited because the ionization densities are too high to give a pulse accurately proportional to energy unless the velocity of the particle is very high (>100 Mev for protons). In this case, the particle would pass right through a crystal of practical size, and the energy *loss* rather than the *total* energy would be measured. However, organic scintillators are very useful for the measurement of electron energy spectra.

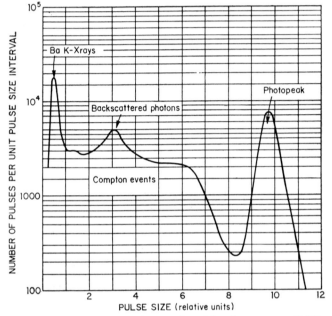

Fig. 12.17. Spectrum of pulses produced by Cs^{137} γ-rays (0.662 Mev) in NaI(Tl) crystal. P. R. Bell, Beta- and Gamma-ray Spectroscopy, K. Siegbahn (ed.), North Holland Publishing Co., Amsterdam, 1955

The organic scintillators may be incorporated in transparent plastics which are easily machined to any required shape. They may be dissolved in organic liquids to provide detectors of very large volume. The use of such a liquid system in the detection of the neutrino was described in Chapter 8.

G. Summary of Counter Types

The properties and uses of the various counter types discussed above are collected for comparison in Table 12.1. The resolving time and

TABLE 12.1. Comparison of the Various Types of Counters

Type of counter	Resolving time	Typical energy resolution	Commonest applications
Grid ion chamber	10 μsec	0.4% (α's)	Measurement α-particle energies
Proportional counter	1 μsec	~1% (charged particles)	1. Measurement particle energies 2. Detection of radiation, no energy measurement involved 3. Measurement energies very low energy γ-rays and X-rays
Geiger counters	~1 msec	None	1. Portable instruments for prospecting, fall-out detection, etc. 2. For economy where large numbers of detectors required, e.g. in cosmic ray experiments
NaI (Tl) scintillation counters	1 μsec	1% (charged particles), 8% (γ-rays, 1 Mev)	1. Detection and energy measurement of γ-rays 2. Detection and energy measurement of charged particles
Organic scintillation counters	1 μsec 10^{-8}–10^{-9} sec	10% (electrons) 15% (heavy charged particles, e.g. He^4).	1. Electron energy measurements 2. Detection charged particles where high speed of response required
Solid state counters	0.1–1 μsec 10^{-8} sec	0.2% (charged particles) ?	1. Energy measurements for charged particles 2. Detection of charged particles when no energy measurement is required

energy resolution figures are only typical, wide variations may occur in particular applications.

H. Counting Statistics

The *average* number of disintegrations taking place in a radioactive source in unit time depends only on the number of nuclei remaining and on the decay constant. However, if the number of disintegrations occurring in, say, one minute is measured several times, the result will not always be the same even when a correction is made for the decay of the sample. This phenomenon is observed in other types of statistical measurements. For example, the death rate, averaged over a large population, might be 1% per year, but this does not mean that in any sample of 100 people, exactly one will die each year. It might be two, zero, or even 100 (but this is not very likely). With nuclei, as with people, statistics become more meaningful when a large sample is observed.

If the number of nuclei present is N, and λ is the decay constant, then the probability $P(n)$ that n disintegrations will be observed in time t is given by the equation which is known as the binomial distribution:

$$P(n) = \frac{N!}{(N - n)!n!} (1 - e^{-\lambda t})^n e^{-\lambda t(N-n)} \qquad (12.6)$$

This equation is inconvenient to use, but it can be simplified if $\lambda t \ll 1$, $N \gg 1$ and $n \ll N$. These approximations assume that the number of nuclei is large, and that the period of observation is much less than one half life. With these assumptions, and some mathematical approximations, the Poisson distribution is obtained:

$$P(n) = \frac{\bar{n}^n e^{-\bar{n}}}{n!} \qquad (12.7)$$

where $\bar{n}$ is the *average* disintegration rate that would be obtained in a very long count. If n is sufficiently large ($\gg 100$), then the Poisson distribution assumes the more familiar Gaussian form:

$$P(n) = \frac{1}{\sqrt{2\pi\bar{n}}} e^{-(\bar{n}-n)^2/2\bar{n}} \qquad (12.8)$$

Figure 12.18 shows the Poisson and Gaussian distributions for $\bar{n} = 15$ counts per minute. Even for so small a value of $\bar{n}$, they are very similar.

We can use the Gaussian equation to calculate the probability of obtaining an error greater than a given amount. The error is $|\bar{n} - n|$, which is the amount that the number n recorded in a measurement differs from the "true" value $\bar{n}$. The probability $P(|\bar{n} - n|)$ that in any measurement we will obtain an error *greater* than $|\bar{n} - n|$ is obtained from

$$P(|\bar{n} - n|) = 2 \int_{|\bar{n}-n|}^{\infty} \frac{1}{\sqrt{2\pi\bar{n}}} e^{-(\bar{n}-n)^2/2\bar{n}} \, dn \qquad (12.9)$$

Values of this integral may be obtained from tables* in terms of the number of times the error $|\bar{n} - n|$ exceeds $\sqrt{\bar{n}}$. The quantity $\sqrt{\bar{n}}$ is called

* *Handbook of Chemistry and Physics*, Chemical Rubber Publishing Company, Cleveland, Ohio.

the standard deviation, and is usually given the symbol σ. The probability of occurrence of errors of various sizes is shown in Table 12.2. The use of this table may be illustrated by some examples. Suppose that, in the measurement of a sample, a total of 10,000 counts is recorded in one minute. We do not know n, the "true" number of events that occur in one minute, but it is probably not far from 10,000. Hence $\sqrt{\bar{n}}$, the

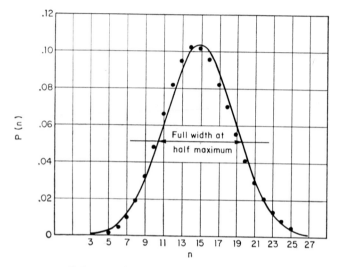

Fig. 12.18. Poisson and Gaussian distribution for $\bar{n} = 15$. The points are the Poisson distribution, the line the Gaussian

standard deviation, must be 100, and from the table, the probability is 31.73% that the error in the measurement is 100 or greater. The probability is only 0.00634% that the error is 400 or greater. We can have 90% confidence that the error is less than 164.49, and so on. The error limit most commonly quoted is the standard deviation. In this example, the result of the measurement would be written as 10,000 ± 100.

TABLE 12.2. Probability of Occurrence of Errors

Error, measured in standard deviations	Probability of occurrence of equal or greater error, %
0.6745	50.00
1.00	31.73
1.6449	10.00
1.9600	5.00
2.00	4.55
3.00	0.27
4.00	0.00634

$\dfrac{|\bar{n}-n|}{\sqrt{\bar{n}}} \rightarrow$

precision $\neq$ confidence $= 100 - X$

Observe that the standard deviation in this example is 1% of the measured value. If only 100 counts were recorded, the standard deviation would be 10 counts, which is 10% of the measured value. The precision increases as the square root of the total number of events recorded.

As a second example, consider the counting rate and error limits in an experiment in which 5000 counts were recorded in 3 minutes. The average counting rate was $\frac{5000}{3}$, or 1667 counts per min. The standard deviation in the number of counts recorded was $\sqrt{5000}$ or 70.6. It was *not* $\sqrt{1667}$. Hence the measured value was $1667 \pm (70.6/3)$, or 1667 ± 23.5 counts per minute.

It is often necessary to combine the results of several measurements each of which has errors. For example, a counter may record unwanted events due to cosmic rays or contamination with radioactive materials. This background counting rate must be measured and subtracted from the observed counting rate of a sample. If the standard deviation in the measurement of the background rate is σ_1, and that in the measurement of (background + sample) is σ_2, then the standard deviation σ in the difference of these quantities is

$$\sigma^2 = \sigma_1^2 + \sigma_2^2$$

$$\sigma_{meas} = \sqrt{\sigma_T^2, \sigma_B^2}$$

$$(12.10)$$

If 50 background counts were observed in 10 minutes, the rate is 5.0 ± 0.71 counts per minute. If sample plus background gave 250 counts in 5 minutes, then the rate is 50 ± 3.16 counts per minute. The rate due to the sample alone is therefore 45 counts per minute, and the standard deviation is $\pm \sqrt{0.71^2 + 3.16^2}$, or ± 3.24 counts per minute.

Equation (12.10) may be applied to cases where two numbers N_1 and N_2 with standard deviations σ_1 and σ_2 are added or subtracted. If N_1 and N_2 are multiplied together or divided, the standard deviation σ of the product or ratio is given by

$$\sigma = N_1 N_2 \sqrt{\left(\frac{\sigma_1}{N_1}\right)^2 + \left(\frac{\sigma_2}{N_2}\right)^2} \quad \text{(for product)}$$

$$\sigma = \frac{N_1}{N_2} \sqrt{\left(\frac{\sigma_1}{N_1}\right)^2 + \left(\frac{\sigma_2}{N_2}\right)^2} \quad \text{(for ratio)}$$

$$(12.11)$$

These equations are useful for calculating standard deviations in any kind of measurement in which the errors obey the Gaussian distribution.

REFERENCES

1. Rossi, B. B., and H. S. Staub, National Nuclear Energy Series, *Ionization Chambers and Counters*, McGraw-Hill Book Co., New York, 1949.

2. Sharpe, J., *Nuclear Radiation Detectors*, Methuen and Co. Ltd., London, 1955.

3. Price, W. J., *Nuclear Radiation Detection*, McGraw-Hill Book Co., New York, 1958.

4. Elmore, W. C., and M. Sands, National Nuclear Energy Series, *Electronics*, McGraw-Hill Book Co., New York, 1949.

5. Shive, J. N., *Semiconductor Devices*, D. Van Nostrand Co., Princeton, N. J., 1959.

6. Arguimbau, L. B. *Vacuum Tube Circuits*, John Wiley & Sons, New York, 1948.

7. Taylor, D., *The Measurement of Radio Isotopes*, Methuen and Co. Ltd., London, 1957.

8. Fretter, W. B., *Introduction to Experimental Physics*, Prentice-Hall Inc., New York, 1954.

9. Friedland, S. S., J. W. Mayer, and J. S. Wiggins, *Nucleonics*, **18,** 54 (1960). (Diffused junction silicon detectors.)

10. Bell, C. G., and F. N. Hayes (eds.), *Liquid Scintillation Counting*, Pergamon Press, London, 1958.

11. Washtell, C. C. H., *An Introduction to Radiation Counters and Detectors*, George Newnes Ltd., London, 1958.

12. Siegbahn, K. (ed.), *Beta- and Gamma-Ray Spectroscopy*, North Holland Publishing Co., Amsterdam, 1955.

PROBLEMS

1. Calculate the amount of electrical charge of both signs (in coulombs) that would be produced by the stopping of a 10 Mev deuteron in argon and silicon. If this charge passed at a uniform rate during 1 μsec through a resistance of 10^6 ohms, what voltage would be generated?

2. Design a tubular proportional counter of sufficient size to completely stop 10 Mev helium ions. Assume that the ions enter the counter through an aluminum foil window at one end of the tube and travel parallel to the axis, but displaced from it by about 1 cm. The gas pressure should not exceed 1 atmosphere. Choose your own wire and tube diameters, foil thickness, and approximate high voltage value. The gas multiplication required is about 1000.

3. If the depletion layer in a silicon detector is just thick enough to stop a 10 Mev helium ion when the bias voltage is 50 volts, what voltage will be required to give a depletion layer thick enough to stop a 15 Mev helium ion? Ignore the thickness of the layer on the donor side of the junction. Assume that the range–energy relationship for silicon is the same as for aluminum.

4. For the detector of Problem 3, calculate the pulse height that would be produced by a 10 Mev proton relative to the pulse produced by a 10 Mev helium ion when the bias voltage is 75 volts.

5. For the counter of Problem 3, operating at a bias of 50 volts, plot a graph showing the relative pulse heights for helium ions of various energies up to 14 Mev.

6. How many counts must be recorded in order to achieve 90% confidence in the result?

7. A determination of the background in a counter gave 357 counts in 10 minutes. With a sample in place, 26,500 counts were observed in 10 minutes. Calculate the counting rate produced by the sample, and its standard deviation. Could the standard deviation be reduced substantially by measuring the background for a longer time?

8. A counter gave 75 background counts in 5 minutes. Samples A and B gave 275 counts and 357 counts respectively in 10 minutes (including background). Calculate the ratio of the counting rates due to the two samples, and its standard deviation.

9. In a certain measurement, the counter background was measured for 1 hour, during which time 150 counts were observed. A sample yielded 25,640 counts in 1 minute. Criticize the way in which this measurement was made.

CHAPTER 13

Particle Accelerators and Reactors

A. Introduction

In principle, the acceleration of charged particles requires only a vacuum system and a source of high voltage. However, the majority of experiments require particle energies of many Mev, or even many thousands of Mev. The production of voltages above about 5 Mev is extremely difficult because of the breakdown of insulators and the appearance of corona discharges which cause loss of charge from objects at high potentials. By means of a series of transformers arranged in cascade so that each one is at a higher potential above ground than the previous one, voltages up to about 1,000,000 volts may be obtained (such devices are often called Cockcroft-Walton machines). These, and the Van de Graaff electrostatic accelerators, are the only machines which operate by the application of a single high potential.

All other accelerators, with the exception of the betatrons, operate by the repeated application of a smaller potential. (We shall not discuss the betatron, because it seems unlikely that this machine will contribute much new knowledge to nuclear physics in the future.) The particles are therefore accelerated in many small steps. In the linear accelerators, the accelerating electrodes are arranged in a straight line; in cyclotrons and synchrotrons, the particles are repeatedly returned to the same accelerating electrode by means of a magnetic field which causes them to move in a circular, or nearly circular, path.

The force F exerted on an electric charge q in an electric field E is

$$F = Eq \qquad (13.1)$$

If the force moves the particle a distance dS, then the work dW done on the particle is

$$dW = F \, dS = Eq \, dS$$

In moving the particle from S_0 to S_1, the work done is

$$\int_{S_0}^{S_1} F \, dS = \int_{S_0}^{S_1} Eq \, dS$$

However,

$$\Delta V = \int_{S_0}^{S_1} E \, dS$$

where ΔV is the potential difference between the points S_0 and S_1. If the particle is free to accelerate, its final kinetic energy T, which is equal to the work done by the accelerating field, is

$$T = \int_{S_0}^{S_1} Eq \, dS = q \, \Delta V \qquad (13.2)$$

If q is expressed in units of the electronic charge and ΔV is in volts, then T will be in units of electron volts. The kinetic energy achieved by a particle depends only on its charge and on the value of the accelerating potential. It does not depend on the mass of the particle or on the distance through which the accelerating field operates.

A charged particle moving in a magnetic field experiences a force which is perpendicular both to the direction of the field and to the direction of motion of the particle. The magnitude of the force F is

$$F = \frac{qvB}{c} \quad \text{dynes} \qquad (13.3)$$

where v is the velocity of the particle in cm per sec, B is the magnetic field strength in gauss, and q is the charge of the particle in esu. The direction of the force is given by the left-hand rule which is illustrated in Figure 13.1. The magnetic field direction (by definition) runs from the north pole towards the south pole. (In vector notation, F is the cross product of $(q/c)\vec{v}$ and $\vec{B}$, i.e., $F = (q/c)\vec{v} \times \vec{B}$.) In a uniform field normal to its direction of motion, a particle of constant charge and velocity experiences a constant force at right angles to its direction of motion, and hence

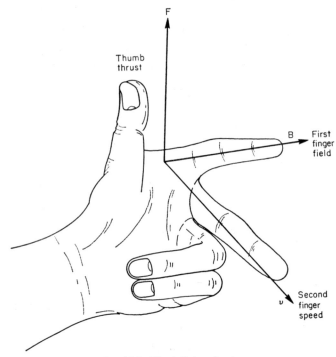

Fig. 13.1. The left-hand rule

describes a circular path. We shall return to this point in the discussion of the cyclotron and synchrotron.

B. The Van de Graaff Machine

R. J. Van de Graaff of the Massachusetts Institute of Technology, invented in 1931 the machine which bears his name. It is an electrostatic source of very high potential. According to a well-known principle of electricity, all the electric charge on an object A (Figure 13.2) will transfer itself to the hollow conductor B when the two are brought into electrical contact. This is true even when the potential of B is already higher than that of A. By repeatedly connecting charged objects to the inside of the hollow conductor, its potential can in principle be raised to an indefinitely high value.   In practice, however, the hollow conductor must be supported on insulators, and the leakage current increases with increasing potential.   In addition, corona discharges cause loss of the charge.   At some potential value, these losses will exactly equal the rate at which the charge is being brought into the hollow conductor, so that its potential will level off at some maximum value.

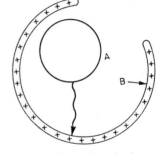

Fig 13.2. Transfer of charge from initially charged object A inside a hollow conductor B

In the Van de Graaff generator, charge is brought into a hollow conductor by means of an endless belt made of an insulating material such as woven cotton.   Positive electric charge is sprayed on to the moving belt by means of corona discharges from sharp needles (corona points) which are connected to a high voltage source (+50 kv); the arrangement is shown in Figure 13.3.   (The electric field E at the surface of a sphere of radius r carrying charge e in a medium of dielectric constant ϵ is

$$E = \frac{e}{\epsilon r^2}.$$

Hence E can be very large for very small spheres (points, for example). It can be large enough to ionize the surrounding medium.   If the charge e

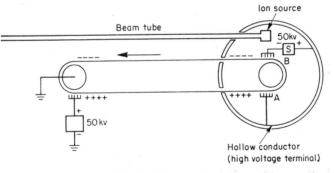

Fig. 13.3. Van de Graaff generator (schematic)

is positive, electrons will be attracted towards it and a "wind" of positive ions will be blown away from the point as a corona discharge.)

The positive ions attach themselves to the moving belt which carries the charge to the inside of the high voltage terminal where it is removed by means of a second set of corona points A.   A third set of points B, connected to the inside of the high voltage terminal through a second high voltage source S, sprays negative charge on to the belt for its return trip. In this way, the charge-carrying capacity of the belt is doubled. To prevent insulator leakage due to dampness, and to obtain better insulation than is possible with air at normal pressures, the whole generator is enclosed in a tank which can be filled with dry gas at high pressure. Sulfur hexafluoride or nitrogen at a pressure of 100 psi are satisfactory, particularly if a small amount of Freon (CCl_2F_2) is added to the nitrogen. (Freon readily captures free electrons to form negative ions of low mobility, thus preventing electrical discharge through the nitrogen.)

Positive ions are produced by bombardment of the appropriate gas with low energy electrons in an ion source which is mounted inside the high voltage terminal. The high positive charge of the terminal repels

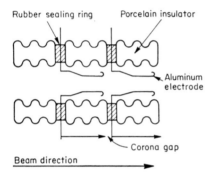

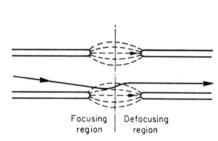

Fig. 13.4. Cross section of high voltage accelerator tube

Fig. 13.5. Focusing by electric field in accelerator tube (second order focusing)

the ions down an evacuated beam tube at the end of which is placed the target to be bombarded. The beam tube consists of many sections of porcelain insulator separated by aluminum ring electrodes which are maintained at progressively decreasing positive potentials as shown in Figure 13.4.

The corona gaps between adjacent electrodes of the beam tube maintain a uniform potential gradient down the tube, and the electrodes protect the insulator sections from bombardment by the beam particles. It was found early in the development of high voltage accelerators that division of the beam tube into several sections was essential. For reasons which are not well understood, it is impossible to maintain a potential difference greater than about 400 kv between the ends of a single insulator section.

Equally important is the focusing of the beam which occurs at the gaps between the electrodes. The electric field at a gap, as shown in Figure 13.5, gives both a focusing and a defocusing action, since the force exerted on the particle is everywhere parallel with the electric field lines. Since the particles are undergoing acceleration in the gap, they spend more time in the focusing region which they enter first, with the result that the focusing action is slightly greater than the defocusing action. Particles are therefore kept bunched together in a narrow beam down the center of the tube.   This type of focusing is called second order, and although it is not very strong, it is adequate for the fairly low particle energies of Van de Graaff machines.

By control of the potential of the high voltage sources which charge the belt, the potential of the high voltage terminal and hence the kinetic energy of the accelerated particles can be regulated very accurately.

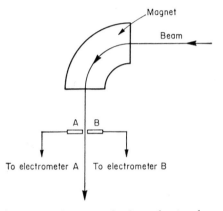

Fig. 13.6. Apparatus for control of accelerator beam energy (schematic)

The arrangement shown schematically in Fig. 13.6 is used to give automatic control of the beam energy.   The beam particles are deflected by means of a magnetic field, and they then pass through a narrow slit between the plates A and B.   If the energy of the particles falls, they will be deflected through a larger angle and some particles will fall on B. A current therefore flows through the electrometer B, and this produces a signal which increases the amount of charge sprayed on to the belt and hence the potential of the high voltage terminal.   In this way, beams of constant energy are obtained.   Even more important, the beams from Van de Graaff accelerators are very nearly monoenergetic; the energy spread may be as small as 20 kev in beams of 6 Mev total energy.   These beams are very useful in the study of closely spaced nuclear levels.   Currents of about 10 μamp of protons, deuterons, tritons, He^3, He^4, and smaller beams of heavier ions such as C^{12} and O^{16} may be obtained.

The tandem Van de Graaff generator is an ingenious modification which permits particles to be accelerated to a kinetic energy twice as high as in a conventional machine. In some gases, electron bombardment in an ion source produces negative as well as positive ions. The negative ions can therefore be accelerated *towards* the high voltage terminal. Inside the terminal, they are allowed to pass through a region of higher gas pressure where collision with the gas molecules strips off two or more electrons, thus converting some of the negative ions into positive ions. Acceleration then continues by repulsion of these positive ions down a beam tube away from the high voltage terminal. Beams of a few μamp of protons, deuterons and tritons with energies of about 14 Mev are obtained. Heavier ions such as C^{12} and O^{16} may be accelerated to about 40 Mev. It is possible to obtain small beams of 20 Mev helium ions even though there is no stable negative helium ion. The process is not well understood.

C. The Cyclotron

The cyclotron was the first practical accelerator to produce high energy particles without the use of high voltages. The principle of magnetic resonance acceleration was discovered by E. O. Lawrence in 1929; the first small cyclotron was built in 1930. It produced 13 kev H_2^+ ions.

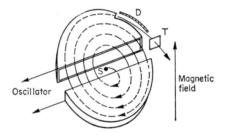

Fig. 13.7. The cyclotron principle

The arrangement of a typical cyclotron is shown in Figure 13.7. The ion source S is an arc struck in the appropriate gas, for example H_2 to provide protons. It is placed between two hollow metal boxes called "dees" by reason of their shape. A large magnet provides a nearly uniform magnetic field across the whole area of the dees and perpendicular to their plane. The dees are connected to a radiofrequency oscillator so that their potentials relative to ground vary from positive to negative. When one dee is positive, the other is negative. The dees are placed inside an evacuated tank (not shown in Fig. 13.7).

Consider the path of a positive ion which is formed at S at a time when the lower dee in Figure 13.7 is negatively charged. The ion will be accelerated towards the dee, but at the same time the magnetic field will force it to move in a curved path.   Inside the dee, no electric field acts upon the particle which, however, will continue to move in a circular path under the influence of the magnetic field.   While the ion is inside the dee, the oscillator reverses the polarities so that the upper dee of Figure 13.7 becomes negative and the lower dee positive.   The ion is therefore accelerated again as it crosses the gap between the dees, and the whole cycle is repeated many times.   Each time the ion crosses the dee gap, it gains kinetic energy equal to the product of its charge and the potential difference between the dees.

Let an ion of charge q and rest mass m be moving with velocity V. The force exerted on it by the magnetic field is

$$F = \frac{qVB}{c}$$

This force causes the particle to move in a circular orbit of radius r such that the centrifugal force is equal to F.   Thus, ignoring the relativistic mass increase,

$$\frac{qVB}{c} = \frac{mV^2}{r} \tag{13.4}$$

The distance traveled in a complete circuit is $2\pi r$ so that the time t required is

$$t = \frac{2\pi r}{V} \quad \text{or} \quad V = \frac{2\pi r}{t}$$

Substituting this value of V into equation (13.4):

$$\frac{qB}{mc} = \frac{2\pi}{t}$$

or
$$t = \frac{2\pi mc}{qB} \tag{13.5}$$

The operation of the cyclotron depends on the circumstance that the time t required for a complete revolution of an ion of given rest mass and charge is independent of the velocity of the ion as long as the velocity is low enough that the relativistic mass increase can be ignored.   From equation (13.4), the radius of an orbit is

$$r = \frac{mcV}{qB} \tag{13.6}$$

and although higher velocity ions travel in larger circles, their higher velocity causes them to make a revolution in just the same time as slower ions.   Because of the result expressed in equation (13.5), the cyclotron can be operated by the application of a constant radiofrequency to the dees, and the dee voltages will always reverse at the right time to cause further acceleration, regardless of the velocity of the ion and the radius of its path.

The ions spiral out from the center of the cyclotron until they approach the deflector D, which is charged to a negative potential of about 50 kv. The deflector pulls the ions from their orbits and causes them to leave the dee system. The energy of the particles, from equation (13.4), will be

$$E = \frac{r^2 q^2 B^2}{2mc^2} \tag{13.7}$$

where r is the radius at which the ions are extracted from their orbits by the deflector. Targets may be inserted at T, or the beam may travel down an evacuated pipe for use at some distance from the cyclotron.

Equation (13.5) shows that the oscillator must have a frequency ν given by

$$\nu = \frac{1}{t} = \frac{qB}{2\pi mc} \tag{13.8}$$

Equation (13.8) gives ν in cycles per second when B is in gauss, q is in esu, and m is in grams.

In most cyclotrons, the frequency is adjustable only over a small range so that the magnetic field strength B is the quantity which is adjusted to satisfy equation (13.8) for the q/m of the particular type of particle which it is desired to accelerate. Acceleration of deuterons or helium ions (+2 charge) requires a magnetic field twice as strong as that required for the acceleration of protons. Reduction of the magnetic field to one half its full value is possible in principle, but leads to a defocusing of the beam for reasons which will be discussed below. Therefore protons are often accelerated as molecular hydrogen ions H_2^+ for which q/m is almost identical with that of deuterons and helium ions. The binding energy of the two protons into the molecule is negligibly small compared with nuclear energies, and they are a long way apart compared with nuclear dimensions. The H_2^+ beam therefore acts just like a proton beam for most purposes, but it can sometimes be troublesome in counter experiments because two protons invariably arrive together in exact time coincidence. A counter will therefore count them together as a single event.

Frequencies of about 12 megacycles per second and magnetic fields of 17,000 gauss are used in many cyclotrons. The diameter of the magnet pole faces is often used as a measure of the size of a given cyclotron. Many machines have pole diameters of about 60 inches; the largest is the Russian 6 meter machine, which gives 680 Mev protons.

To obtain a useful beam intensity, the motion of the particles must be confined to a horizontal plane in the center of the dees (the median plane).

If there is no focusing of the beam in the vertical direction, the particles will wander away from the median plane and eventually be lost by striking the top or bottom surfaces of the dees.   The required vertical stability of the orbits can be achieved if the magnetic field decreases by a few per-cent between the center and the edge of the magnet.   The magnetic field lines thus obtained are shown in Figure 13.8.   A particle traveling in spirals in the plane AB will experience a force downwards to restore it to the median plane, since it is not crossing the field lines at right angles. This type of focusing is similar to the focusing of particles in the fringing

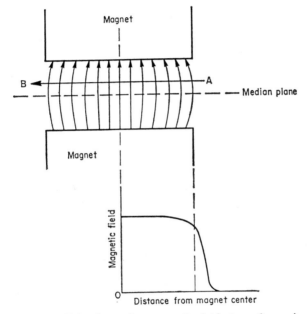

Fig. 13.8. Radially decreasing magnetic field strength required for vertical stability in cyclotron

fields of magnets, which is discussed in Chapter 14.   If the magnetic field is drastically reduced to permit the acceleration of protons, the frac-tional reduction in the magnetic field strength at large radii is reduced, so that vertical focusing is lost.   It is for this reason that many machines accelerate H_2^+ rather than protons.

The frequency and magnetic field required for acceleration [equation (13.8)] are a function of the mass of the particle.   When the velocity of the particle becomes high, its relativistic increase of mass can no longer be ignored.   As the particle spirals outwards, a greater magnetic field is required to satisfy equation (13.8) with the greater mass of the particle, but then the vertical stability is lost.   For this reason, conventional cyclotrons cannot accelerate particles to velocities greater than about

0.2c.   The relativistic increase in mass at this velocity is about 2%; the kinetic energy is about 20 Mev (for a proton).

Two ways of obtaining higher energies from cyclotrons have been devised.   In the first, the magnetic field is allowed to increase with increasing radius to compensate for the increasing mass of the particles. This is done by suitable shaping of the pole faces.   Vertical stability is then obtained by the use of radial ridges in the form of spirals on the faces of the poles, so that the particles pass alternately through regions of higher and lower magnetic field as shown in Figure 13.9.   The pole gap is smaller between the ridges, so that the magnetic field strength is greater there.   Since the magnetic field lines are not perpendicular to the median plane in regions where the magnetic field is increasing or decreasing,

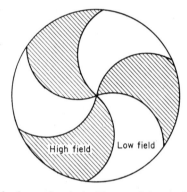

Fig. 13.9. Pole face of spiral ridge cyclotron.   Shaded areas represent ridges, blank areas are valleys.   The other pole has identical ridges and valleys.   Vertical focusing is obtained for particles moving either with or against the spirals

vertical forces act on the particles with the result that they are strongly confined to the median plane, even though the *average* field strength is increasing with increasing radius.   Several spiral ridge cyclotrons are planned—for example, at Oak Ridge, Saclay, and the University of Colorado.   The 88 inch spiral ridge cyclotron at the Lawrence Radiation Laboratory, Berkeley, was built to produce large beams of 50 Mev protons, 60 Mev deuterons, and 120 Mev helium ions.   According to calculations made at Oak Ridge National Laboratory, it should be possible to obtain 850 Mev protons from a spiral ridge cyclotron.

In the frequency modulated (FM) cyclotron, the frequency [equation (13.8)] is changed as the mass of the particles increases.   The constantly changing frequency permits a group of particles to go through their accelerating cycle until they are at full energy.   In the meantime, though, no more particles can start from the ion source because the frequency is too low for slow particles to satisfy equation (13.8).   As soon as a group of particles has reached full energy, the frequency of the oscillator is changed back to its maximum value to permit another group to start from the ion source.   Thus the beam from a frequency modulated cyclotron (synchrocyclotron) consists of bursts of particles.   The average beam intensity is about 100 times lower than from conventional or spiral ridge machines.   High particle energies require magnets of very large radius, and for energies above about 1000 Mev, the cost of the magnet becomes excessive.

Although the energy of the particles in a beam can be reduced by the insertion of absorbers, it is much better to accelerate them in the first place only as far as the energy desired for the particular experiment. Absorbers scatter the beam, and introduce a considerable energy dispersion so that the beam is not truly monoenergetic.   A few variable energy cyclotrons have been built.   To bring lower energy particles out to the extraction radius requires a reduction both in the oscillator frequency and in the magnetic field.   Reduction of the magnetic field reduces the amount that the field falls off as a function of radius, and therefore reduces the vertical focusing.   It is therefore necessary to build on the pole faces of the magnet supplementary coils whose currents can be adjusted to give the right magnetic field shape.   The Berkeley variable energy spiral ridge cyclotron has seventeen pole face coils, in addition to the main coils of the magnet.

The beam from a cyclotron typically has an energy dispersion whose full width at half maximum intensity is about 1%.   The beam is therefore much less accurately monoenergetic than the beams from Van de Graaff accelerators.   However, the cyclotron beam can be magnetically analyzed by the methods described in Chapter 14 to give a dispersion as small as 0.1% in energy.   Some 90% of the beam is lost in this analysis, but this is not serious since conventional and spiral ridge cyclotrons are usually capable of producing far greater beam currents than are normally required for experiments.

D. The Synchrotron

The magnetic field of the cyclotron extends from the center out to the extraction radius.   If particles could be constrained to move in an orbit of constant radius as they accelerate, then the magnet could be constructed in the form of a ring, like a cyclotron magnet with its center cut out.   Such a magnet would require far less iron, copper conductor, and electrical power than a cyclotron magnet of the same outer radius.

The synchrotron uses a ring-shaped magnet in which the field is increased as the particles accelerate so that the radius of their orbits remains constant.   After a group of particles has reached full energy, the magnet is switched off and acceleration of a new group of particles is started.   The principle of the synchrotron was discovered independently by V. Veksler in 1944 and by E. M. McMillan in 1945.   Since then, several machines of enormous size have been built for the acceleration of protons.   Smaller machines of the same type are also used for accelerating electrons.   The synchrotron is illustrated in Figure 13.10.

The protons originate in an ion source which is external to the machine. They are first accelerated to energies of a few Mev in a completely independent accelerator.   The Berkeley machine accomplishes this preliminary acceleration by means of a 500 kv DC supply followed by a

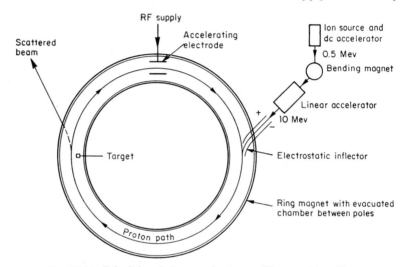

Fig 13.10. Principle of the synchrotron.   The machine illustrated is actually the 6.2 Bev "bevatron" at Berkeley

10 Mev linear accelerator (see Section E below).   The protons then pass into the synchrotron magnet, which is operating at a very low field strength.   The electrostatic field of the inflector bends the path of the protons to be tangential to the main ring magnet.   During injection of the protons from the ion source, the synchrotron magnet is turned on, and the slow increase in the field strength causes the proton orbits to shrink so that on their second trip around, they miss the end of the inflector.

A sinusoidal alternating potential is now applied to the tubular accelerating electrode.   Protons which enter the electrode at time t_1 (Fig. 13.11) and leave at time t_2 experience a small acceleration because the positive potential of the electrode increases between t_1 and t_2.   The energy increase is ΔV, which is only 1500 volts in the Berkeley machine. As the particles accelerate, the magnetic field continues to increase in such a way that the radius of the proton orbit remains constant. The frequency of the oscillating voltage applied to the accelerating electrode must also increase, since the time required for a complete circuit becomes shorter and shorter until the velocity of the protons approaches the velocity of light, after which the circuit time remains constant. The whole accelerating cycle requires several seconds, during which time the protons make many millions of circuits.

As the magnetic field strength approaches its maximum value, the accelerating voltage is turned off and a target is pushed towards the circulating beam on a pneumatically operated rod. The magnetic field continues to increase slightly so that the radius of the proton orbit decreases and the particles strike the target. Scattered beams of protons, neutrons, mesons of various kinds, and antiprotons and antineutrons may be obtained from a thin window in the wall of the vacuum chamber.

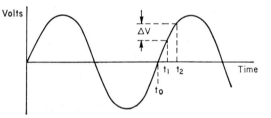

Fig. 13.11. RF voltage on synchrotron accelerating electrode

Finally, the magnet current is turned off and the field collapses to its initial value, ready for the next injection and acceleration cycle. Each burst of protons contains about 10^{11} particles, and in the Berkeley machine there is one burst every six seconds. The average beam intensity is therefore much lower than in cyclotrons.

The successful operation of the synchrotron depends on the existence of phase stability. If a proton gains too little energy in any turn, its radius of curvature will be smaller than the average, and hence it will arrive at the accelerating electrode a little *sooner* than the main group of protons. At relativistic energies, all the particles, regardless of their energy, are traveling at very nearly the same velocity, but the radius of the path in a given magnetic field is still a function of the energy of the particle. As Figure 13.11 shows, the rate of increase of the accelerating electrode voltage is greater just before t_1, so that the slower particle, arriving earlier at time t_0, receives a greater acceleration and catches up in energy with the rest of the proton group. Conversely, a particle with too much energy arrives late when the accelerating voltage is increasing more slowly, so it receives less acceleration. Thus there is an automatic mechanism which ensures that all the protons which start the accelerating cycle will continue to arrive at the accelerating electrode at such a time that they continue to be accelerated.   A few particles are lost in collisions with residual gas molecules during their enormously long flight path around the magnet.

The machines at Brookhaven National Laboratory and Geneva produce 30 Bev protons.   These machines use nonuniform magnetic fields which strongly focus the protons.   The circulating beam therefore stays tightly bunched together in space so that a vacuum chamber with only a relatively small aperture is required.   The size of the magnet pole gap can therefore be correspondingly small, and the whole machine becomes much cheaper to build—or rather a bigger diameter magnet can be built for the same price so that higher energy particles can be obtained.   The Berkeley machine, which produces 6.2 Bev protons, was designed before the discovery of this focusing principle.   In the future, machines of truly monumental size seem certain to be built.   For the production of 100 Bev protons, a ring magnet with a diameter of nearly half a mile is required.

E. The Linear Accelerator

The linear accelerator was actually the first particle accelerator to be built (other than machines using high voltages).   In 1931, D. H. Sloan

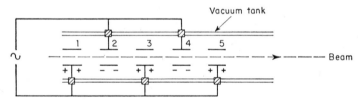

Fig. 13.12. Principle of the linear accelerator

and E. O. Lawrence produced 2.9 Mev mercury ions, but further development was slow because of the enormous success of the cyclotron and because the electrical equipment required for further progress was not available until after the Second World War.

The linear accelerator, in its simplest form, consists of a large vacuum tank along the axis of which there are a number of metal tubes which are called drift tubes.   The beam of particles passes down the center of the tubes as shown in Figure 13.12.   The drift tubes are connected to a high frequency oscillator as shown in the figure.   Suppose that a group of positively charged particles leaves the right-hand end of tube 1 when its polarity is positive and that of tube 2 is negative.   The particles will be accelerated as they cross the gap, but once inside tube 2 they will experience no further force.   If their drift time through tube 2 is exactly equal to the time required for the oscillator to reverse the polarity of all the tubes, then there will be a further acceleration between tubes 2 and 3, and so on.   The length of the tubes must increase from left to right so that the time required by the particles to pass through each tube is constant and equal to half the reciprocal of the frequency of the oscillator. Particles are injected into the first drift tube with an energy of about 1 Mev (obtained from an independent accelerator such as a Van de Graaff generator), so that the length of the first few tubes need not be too small.

The linear accelerator exhibits a phase stability which resembles that of the synchrotron.   If the potential difference between two drift tubes is increasing, a particle arriving late at the gap will receive extra acceleration, whereas if it arrives early, it will receive less.   The particles therefore remain together in bunches which cross the gaps in phase with the oscillator frequency.   However if the particles are traveling with velocities very nearly equal to c, the effect of the acceleration is to increase the mass of a particle but to leave its velocity almost unchanged.   Phase stability is therefore lost.

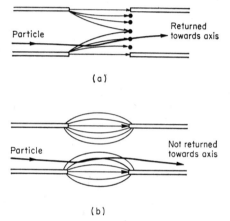

Focusing of the beam is a major problem in linear accelerators.   If particles cross a gap as the electric field is increasing (as they must to obtain phase stability), then the second-order focusing at the gap is lost and the beam can "blow up" in a radial direction.   This problem can be

Fig. 13.13. Action of focusing grids in a linear accelerator

solved by placing a wire grid at the entrance of each drift tube so that the electric field lines are like those shown in Figure 13.13 (a) rather than those of Figure 13.13 (b).   Many particles are lost by scattering from the grid wires, however.   A more satisfactory, but more expensive solution, is to place a focusing magnet inside each pair of drift tubes.   (Magnets of this type are described in Chapter 14.)   The heavy ion linear accelerators at Berkeley and Yale operate in this way.

If an electromagnetic wave can be set up in an evacuated tube in such a way that particles traveling down the axis always experience an accelerating force, then there is no need for drift tubes (whose function, after all, is only to shield the particles from the field when its phase is incorrect). This possibility is realized in the traveling wave linear accelerator in which the particles ride along the electromagnetic wave like surf riders. The phase velocity of the traveling wave is adjusted by means of the cavities shown in Figure 13.14 so that it is equal to the velocity of the particles all the way down the tube. Machines of this type are particularly suitable for the acceleration of electrons, since once the electron energy exceeds 1 Mev, the velocity is very nearly equal to c, and hardly increases as the energy of the electrons increases.

Linear accelerators have certain advantages and disadvantages when compared with cyclotrons. Since the ion source can be outside the machine, it is easier to design and operate than the cyclotron, whose ion source must fit into the space between the dees. In the heavy ion linear accelerators at Berkeley and Yale, the ion source produces partly ionized particles—e.g., $(C^{12})^{+2}$—which are first accelerated by means of a DC potential and then by a short linear accelerator to an energy of about $1A$ Mev (where A is the mass number of the ions). The ions then pass through a transverse jet of mercury vapor; collisions with mercury atoms strip several more electrons from the ions. Acceleration is then continued in a second linear accelerator section to a final energy of $10A$ Mev.

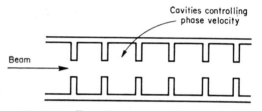

Fig. 13.14. Traveling wave accelerator tube

Beams of ions from He^3 (30 Mev) to A^{40} (400 Mev) have been obtained. Since the radiofrequency power requirements are very large, these machines can only operate in a pulsed manner. Bursts of particles lasting about 0.002 sec are generated about 20 times per second. The average beam is about 1 μamp (for C^{12}), which is much less than the p,d, or He^4 beams from conventional cyclotrons. However, it is hard to obtain beams of high energy, heavy ions like C^{12} from cyclotrons designed to accelerate deuterons and helium ions because the ion source must produce highly ionized particles to give q/m values suitable for acceleration. Ion sources naturally produce much lower yields of, for example, $(C^{12})^{+4}$ than of $(C^{12})^{+2}$. In most cyclotrons, the beam starts out as C^{+2}, but some of the ions lose electrons by collision with gas molecules. The final beam therefore contains a few C^{12} ions of full energy and many ions of low energy which only heat up the target without producing nuclear reactions.

The linear accelerator is particularly suitable for the acceleration of electrons. In circular machines, the continual acceleration of the particles towards the center by the magnetic field produces enormous energy losses by bremsstrahlung radiation for high energy electrons and further acceleration becomes virtually impossible. At Stanford

University, a linear accelerator of the traveling wave type produces electrons of 900 Mev, and there are plans for a far bigger machine of the same type.

F. Reactors

In Chapter 10, we saw that the fission of certain heavy nuclei can be induced by capture of neutrons even of essentially zero energy, and that the fission act is accompanied by the liberation of between two and three neutrons. The possibility of producing a chain reaction was realized very shortly after the discovery of fission. However, the number of neutrons liberated is not great enough to permit the chain reaction to continue if many neutrons are wasted. Very carefully controlled conditions must be established. If so many neutrons are lost or absorbed in unproductive ways that, on the average, each generation of neutrons fails to produce at least as many for the next generation, then the chain reaction will stop. If the quantity k is defined as

$$k = \frac{\text{Number of neutrons in } (n+1)\text{th generation}}{\text{Number of neutrons in } n\text{th generation}} \qquad (13.9)$$

then k must be equal to or greater than unity in a self-sustaining chain reaction. If k is greater than unity, then the chain reaction is divergent —that is, the number of neutrons produced and the number of fission events per unit time will continually increase until a disaster occurs. Atomic bombs operate in this manner. For steady operation of a reactor, k must be kept precisely equal to unity. For the sake of definiteness, we shall consider the example of a reactor operating with natural uranium fuel.

Neutrons may be lost in the following three ways:

1. *Non-fission capture in the fuel.* The fuel contains only 0.7% of U^{235}, which is the only isotope present in natural uranium capable of fission on the capture of a low energy neutron. The major part of the fuel is U^{238} (99.3%) which only fissions following the capture of a neutron of energy greater than about 1 Mev. The energy spectrum of fission neutrons (see Fig. 9.6) contains many neutrons whose energies are too low to induce fission in U^{238}; many of these will be captured in the reaction $U^{238}(n,\gamma)U^{239}$, which of course is unproductive as far as renewing the neutrons for the next generation is concerned.

This difficulty can be avoided by placing the lumps of uranium fuel in a *moderator* whose function is to slow down the fission neutrons into the thermal energy range. For thermal neutrons, the fission cross section of U^{235} is large (550 barns), whereas the (n,γ) cross section of U^{238} is only 2.8 barns. The unproductive capture cross section of U^{235} is also rather large (100 barns), but the inevitable loss of neutrons by formation of U^{236} is not great enough to stop the chain reaction if the other sources of loss are carefully minimized.

As we saw in Chapter 11 E, neutrons are slowed down most rapidly by collisions with light nuclei. The moderator is then some substance containing a high proportion of light nuclei whose neutron capture cross sections are very small. Heavy water, graphite (carbon), or beryllium are particularly suitable. The (n,γ) cross section of light hydrogen is 0.33 barns for thermal neutrons, which is too large to permit ordinary water to be used as the moderator in reactors fuelled with natural uranium. Light water can be used if the U^{235} content of the fuel is increased above the natural proportion.

The lumps of fuel must be sufficiently small to permit the fission neutrons to escape into the moderator before they have had an opportunity to undergo (n,γ) reaction with U^{239}. In practice, the problem of heat removal from the fuel often determines the maximum size of the fuel elements.

The distance between the elements must be great enough to permit the neutrons to be reduced in energy to below 1 ev before they have an appreciable probability of entering another fuel element. In the neutron energy range 5–200 ev, there are several large (n,γ) resonances in U^{238}, and neutrons in this energy range are very likely to be captured unproductively to produce U^{239}. The thermal neutrons (about 0.025 ev) are safely below this resonance capture region.

2. *Neutron Absorption in Structural Materials.* Neutrons will be absorbed, mainly in (n,γ) reactions, in the moderator and the structural materials of the reactor core. Uranium metal fuel elements must be covered with a protective layer, usually aluminum, to protect them from corrosion and to prevent the escape of radioactive fission products. A cooling fluid, usually ordinary water, must be passed over the fuel elements to remove the heat, and neutrons are necessarily lost by absorption in this coolant.

Some loss is inevitable, but it must be minimized by choosing structural materials with low (n,γ) cross sections. Particular care must be paid to purity; traces of elements with high (n,γ) cross sections, such as B^{10} and Cd^{113}, must be eliminated as well from the uranium fuel as from the structural materials and the moderator.

3. *Neutron Escape.* The third important source of neutron loss is by escape from the outer surface of the reactor. This loss may be reduced by surrounding the core of the reactor with pure graphite. Some escaping neutrons undergo elastic collisions with C^{12} nuclei which reflect them back into the reactor core.

Loss by escape, even with a reflector, is a function of the size of the core.   An infinitely large reactor, having no boundaries, would lose no neutrons in this way.   For any reactor design, there will be a certain critical size below which a value of k equal to unity cannot be obtained. Reactors, especially those containing a rather dilute fuel such as natural uranium, are therefore necessarily rather large in order to minimize the surface loss of neutrons.   For example, the natural uranium, heavy water moderated reactor at Chalk River, Ontario, contains about 10 tons of uranium and 17 tons of pure heavy water.   The necessary steel and concrete shielding required to protect employees against escaping neutrons and γ-rays makes the total diameter of this rather small reactor about 34 feet.   Graphite moderated reactors are even larger.

We can now consider the fate of the fission neutrons in a somewhat more quantitative manner.   Let ν be the average number of neutrons produced per fission of U^{235}; its value is 2.5.   Let η be the average number of neutrons produced per thermal neutron absorbed in the fuel (U^{235} + U^{238}).   Clearly, η will be less than ν, since some of the neutrons are absorbed in the fuel to produce nonfission reactions.   Then

$$\eta = \frac{\nu \sigma_f^{235}}{\sigma_f^{235} + \sigma_c^{235} + b\sigma_c^{238}} \tag{13.10}$$

where the σ_f and the σ_c's are the appropriate thermal neutron fission and capture cross sections, and b is the atomic ratio of U^{238}/U^{235}.   For U^{235} in natural uranium, $\eta = 1.3$.   If the U^{235} content of the fuel is higher than the natural mixture, then η will also be greater.

Some of the fission neutrons which are formed in the nth generation will be captured by U^{238} resonances before they ever reach the thermal range.   Let P be the probability that a neutron will *escape* resonance capture.   Clearly, the maximum value which k can achieve, even in a reactor of infinite size, is equal to $P\eta$. P depends on the diameter of the fuel elements and on the distance between them; it is equal to unity for elements of zero size.

$P\eta$ is the number of neutrons which arrive at thermal energies per neutron initially absorbed in the fuel.   However, some thermal neutrons are lost by absorption in the moderator, cooling fluid, or structural materials.   Let the fraction *not* lost in this way be f, which is called the thermal utilization factor.   Unfortunately, f varies with fuel element size and spacing in exactly the opposite way to P, so that a compromise must be made.   For natural uranium, heavy water moderated reactors, P and f may both be about 0.95.   The maximum value of k is $P\eta f$.

Some neutrons in the fission neutron spectrum are energetic enough to induce fission in U^{238}, which is of course a productive reaction. k will therefore in fact be slightly greater than $P\eta f$ by the factor ϵ, the fast fission factor, for which 1.03 is a typical value.

We now arrive at a value of k for an infinite reactor, given by

$$k_\infty = P\eta f\epsilon \tag{13.11}$$

With the values given above, k_∞ would be 1.21, which is more than sufficient to maintain the chain reaction. The reactor can therefore be made of less than infinite size, and some neutron-absorbing control rods can be inserted so that k can be raised and lowered at will.

For steady operation of the reactor, k must be kept precisely equal to unity, but it is not at all likely that this can be achieved in practice. All forms of control, whether human or automatic, operate by alternately raising and lowering the quantity to be controlled above and below the required value. Suppose that k momentarily becomes greater than unity. If the rate of increase in the number of neutrons were exceedingly fast, disaster would occur before the neutron-absorbing control rods could be inserted to reduce k. The rate of increase depends on the time lapse between successive generations. If this time is τ, then n, the number of neutrons at time t, will be

$$n = n_0 \; \exp \left[\frac{(k-1)t}{\tau} \right] \tag{13.12}$$

where n_0 is the number of neutrons at time zero. For $k = 1$, $n = n_0 =$ constant.

The time taken for slowing down and reabsorption of a neutron is only about 10^{-3} sec, but fortunately about 1% of the fission neutrons are delayed (see Chapter 10 D). k may therefore be divided into two parts, kd and $k(1 - d)$, where d is the fraction of the fission neutrons which are delayed. Provided that $k(1 - d)$, the part of k due to prompt neutrons, is less than unity, the rate of increase in the number of neutrons will be determined by equation (13.12) with $\tau = 0.1$ sec. (This value is an effective weighted average for the delayed neutron groups.) Thus the chain reaction will diverge slowly, and control will be easy. However, if $k(1 - d)$ ever exceeds unity, so that the reactor becomes divergent without waiting for the delayed neutrons, then the value $\tau = 10^{-3}$ sec must be used, and control is much more difficult.

Depending on their purpose, reactors may be operated at power levels ranging from practically zero up to hundreds of megawatts. The neutron fluxes range from 10^8 to about 10^{15} neutrons per cm^2 per sec. At the highest fluxes, the fuel is burned up very rapidly, and the levels of radioactivity induced inside the core are extremely high. Tubes are provided through which samples may be introduced through the shielding into the core of the reactor for bombardment with neutrons. In many reactors, the shielding on one side is replaced with blocks of graphite which filter out electrons and γ-rays, but allow slow neutrons to escape freely. In this way, intense beams of neutrons may be obtained for experiments outside the reactor.

G. Production of Transuranium Elements in Reactors

For the most part, reactors are operated for research purposes or for the production of Pu^{239} for use in nuclear weapons. Economical power production has not been achieved, although for certain purposes such as submarine propulsion, the advantages of nuclear power offset the additional cost of the power.

Capture of neutrons by U^{238} is responsible for the formation of the fissionable nuclide Pu^{239} by the following series of reactions:

$$U^{238}(n,\gamma)U^{239} \xrightarrow{\beta^-} Np^{239} \xrightarrow{\beta^-} Pu^{239}$$

Pu^{239} accumulates at the rate of about 1 gm per day per 1000 kw of reactor power. If the Pu^{239} is required for making weapons or as fuel in another reactor, the fuel elements may be removed, dissolved, and the Pu^{239} separated chemically from the uranium and the fission products. If the Pu^{239} is allowed to accumulate in the fuel elements, it partly compensates for the loss of reactivity due to the decrease in the U^{235} content of the fuel. Capture of neutrons by Pu^{239} produces heavier nuclides by the sequence of successive neutron captures and β^--decays shown in Table 13.1

The rate of production of the heavy nuclides increases very rapidly with the neutron flux of the reactor. With a neutron flux of 3×10^{14} neutrons per cm^2 per sec, microgram amounts of berkelium and californium isotopes can be produced from 1 gm of plutonium in about three years.

There seems to be little possibility of synthesizing nuclides heavier than Fm^{256} in this way. Fm^{256} decays by spontaneous fission with a half life of only 3 hours, so that there is very little chance that it will capture a neutron before it decays unless the neutron flux is much higher than anything yet proposed.

In fuel elements containing U^{238}, the reaction $U^{238}(n,2n)U^{237}$ is induced by fission neutrons in the high energy "tail" of the fission neutron spectrum. The sequence of reactions is shown in Table 13.2. Gram amounts of Np^{237} (α, 2.20×10^6 yr) have been extracted from fuel elements, permitting a detailed study of the chemical properties of this interesting element. Pu^{239} contains a small amount of Pu^{238} formed by the reactions shown in Table 13.2. Since the Pu^{239} is formed as a result of a single neutron capture whereas Pu^{238} is a two-stage product, the ratio

TABLE 13.1 Production of the Heavy Elements by Successive Neutron Captures and β^--Decays[a]

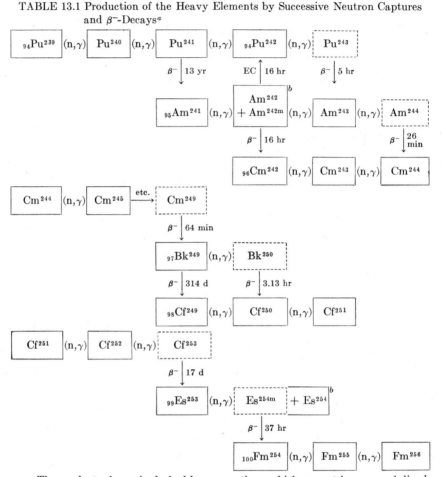

[a] The products shown in dashed boxes are those which are not long enough lived, or produced in sufficient yield, to be useful for chemical studies or as targets for further bombardments.

[b] Both Am²⁴² and Es²⁵⁴ exist in two isomeric forms. "m" denotes the higher energy member of the pair, or the shorter lived species if the energies are unknown.

TABLE 13.2. Synthesis of Np²³⁷ and Pu²³⁸ in Reactor Fuel Elements

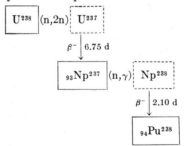

Pu^{238}/Pu^{239} increases as the first power of the total neutron flux which has passed through the fuel element.   Pure Pu^{238} can be prepared by thermal neutron bombardment of Np^{237}.   After decay of the Np^{238}, the plutonium is chemically separated from the neptunium.

REFERENCES

1. Livingston, M. S., "Particle Accelerators." *Advances in Electronics*, Vol. I, Academic Press, New York, 1948.

2. Segrè, E. (ed.), *Experimental Nuclear Physics*, John Wiley & Sons, New York, 1959: Vol. III/12, E. M. McMillan, "Particle Accelerators."

3. Livingston, M. S., *High Energy Accelerators*, Interscience, New York, 1954.

4. Livingston, M. S., and E. M. McMillan, "The History of the Cyclotron," *Physics Today*, **12,** No. 10 (Oct. 1959).

5. Niemenn, F. L., "Low Energy Particle Accelerators for Precision Nuclear Research," *Nuclear Instruments and Methods*, **7,** 338 (1960).

6. *Soviet Reviews of Nuclear Science on the 40th Anniversary of the Revolution*, Pergamon Press, London, 1959 (in English).

7. Lofgren, E. J., *Proc. Natl. Acad. Sci. U. S.*, **45,** 451 (1959), (Description of the University of California 6 Bev proton synchrotron.)

8. Flügge, S. (ed.), *Handbuch der Physik*, Vol. XLIV, *Instrumentelle Hilfsmitel der Kernphysik*, Julius Springer Verlag, Berlin, 1959.   Contains articles in English on various types of accelerators.

9. Lehr, G., *Atomwirtschaft*, **4,** 277 (1959).   (Tabulation of the principle accelerators of the world.)

10. Malmberg, C., *Abstract Bibliography on Linear Accelerators*, Los Alamos Scientific Laboratory Reports AECU 4009, 4010 and 4012, Los Alamos, N. M., 1958.

11. de Broglie, L. (ed.), *Les Accélérateurs de Particules*, Editions de la Revue d'Optique Théorique et Instrumentale, Paris, 1950.

12. Nahmias, M. E., *Le Cyclotron*, Editions de la Revue d'Optique Théorique et Instrumentale, Paris, 1945.

13. Nahmias, M. E., *Machines Atomiques*, Editions de la Revue d'Optique Théorique et Instrumentale, Paris, 1950.

14. Fretter, W. B., *Introduction to Experimental Physics*, Prentice-Hall, Inc., Englewood Cliffs, N. J., 1954.

15. Mann, W. B., *The Cyclotron*, Methuen and Co. Ltd., London, 1945.

16. Liverhant, S. E., *Elementary Introduction to Nuclear Reactor Physics*, John Wiley & Sons, New York, 1960.

17. Sordak, H., and E. C. Campbell, *Elementary Pile Theory*, John Wiley & Sons, New York, 1950.

18. Glasstone, S., and M. C. Edlund, *The Elements of Nuclear Reactor Theory*, D. Van Nostrand, New York, 1952.

19. Syrett, T. J., *Nuclear Reactor Theory*, Temple Press, London, 1958.

20. Glasstone, S., *Principles of Nuclear Reactor Engineering*, D. Van Nostrand, New York, 1955.

21. Hughes, D. J., *Pile Neutron Research*, Addison-Wesley Publishing Co., Cambridge, Mass., 1953.

PROBLEMS

1. Calculate the maximum energy that can be acquired by protons, deuterons, and helium ions in a cyclotron whose maximum radius is 25 inches, and whose frequency is 12 Mc per sec. What magnetic field would be required in each case?

2. Calculate the ratio of the highest to the lowest frequency required in a frequency modulated cyclotron which is capable of accelerating protons to 700 Mev.

3. Assuming no losses in friction, etc., calculate the power required to drive the belt of a Van de Graaff accelerator when the machine is accelerating 100 μamp of protons to an energy of 5 Mev.

4. Calculate the rate of consumption of U^{235} in a reactor operating at a power of 100,000 kw. How much natural uranium would be consumed per year, assuming that only 5% of its U^{235} content could be used before the fuel had to be removed from the reactor?

5. Calculate the equilibrium amount of Rb^{91} in the reactor of Problem 4 (in curies). Use the fractional chain yield given in Chapter 10.

6. What would be the maximum energy to which C^{12} ions with charge +4 could be accelerated in a 25 inch radius cyclotron whose maximum magnetic field is 17,500 gauss? What frequency would be required?

7. What would be the length of the last drift tube in a linear accelerator which produces 120 Mev C^{12} ions, using a frequency of 70 Mc per sec? What would be the energy of the O^{16} ions from this machine?

8. Using a fission neutron distribution of the $P(E) = Ee^{-E/T}$, with $T = 1.3$ Mev, calculate the fraction of the fission neutrons that are capable of inducing the reaction $U^{238}(n,2n)U^{237}$, whose threshold is 7 Mev.

9. Show that the remaining quantity of a nuclide exposed to a neutron flux of F neutrons per cm^2 per sec decreases exponentially with a law identical to radioactive decay, except that the decay constant λ is replaced by $F\sigma$, where σ is the total neutron cross section of the nuclide.

10. Calculate the atomic ratio of U^{236} to U^{235} in a sample of initially pure U^{235} after exposure to a flux of 10^{14} neutrons per cm^2 per sec for 10 days. Assume that none of the U^{236} is destroyed by further reactions with neutrons. *Hint:* The rate of disappearance of U^{235} is determined by its total cross section $\sigma_c + \sigma_f$.

CHAPTER 14

Magnetic Analyzing
Equipment

A. Introduction

The deflection of charged particles by means of electric and magnetic fields is extremely useful in a wide variety of applications. Particles of a given mass can be sorted out according to their velocity, and particles of a given velocity can be sorted out according to their mass. Beams of charged particles can be focused and bent in ways which strongly resemble the focusing and bending of beams of light by lenses and prisms. Although the applications of magnetic and electrostatic analysis cover a very wide field, there are sufficient basic similarities to justify their

inclusion in a single chapter.   We shall mainly discuss the use of magnetic fields, since they are more generally useful, but for every example
there exists an electrostatic analogue.   We start by discussing the bending and focusing of charged particle beams in uniform magnetic fields,
and then take up the subject of beam focusing by means of nonuniform
magnetic fields.

B. Deflection of Charged Particles in Magnetic Fields

The force acting on a particle of charge q moving with velocity v in a
magnetic field of strength B is

$$F = \frac{qvB}{c} \text{ dynes} \tag{14.1}$$

where q is in esu, B is in gauss, and v and c in cm per sec.   The direction
of the force is perpendicular both to the velocity and to the magnetic

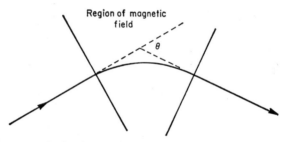

Fig. 14.1. Deflection of charged particles in a magnetic field

field direction (see Fig. 13.1).   In a uniform magnetic field, the path of
the particle is circular, and its radius r is

$$r = \frac{mcv}{qB} \text{ cm} \tag{14.2}$$

where m is the mass of the particle in grams.   Since r is a function both of
m and v, particles of the same mass and charge can be separated from each
other if their velocities are different, while particles of the same velocity
and charge can be separated if their masses are different.

Figure 14.1 shows the path of a charged particle through a magnetic
field. θ is the angle by which the direction of motion of the particle is
changed.   By differentiation of equation (14.2),

$$dr = \frac{c}{Bq} d(mv)$$

$$\therefore \quad \frac{dr}{r} = \frac{d(mv)}{mv} \tag{14.3}$$

The distance l traveled by the particle in the magnetic field is

$$l = r\theta$$

$$\therefore \quad dr = -\frac{l}{\theta^2}\,d\theta$$

$$\therefore \quad \frac{dr}{r} = -\frac{d\theta}{\theta}$$

Substituting this value of dr/r into equation (14.3) gives

$$-\frac{d\theta}{\theta} = \frac{d(mv)}{mv}$$

$$\therefore \quad d\theta = -\frac{\theta}{mv}\,d(mv) \qquad\qquad (14.4)$$

Equation (14.4) means that the difference $d\theta$ in deflection angle for two particles whose momenta differ by $d(mv)$ is proportional to this

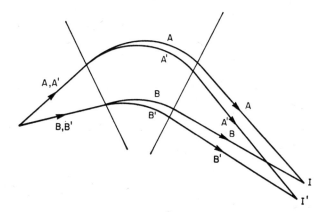

Fig. 14.2. Horizontal deflection and focusing of charged particles in a uniform magnetic field

momentum difference and to the total angle of deflection, θ. The quantity $d(mv)/mv$ is the momentum resolution of the magnet.

Besides giving momentum resolution, uniform field magnets also act in the first approximation as focusing lenses for charged particles. Consider four equally charged particles A, B, A′, and B′, all originating from the point source S of Figure 14.2 and all moving in the plane of the page, which is normal to the direction of the magnetic field. Let particles A and B have equal momenta, greater than the momenta of A′ and B′, which are also equal. Particle A travels further in the region of the magnetic field than particle B, and is therefore deflected through a greater angle, with the result that an image of the source is formed at some point I. Likewise, another image of the source is formed at the point I', such that all particles originating from S and moving in a plane parallel to the magnet pole faces (the horizontal plane), with momenta equal to the momentum of A′ and B′ will pass through the point I'.

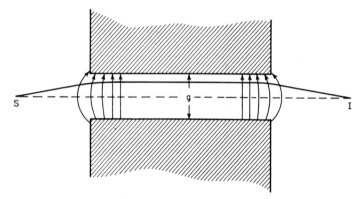

Fig 14.3a. Vertical focusing by the fringing field of a magnet

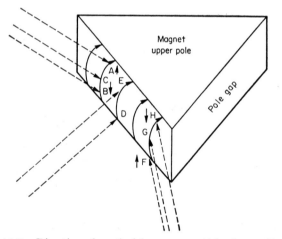

Fig. 14.3b. Direction of vertical forces on particles in a uniform magnetic field

However, particles leaving the source in a direction which is not in a plane parallel to the pole faces will not in general pass through I or I'.

Focusing does exist in the plane normal to the pole faces (the vertical plane), because of the fringing field illustrated in Figure 14.3 (a). The vertical focusing action does not depend on the details of the fringing field shape as long as the pole gap g is small compared with the radius of curvature of the particles. Figure 14.3 (b) shows the direction of the vertical force acting on positively charged particles moving from left to right.   The force is downwards on particles entering at B and H, upwards on particles entering at A and F, and zero for particles entering at D and E, normal to the field boundary.   It is also zero for all particles such as those at C and G which enter normal to the field lines.

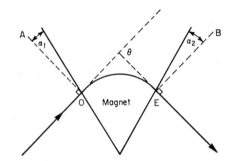

Fig. 14.4a. Definition of entry and exit angles α_1 and α_2.   As shown, α_1 and α_2 are taken as positive.   If OA and EB lie inside the magnet, the α's are taken as negative for use in Equation 14.5

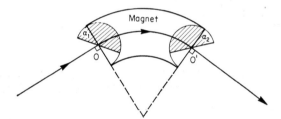

Fig. 14.4b. Magnet with variable entrance and exit angles.   The shaded portions of the upper and lower poles can be rotated about 0 and 0', thus changing the entrance and exit angles but leaving the path length and angle of deflection unchanged.   As shown, α_1 and α_2 negative

Wedge-shaped magnets such as those shown in Figures 14.1, 14.2, and 14.3 (b) thus behave like lenses, but there will in general be two focal lengths, one for the horizontal plane and another for the vertical plane. The magnitudes of these focal lengths are given by the following equations, in terms of the angles α_1, α_2, and θ defined in Figure 14.4 (a).   (In the equation for the vertical plane focal length, θ must be in radians, of course.)

$$f_{\text{horiz}} = r\{(\sin \theta)(1 - \tan \alpha_1 \tan \alpha_2) - (\cos \theta)(\tan \alpha_1 + \tan \alpha_2)\}^{-1}$$

$$f_{\text{vert}} = r\{(\tan \alpha_1 + \tan \alpha_2) - \theta \tan \alpha_1 \tan \alpha_2\}^{-1}$$

(14.5)

Here r is the radius of curvature of the trajectory, so that the focal lengths are functions of the momenta and charges of the particles. Notice that if the angles α_1 and α_2 are both zero (i.e., the particles enter and leave the field normal to its boundary), then

$$f_{\text{horiz}} = \frac{r}{(\sin \theta)}$$

$$f_{\text{vert}} = \infty$$

(14.6)

In this case, there is no vertical focusing action at all.

By suitable choice of the angles α_1 and α_2, it is possible to make the focal lengths in the two planes equal; the wedge magnet then acts as a combination of a spherical lens and a prism, and all particles of a given momentum originating from a point source are focused to a point whether or not they enter the magnet in a plane parallel to its pole faces. Figure 14.4 (b) shows a method by which α_1 and α_2 can be varied to control the focal lengths, while leaving θ unchanged.

If the focal lengths are long compared with the distance that the particles travel in the magnetic field, then the distance q of the image from the magnet is related to the distance p of the source by the familiar thin lens equation:

$$\frac{1}{p} + \frac{1}{q} = \frac{1}{f}$$

(14.7)

However, the thin lens criterion is not usually very well satisfied for magnets, so that thick lens calculations, entirely equivalent to those of geometrical optics, are usually required.

The position of the horizontal focus can rapidly be calculated by means of Cartan's construction, which is shown in Figure 14.5. Particles from the source slit S enter the magnet at A, describe a circular path whose center is C, and leave the magnet at B. Construct AD and BG to be perpendicular to the magnet faces. Draw FS perpendicular to AS. Join FC and continue this line to E, its point of intersection with BG. Drop a perpendicular from E to the line BH at I. The image of the slit S will be at I. To obtain the conditions for which the vertical and horizontal images coincide, reference should be made to a paper by W. G. Cross.*

Special cases of horizontal focusing are often used in various kinds of spectrometers and mass separators. Two of these are illustrated in Figures 14.6 (a) (60° instrument) and 14.6 (b) (180° instrument). Like optical devices, magnets suffer from aberrations, which are often corrected by making small adjustments in the shape of the pole faces. Many instruments use magnetic fields which are deliberately made non-uniform in order to obtain special deflecting and focusing properties.

* Cross, W. G., *Rev. Sci. Instr.*, **22**, 717 (1951).

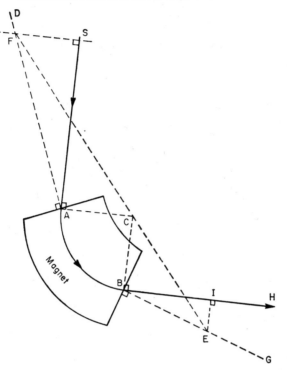

Fig. 14.5. Cartan's construction for finding the position of the image in the horizontal plane

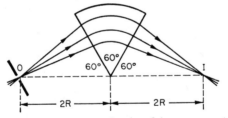

Fig. 14.6a. 60° sector magnet often used in mass spectrometers and α-particle spectrographs.   R is the radius of the particles' paths in the magnetic field

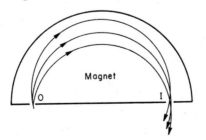

Fig. 14.6b. 180° magnet often in mass separators, α- and β-particle spectrographs

C. Deflection of Charged Particles in Electric Fields

The force exerted on a particle of charge q in an electric field of strength E is

$$F = Eq$$

In a constant uniform field, the particle will follow a circular path whose radius is given by

$$Eq = \frac{mv^2}{r} \qquad (14.8)$$

The usual form of electrostatic deflector is shown in Figure 14.7. The curved, parallel metal plates at a potential difference of V volts give a

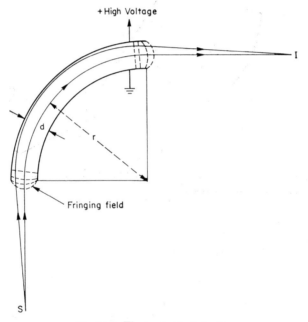

Fig. 14.7. Electrostatic deflector

field V/d volts per cm, where d is the distance between them in cm. Since the force exerted on the particle is everywhere parallel with the direction of the field, there is a fringing field focusing effect which is illustrated in Figure 14.7.

D. Mass Spectrometers and Separators

Deflection by electric and magnetic fields is the most useful and general method for the separation of isotopes. The purpose of the separation may be to measure the relative abundance, to measure precisely the atomic mass of each isotope, or to obtain samples of isotopic composition different from the natural element. Somewhat different machines are used in each case.

For abundance measurements, a 60° magnetic instrument is often used. The element to be analyzed is placed on a tungsten filament (by evaporation of a solution, usually) and the filament is then heated electrically to a temperature sufficient to evaporate the specimen slowly. Most of the material leaves the filament in the form of neutral atoms, which of course cannot be deflected. A higher yield of ions is obtained by allowing the stream of atoms to pass through a beam of electrons coming from a second filament. In some machines, the atoms fall on a second, much hotter filament from which they are immediately reevaporated with a much greater chance of being ionized. In this way, the temperature of the first filament can be chosen to give a convenient rate of evaporation, while the temperature of the second can be high enough to give a high ionization efficiency.

Ions obtained in this way will be moving with a Maxwellian distribution of kinetic energies. Some ions will therefore have velocities many times greater than others, so that ions of the same mass and charge will not all be deflected to the same extent in the magnetic field. This difficulty is overcome by accelerating the ions by means of a DC potential of a few kilovolts, which gives them all kinetic energies much greater than thermal energies. The initial differences in kinetic energy are then relatively much less important, so that ions of the same mass and charge will all be deflected to the same extent.

After analysis by the magnet, the ions are recorded in a variety of ways. They may pass through a slit which selects ions of a given mass, and then fall upon a metal plate connected to a sensitive electrometer which measures and records the ion current. By changing either the magnetic field or the DC accelerating potential, ions of different masses can be made to fall on the slit and the relative ion currents measure their relative abundances in the sample. Alternatively, the ions may pass through the slit and then fall on the first dynode of a photomultiplier tube which is built into the vacuum system of the mass analyzer. The arrival of individual ions can thus be detected and counted. By this method, samples as small as 10^{-10} gm may be analyzed. Figure 14.8 shows a two-stage magnetic analyzer which was built to give very good separation between adjacent mass numbers. Figure 14.9 shows the results of a analysis of ordinary lead with the same machine.

For precise mass measurements, special instruments with very large dispersion are required. In a machine built by A. O. Nier and his collaborators, the ions are deflected first through 90° by an electrostatic

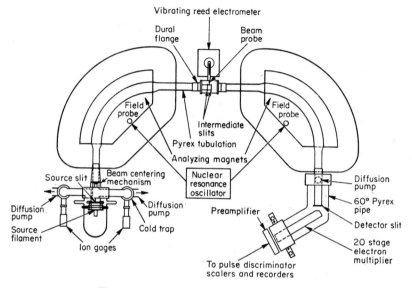

Fig. 14.8. Two-stage magnetic mass analyzer with two 90° 12 inch radius magnets and photomultiplier detection. F. A. White, T. L. Collins, and F. M. Rourke, *Phys. Rev.* **101**, 1786 (1956)

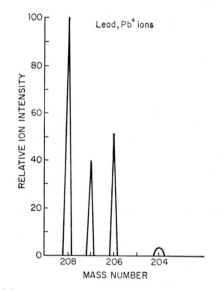

Fig. 14.9. Mass spectrum of lead made with the apparatus shown in Figure 14.8

analyzer and then through 60° in a magnetic field. By eliminating the velocity v between equations (14.2) and (14.8), we obtain

$$m = \frac{qB^2 r_m^2}{E c^2 r_e} \tag{14.9}$$

where r_m and r_e are the radii of curvature of the ion paths in the magnetic and electrostatic fields respectively. For fixed values of B and E, equation (14.9) will be satisfied for ions of a given mass *regardless of their velocity*. Hence no problems arise with dispersion due to the thermal distribution of kinetic energy of the ions leaving the ion source.

The dispersion of such an instrument is sufficient to permit complete separation of two ions of the same mass number but different exact atomic mass. Measurements are made by the method of doublets, in which the mass differences between pairs of ions of the same mass number are obtained. By a suitable choice of pairs, an unknown atomic mass can be referred directly to that of the chosen standard (C^{12}, or, in the past, O^{16}). Many of the doublets involve molecular ions such as C_4^+. These unstable species are produced in sufficient quantity by the ion source and last long enough to travel to the detector before decomposing. Some typical doublets and their mass differences are shown in Table 14.1.

TABLE 14.1. Some Doublet Mass Differences Giving the Relation Between the Atomic Masses of C^{12} and O^{16a}

Designation	Doublet	Mass difference, mMU[b]
a	$C_4^+ - SO^+$	33.0269
b	$O_2^+ - S^+$	17.7599
c	$(C_4H_4O)^{++} - H_2S^+$	25.3926

[a] After K. S. Quisenberry, T. T. Scholman, and A. O. Nier, *Phys. Rev.*, **102**, 1071 (1956).

[b] 1 mMU = 10^{-3} atomic mass units.

From these three doublets, the mass of O^{16} can be obtained in two ways, using $C^{12} = 12.000 \cdots$ as the standard substance:

or

$$O^{16} = 16 - \tfrac{1}{3}(a - b) \qquad \text{Result: } O^{16} = 15.9949110$$
$$O^{16} = 16 - \tfrac{2}{3}(c - b) \qquad \text{Result: } O^{16} = 15.9949115$$

(A more precise value for the mass of O^{16}, taking account of all the experimental results, is 15.99491494.)

In the first calculation above, the quantity $16 - \tfrac{1}{3}(a - b)$ can be written as follows in terms of the atomic masses M_O, M_C, and M_S of O^{16}, C^{12}, and S^{32}:

$$16 - \tfrac{1}{3}(a - b) = 16 - \tfrac{1}{3}(4M_C - M_S - M_O - 2M_O + M_S)$$

$$= 16 - \tfrac{4}{3}M_C + M_O$$

If M_C is taken as 12 by definition, then $\tfrac{4}{3}M_C$ equals 16, and the expression reduces to M_O as required.   If on the other hand, the mass of O^{16} is taken as 16 by definition, then the mass of C^{12} becomes, from the mass differences given above, $12 \times 16/15.9949112$, or 12.0038178.   (A more precise value, taking into account all the experimental results, is 12.00381501.)

Mass separators using magnetic deflection of ions through 180° are used at the Oak Ridge National Laboratory to produce separated isotopes of many elements in quantities as large as grams.   If the accelerating potential is V volts, then the velocity v of ions of mass m and charge q will be

$$v = \left(\frac{2Vq}{m}\right)^{1/2}$$

Substitution of this value into equation (14.2) gives

$$r = \frac{mc\left(\dfrac{2Vq}{m}\right)^{1/2}}{qB} = \frac{c\left(\dfrac{2Vm}{q}\right)^{1/2}}{B}$$

By differentiation,

$$dr = \frac{c\left(\dfrac{2V}{qm}\right)^{1/2}}{2B}\,dm$$

$$\therefore \quad \frac{dr}{r} = \frac{dm}{2m}$$

In a 180° instrument such as that shown in Figure 14.6 (b), the distance ds between two particles whose radii differ by dr will be just $2\,dr$.   Hence

$$ds = r\,\frac{dm}{m} \qquad (14.10)$$

Hence if the radius of the instrument is 1 meter, ions differing in mass by 1% will arrive at the collector 1 cm apart.   Pockets are placed in the proper positions to collect the separated isotopes, which are finally scraped or dissolved from the pockets.

In most neutron and charged particle bombardments, several different radioactive products are formed simultaneously, and the problem of identifying the radiations can become very difficult.   Small mass separators capable of handling milligram amounts of material and giving yields of about 1% are therefore more and more used in the preparation of monoisotopic sources for decay scheme studies. They do not differ in principle from the instruments described above.

E. Electron and α-Particle Spectrographs

Magnetic deflection instruments like those described above are used for the study of β-particle, conversion electron, and α-particle spectra. The magnetic fields required to deflect electrons are much smaller than those required in α-particle investigations, and it is possible to use 180° instruments with permanent magnets of only a few hundred gauss. Figure 14.10 shows a conversion electron spectrum obtained with such an instrument. In electron spectrographs, a momentum resolution of about 0.1% can be obtained, but the transmission of the instrument is then necessarily low (i.e., only a small fraction, perhaps 0.1%, of the

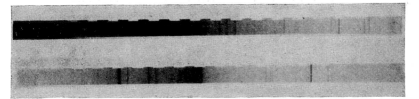

Fig. 14.10. Conversion electron spectra of Bi^{203} (upper) and U^{237} (lower), obtained with 180° permanent magnet spectrograph. J. M. Hollander, private communication

electrons leaving the source actually reach the detector). In α-particle instruments, line widths as low as 1.2 kev have been obtained, again with low transmission.

The study of the low energy end of β-ray spectra is complicated by the presence of electrons which were initially emitted by the source in the direction of the plate on which the source is mounted, and then scattered back in the direction of the analyzer. Unwanted electrons can also scatter from surfaces inside the vacuum chamber of the analyzer and finally arrive at the detector. These problems are reduced by making very thin sources on backings of very thin plastic films, so that there is little material behind the source to cause backscattering. Scattering inside the analyzer is reduced by means of baffles which stop electrons unless they are following a normal flight path from source to detector. These problems are much less severe in α-particle instruments, but the sources must be thin if high energy resolution is required, to avoid energy loss by particles as they travel through the source material on their way to the analyzing system. Some methods for preparing thin sources are described in Chapter 15.

Electron spectra are often studied with instruments using axial magnetic fields generated by means of solenoid coils.   The path of an electron in such a field is shown in Figure 14.11, where it is wrapped around a fictitious rod to show its spiral nature.   If the electron starts from a point S on the axis of the magnetic field, it will periodically return to that axis, for example at the point D.   It can be shown that all the electrons of a given momentum, leaving the source at a fixed angle, will pass through the annular ring baffle R and return to the axis at the same point

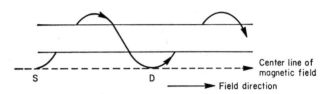

Fig. 14.11. Spiral path of electron in axial magnetic field

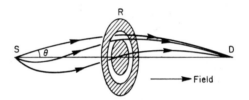

Fig. 14.12. Path of electrons from source S through ring baffle R to detector D, in an axial magnetic field

D, as shown in Figure 14.12.   A detector such as a scintillator–photomultiplier combination or a Geiger counter can be placed at D, and electrons of different momenta can then be counted as the magnetic field is changed.

Instruments of the axial type have higher transmissions (e.g., 8%) than transverse deflection instruments, but they are not capable of such high momentum resolution.

F. Quadrupole Focusing Lenses

A magnetic field originating from the quadrupole arrangement shown in cross section in Figure 14.13 can be used as a lens for focusing charged particle beams without deflecting them.   The quadrupole lens consists of four poles and coils, the poles being alternately north and south.   The magnetic field is zero along the central axis, and increases linearly with distance from the axis in both the x and y directions.   This result is obtained by making the pole pieces hyperbolic in cross section.   In the magnet shown in Figure 14.13, a positively charged particle displaced from the z axis in the $\pm x$ direction feels a force *away* from the axis, but a particle displaced in the $\pm y$ direction feels a force *towards* the axis.   The magnet therefore acts as a focusing lens in the yz plane, but as a defocusing lens in the xz plane.

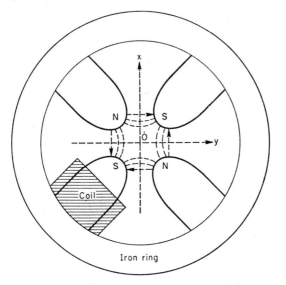

Fig. 14.13. Cross section of quadrupole magnet.   Only one of the four coils is shown

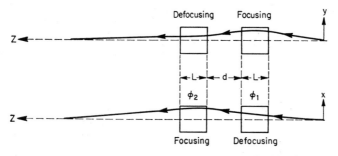

Fig. 14.14. Path of particle through quadrupole doublet in y-z plane (upper) and x-z plane (lower)

If a beam of particles is allowed to pass through two quadrupole lenses, (a doublet), which are rotated with respect to each other so that the defocusing plane of the first lens becomes the focusing plane of the second, then the beam can be focused in both planes rather like a beam of light in a spherical lens.   The trajectory of a particle in the two planes is shown in Figure 14.14.

The focal length of a quadrupole lens depends on the length L of the magnet, the rate of change of the magnetic field with displacement from the axis, dB/dx, the momentum p of the particles, and their charge q. It is convenient to express focal lengths in terms of the parameter ϕ, defined as follows:

$$\phi = L \left[\frac{q\left(\frac{dB}{dx}\right)}{pc} \right]^{1/2}$$

In the plane in which the first lens of the doublet is converging (the yz plane of Fig. 14.14), the focal length f_y is

$$f_y = L \left\{ \frac{d}{L} \phi_1\phi_2 \sin \phi_1 \sinh \phi_2 + \phi_1 \sin \phi_1 \cosh \phi_2 - \phi_2 \cos \phi_1 \sinh \phi_2 \right\}^{-1}$$

$$(14.11)$$

In the other plane (first lens diverging), the focal length f_x is

$$f_x = L \left\{ \frac{d}{L} \phi_1\phi_2 \sin \phi_2 \sinh \phi_1 + \phi_2 \sin \phi_2 \cosh \phi_1 - \phi_1 \cos \phi_2 \sinh \phi_1 \right\}^{-1}$$

$$(14.12)$$

In the above equations, d is the distance between the two halves of the doublet. The focal lengths can be changed simply by changing the current in the coils, which alters dB/dx, and hence ϕ_1 and ϕ_2.

If a beam of particles originates from a source at a distance p from the lens doublet, then an image will be formed at a distance q from the doublet, where p, q, and f are related by equation (14.7) if p, q, and f are large compared with L and d (the thin lens approximation). The image will appear at the same distance q in both planes only when the focal lengths f_x and f_y are equal. The linear magnification of the image, as for an optical lens, is

$$M = \frac{q}{p} = \frac{\text{(Linear size of image)}}{\text{(Linear size of source)}} \qquad (14.13)$$

Calculations with quadrupole lenses are greatly facilitated by the use of graphs published by H. A. Enge.*

By the use of quadrupole lenses, beams of charged particles may be made to travel long distances through evacuated pipes without loss. Their use as the focusing elements in linear accelerators was mentioned in Chapter 13.

* Enge, H. A., Rev. Sci. Instr., **30**, 248 (1959).

REFERENCES

1. Segrè, E. (ed.), *Experimental Nuclear Physics*, John Wiley & Sons, New York: Vol. I/5 (motion of charged particles in uniform fields), Vol. III/9 (α-particle spectrographs), Vol. III/11 (electron spectrometers).

2. Flügge, S. (ed.), *Handbuch der Physik*, Vol. XXXIII, Julius Springer Verlag, Berlin, 1956: H. Ewald, "Massenspektroskopische Apparate"; T. R. Gerholm, "Beta-Ray Spectroscopes"; W. Glaser, "Elektronen- und Ionenoptik."

3. Aston, F. W., *Mass Spectra and Isotopes*, Edward Arnold and Co., Ltd., London, 1942.

4. Inghram, M. G., "Modern Mass Spectroscopy," *Advances in Electronics*, Vol. 1, Academic Press, New York, 1948.

5. Barnard, G. P., *Modern Mass Spectrometry*, Institute of Physics, London, 1953.

6. Siegbahn, K. (ed.), *Beta- and Gamma-Ray Spectroscopy*, (ed.), North Holland Publishing Co., Amsterdam, 1955.

7. Koch, J. (ed.), *Electromagnetic Isotope Separators and Applications of Electromagnetically Enriched Isotopes*, North Holland Publishing Co., Amsterdam, 1958 (Articles by R. H. M. V. Dowton, M. L. Smith, and W. Walcher).

8. Duckworth, H. E., *Mass Spectroscopy*, Cambridge University Press, Cambridge, 1958.

9. Smith, M. L., "Electromagnetic Enrichment of Stable Isotopes," *Progress in Nuclear Physics*, Vol. 6, Pergamon Press, London, 1957.

10. Inghram, M. G., and R. J. Hayden, *A Handbook on Mass Spectroscopy*, Nuclear Science Series Report No. 14, National Academy of Sciences–National Research Council, Washington D. C., 1954.

11. Hintenberger, H. (ed.), *Nuclear Masses and Their Determination*, Pergamon Press, London, 1957.

PROBLEMS

1. Verify, by Cartan's construction, the focusing conditions for the 60° wedge magnet shown in Figure 14.6 (a).

2. Calculate the horizontal and vertical focal lengths of the magnet shown in Figure 14.4 (a) for particles whose radius of curvature is 20 cm, given $\theta = 90°$ and $\alpha_1 = \alpha_2 = 30°$. Verify the horizontal focal length by means of Cartan's construction by placing the source a long way from the magnet compared with 20 cm. Find the image position and then use equation (14.7). The result is only approximate, since the thin lens assumption is not accurate.

3. Three thin conducting plates 100 cm long are placed parallel to each other with a gap of 3 cm between each pair. A narrow beam of 48 Mev $(He^4)^{2+}$ ions falls upon one end of the center plate. The beam moves in the direction of the long (100 cm) dimension of the three plates. By making the potential of the center plate $+50,000$ volts with respect to the two outer plates, the beam is split into two beams. Calculate the separation between the two beams at the far end of the plates.

4. A quadrupole doublet consists of two elements each 20 cm long, and 20 cm apart. The field gradient dB/dx is 2000 gauss per cm. Calculate the focal lengths for 12 Mev protons. Where will be the image of a source which is 10 meters from the magnet?

5. Given the following mass doublets, calculate the atomic mass of O^{16} relative to $C^{12} = 12$:

$$C_3^+ - A^{36+} \qquad 32.4729 \text{ mMU}$$
$$CH_4^+ - O^+ \qquad 36.3933$$
$$H_2O^+ - A^{36++} \qquad 26.7937$$

6. Calculate the potential difference between two charged plates 5 cm apart which can deflect 2 Mev deuterons in a path of radius 15 cm. What is the magnetic field strength which would give the same radius?

7. Satisfy yourself by means of the left-hand rule, or otherwise, that a quadrupole magnet provides a focusing action in one plane and a defocusing action in the other.

CHAPTER 15

Chemical Techniques

A. Introduction

Chemical operations are often essential for the successful prosecution of nuclear experiments. Targets must be prepared in suitable form for bombardment, and the new nuclei thus formed must often be subjected to chemical separations to separate one element from another. As a final step, it is often necessary to prepare very thin and uniform deposits of radioactive material so that the emitted particles suffer the minimum energy loss in leaving the source.

Chemical techniques have been developed which permit quantities of material as small as a single atom to be separated from other elements. These small quantities of material are normally handled in solutions whose volumes are typically a few tenths of a cubic centimeter, which is a very convenient quantity. In these solutions, of course, the concentration of the material of interest may be fantastically low. Quantities as small as a few tenths of a microgram can also be handled in "normal" concentrations, or even in solid form, by the use of microchemical techniques. However, great personal skill and some specialized equipment are required. Although there are no differences in principle between the chemical methods used in handling radioactive materials and those used in ordinary chemical work, there are nevertheless certain techniques which have been found most useful in nuclear work. The following discussion will be limited just to those techniques.

B. Coprecipitation Methods

Ions can be selectively removed from a solution by causing the formation in the solution of a precipitate, called a *carrier*. For example, a precipitate of lanthanum fluoride, LaF_3, formed by addition of a milligram or two of a soluble lanthanum salt followed by hydrofluoric acid, will remove from the solution all the rare earth ions and many heavy element ions, even though they may be present in extremely low concentrations. Elements whose fluorides are soluble will remain in the solution. A few milligrams of the carrier precipitate per milliliter of solution is normally sufficient to obtain a high yield of the carried ions.

Three types of carrier precipitates can be distinguished. In the first, the carrier ions are isotopic with the ions carried. For example, copper ions formed in a bombardment could be selectively removed from solution by formation of a copper sulfide carrier precipitate by addition first of ordinary copper ions and then of H_2S. As the copper ions enter the sulfide crystal lattice, no distinction is made between the radioactive species and the added copper carrier ions, provided that they both exist in solution in the same chemical form. The fraction of the radioactive ions entering the precipitate will therefore be equal to the fraction of the added copper which precipitates, and this should be well over 99% of the total. An isotopic carrier precipitate is sure to carry the radioactive ion in good yield provided that the carrier ion itself is nearly completely precipitated, and provided that the carrier and carried ions exist in the solution in the same chemical state. The latter requirement is usually, but not always, easy to satisfy.

Even if the trace ion is present in the form of a complex ion, there will usually be sufficient dissociation of the complex to give complete interchange between the carrier and carried ions. In a few cases, however, difficulties arise. For example, a trace amount of uranium present in solution as the ion UO_2^{++} would not be coprecipitated with the insoluble fluoride UF_4, containing the ion U^{4+}. Elements with multiple oxidation states such as iodine and sulfur are most likely to be troublesome. The most difficult of all the elements is probably ruthenium, which not only has several oxidation states but also forms many complex ions which are so stable that they often fail to exchange their ruthenium with the added carrier ruthenium.   In most cases, strong oxidation or reduction will put the carrier and carried ions into the same oxidation state.   For example, a precipitate of $BaCrO_4$ would not carry chromium ions present as Cr^{3+}, but in the presence of a strong oxidizing agent, there would be hardly any Cr^{3+} because this ion would be oxidized to CrO_4^{--} which would coprecipitate very completely.

The disadvantage of adding an isotopic carrier is that the radioactive species cannot subsequently be chemically separated from the carrier. If a thin, virtually weightless deposit is finally required for counting, the use of isotopic carriers must clearly be avoided.   Fortunately, an ion will coprecipitate very completely as long as it forms an insoluble compound which is isomorphous with the carrier precipitate.   Thus LaF_3 can be used as a carrier for *all* the rare earth ions.   Other rare earth ions, in minor amount at least, can enter the LaF_3 lattice as the precipitate forms, and substitute for La^{3+} ions with very little strain.   The carried ions can then be subsequently separated from the lanthanum if necessary.

It is not always necessary that the carrier and carried ions form isomorphous compounds.   Often the coprecipitation will work very well if the carried and carrier ions both form insoluble compounds with the added anion.   Thus a precipitate of CaF_2 works quite well as a carrier for rare earth and heavy metal ions whose fluorides are insoluble but not isomorphous with CaF_2.   This type of coprecipitation has some of the characteristics of adsorption; it is most likely to succeed when the precipitates are gelatinous solids with large surface areas.   The very gelatinous hydroxide $Fe(OH)_3$, for example, is an excellent carrier for all the many metal ions whose hydroxides are insoluble.

To obtain high yields in coprecipitations, the order of addition of the reagents is important.   For example, to carry Zr^{4+} on a precipitate of $Fe(OH)_3$, the Fe^{3+} ion must be added first to an acidic solution containing the Zr^{4+}, and well mixed.   The reagent providing the OH^- ions (ammonium hydroxide or an alkali metal hydroxide) is then added.   Thus the carried ion is in the closest possible proximity to the carrier ions as the latter enter the solid phase, which gives it the best possible chance of going with them.

If, however, the order of addition is reversed, the result may be disappointing.   In the example given above, even if the Zr^{4+} ions did not partially precipitate on the addition of ammonia, they would immediately hydrolyze to give species such as $Zr(OH)_3^+$ which very readily attach themselves to any surfaces which happen to be present, such as the sides of the test tube.   Addition of Fe^{3+} to the already alkaline solution immediately produces a precipitate of $Fe(OH)_3$, but only in the immediate vicinity of the drops of added Fe^{3+} solution and not uniformly throughout the solution. Thus some of the Zr^{4+} ions may well fail to be carried, because they were never near any Fe^{3+} ions at the moment that these were entering the solid phase. Other Zr^{4+} ions are lost by surface adsorption on the walls of the vessel.

Occasionally, though, it is necessary to carry out a coprecipitation in the wrong order (so-called *preformed precipitation*). Satisfactory results can be obtained in many cases. In the example used above, the Fe^{3+} solution should be added very slowly with good stirring so that all parts of the Zr^{4+} solution have an opportunity to be close to Fe^{3+} ions in the act of precipitation. The solution and precipitate should then be heated and stirred for a few minutes to permit a slow adsorption of Zr^{4+} on to the surface of the precipitate.

The final step in a coprecipitation procedure is to separate the solid and liquid phases, preferably by centrifugation or filtration. The precipitate can then be washed to remove the remaining traces of unwanted unprecipitated ions. The washing solution should contain a trace of the precipitating reagent—ammonia, in the case of $Fe(OH)_3$—to prevent it from redissolving or peptizing.

Some precipitates, especially the gelatinous types, adsorb small quantities of almost all ions, even those which, according to the rules presented above, would not be expected to coprecipitate. Some of the unwanted ions can usually be removed by washing the precipitate, but the rest cannot. If the precipitate is redissolved and reprecipitated, much greater purity can be obtained. Thus $Fe(OH)_3$ should carry 99–100% of the La^{3+} present in a solution, but it might also carry 10^{-2}% of any Ba^{++}. If the object of the precipitation is to obtain a sample of an isotope of lanthanum as free as possible from barium, the $Fe(OH)_3$ should be dissolved in a small quantity of acid and then reprecipitated by the addition of a base. If the fraction of the Ba^{++} carried down is again 10^{-2}%, then the two precipitations will have resulted in an increase in the ratio of La^{3+} to Ba^{++} by a factor of 10^8.

In nuclear experiments, it is usually the degree of separation of wanted from unwanted radioactive species which is important rather than the absolute chemical purity. Thus it might not matter if, in the example above, the La^{3+} contained some Ba^{++} as long as were not a radioactive isotope of barium. Coprecipitation of unwanted radioactive species can sometimes be reduced by diluting them with stable isotopes of the same element. If a given precipitate is capable of carrying only a certain fixed quantity of an unwanted ion before it becomes "saturated," then addition of inactive ions ("holdback carriers"), will help. If, however, there is no saturation, and a constant fraction of the impurity ions is carried, then holdback carriers are no help.   In practice, carrying of impurities is often somewhere between constant in amount and constant in fraction, so that the wisest procedure is to add a holdback carrier *and* to repeat the precipitation.

C. Ion Exchange

Ion exchange substances are insoluble solids with acidic or basic properties, capable of forming loosely bound compounds with cations or anions respectively.   Those which are most widely used in the separations of small amounts of materials consist of an organic matrix produced by the polymerization of a mixture of styrene and vinyl benzene.   The acidic properties of a cation exchange resin such as Dowex-50 (Dow Chemical Company) or IR-120 (Rohm and Haas Company) are due to the presence in the matrix of sulfonic acid groups, $—SO_3H$.   Anion exchange resins such as Dowex-1 or Amberlite IRA-400 (Rohm and Haas Company) obtain their properties from the presence in the matrix of basic quaternary ammonium groups.

If a few beads of a cation exchange resin in the hydrogen ion form are placed in a solution containing, for example, sodium ions, the following reaction occurs:

$$R—SO_3^- \cdots H^+ + Na^+ \rightleftharpoons R—SO_3^- \cdots Na^+ + H^+$$

$R—$ represents the organic matrix of the resin.   The dotted lines represent the forces which hold the cations H^+ or Na^+ in the resin phase.

An equilibrium constant K_1 can be written for the reaction given above:

$$K_1 = \frac{[R—SO_3^- \cdots Na^+][H^+]_a}{[R—SO_3^- \cdots H^+][Na^+]_a} \tag{15.1}$$

where $[R—SO_3^- \cdots Na^+]$ represents the concentration of Na^+ in the resin phase and $[H^+]_a$ and $[Na^+]_a$ are the concentrations of H^+ and Na^+ in the solution phase.   (More properly, thermodynamic activities should be used rather than concentrations.)

If the solution contains several species of ions, there will be an equilibrium equation similar to (15.1) for each of them, and it is found that the equilibrium constants are nearly always different.   In other words, ions are removed from the solution phase into the resin to different extents, and thus chemical separations can be obtained.   However, the differences in equilibrium constants are often very small, so that to obtain a complete separation, the equilibration must be repeated perhaps several thousands of times.

Fortunately, this result can be achieved very simply by the use of a small tube filled with the ion exchange resin. For the separation of trace amounts of material, the column of resin (in the form of tiny spherical beads) need be only a few millimeters in diameter and a few centimeters in length. A solution of the ions to be separated is allowed to flow slowly into the resin bed from the top so that the ions are completely absorbed in a very narrow band of resin. The ions are then slowly washed down through the column (eluted) by a slow current of some solution which partially reverses the equilibrium, so that a given ion spends part of its time fixed in the resin bed and part of its time moving downward with the solution. If the equilibria are even slightly different for two species of ions, then the species which is less strongly absorbed by the resin will move more rapidly and will therefore appear first in the drops of solution falling from the bottom of the column.

This method is widely used for the separation of the actinide and lanthanide elements, whose chemical properties are so similar that the ion exchange column is the most practical method. The eluant solution in this case contains some organic anion which forms complexes with the ions to be separated; the α-hydroxyisobutyrate ion is particularly successful. The equilibrium between the actinide ion Cm^{3+} and the eluant anion is of the following type:

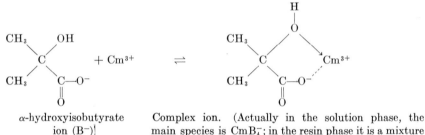

α-hydroxyisobutyrate ion (B⁻)

Complex ion. (Actually in the solution phase, the main species is CmB_4^-; in the resin phase it is a mixture of CmB^{++} and CmB_2^+.)

Reduction of the Cm^{3+} concentration in the solution phase as a result of the formation of the complex ions reverses the absorption of Cm^{3+} in the resin phase to an extent which can be controlled by adjusting the α-hydroxyisobutyrate ion concentration. (This can be done easily by controlling the pH of the eluant solution, since α-hydroxyisobutyric acid is quite a weak acid.) Passage through a column 5 cm in length, 3 mm in diameter, at a flow rate of about 0.01–0.03 ml per min gives a separation of Cm^{3+} from the adjacent actinide elements Bk^{3+} and Am^{3+} which is virtually complete; it is equivalent to about 500 individual fractionizations. As shown in Figure 15.1, the heaviest elements within the actinide group are the first to appear at the bottom of the column. The same phenomenon is observed within the lanthanide element group.

The equilibria between anion exchange resins and anions in solution

can be described in exactly the same way. The most important applications have been to the separation of cationic elements by first converting them into anionic complex ions, usually chloride complexes. For
example, a complete separation of Fe^{3+}, Co^{3+}, and Ni^{++} can be made in
a few minutes by the use of a column of Dowex-1 anion exchange resin.
The mixture of ions in $8M$ hydrochloric acid is poured into the top of the
resin bed. Fe^{3+} and Co^{3+} form negatively charged anion complex ions
of the type $FeCl_6^{3-}$. Ni^{++} remains cationic and so is not absorbed by

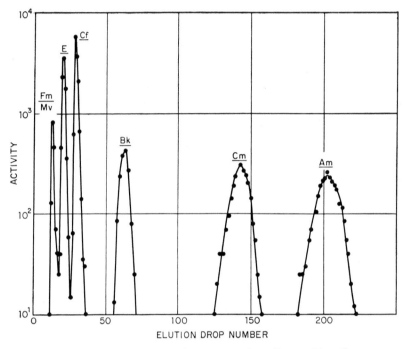

Fig. 15.1. Elution of actinide elements from Dowex-50 cation
resin column by ammonium α-hydroxyisobutyrate

the resin. It can therefore be removed completely by passing a small
amount of $8M$ hydrochloric acid through the column. After the last
trace of Ni^{++} has been washed away and collected, the Co^{3+} can be
removed by changing to $3M$ hydrochloric acid, in which the chloride ion
concentration is high enough to keep the Fe^{3+} in the anionic complex
form, but not the Co^{3+}. Finally, after collection of all the Co^{3+}, the
Fe^{3+} can be removed by washing the resin bed with very dilute hydrochloric acid (about $0.1M$).

By suitable choice of cation and anion exchange columns, virtually
any mixture of elements can be separated quite rapidly. No carriers are

required, and the columns work even with the lowest concentrations of the ions (in fact they give in most cases better separations when the concentrations are very low). Figure 15.2 shows the volume of hydrochloric acid required to wash various elements through a small anion exchange resin column, as a function of the concentration of the acid. The figures

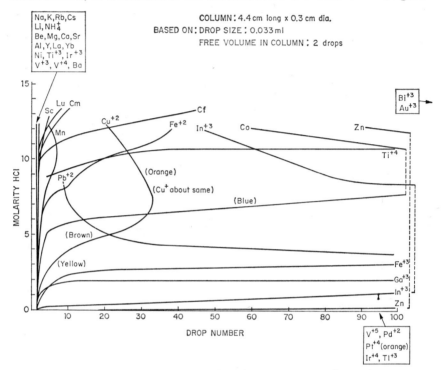

Fig. 15.2. Elution of various ions from Dowex-1 anion resin column by hydrochloric acid. A. Chetham-Strode, private communication

are only approximate, but they serve as a useful guide in planning separations. Further information has been published by Kraus, Moore, and Nelson* and by Kraus and Nelson.†

D. Solvent Extraction

Although not as general a method as ion exchange and coprecipitation, solvent extraction sometimes permits very rapid and complete chemical separations to be made. It operates by the selective extraction of some

* Kraus, K. A., G. E. Moore and F. Nelson, *J. Am. Chem. Soc.*, **78**, 2692 (1956).
† Kraus, K. A., and F. Nelson, *Proceedings of the First United Nations Conference on the Peaceful Uses of Atomic Energy*, Vol. 7, United Nations, Geneva, 1955.

compounds from (usually) an aqueous solution into an immiscible organic solvent. The extraction of iodine (as I_2) from aqueous potassium iodide solution into carbon tetrachloride provides a very well-known example.

Ionic compounds are not soluble in covalent organic liquids; the solvent extraction of metallic ions therefore requires the presence of some substance which converts them into neutral soluble complexes. The use of organic complexing agents such as 8-hydroxyquinoline for this purpose is very well known in analytical chemistry, and will not be further discussed here. In some cases, chloride complexes can be extracted. For example, the ferric ion can be removed very completely from $7M$ hydrochloric acid solution by agitation with diethyl or diisopropyl ether. However, several other elements, especially Ga, Au, and As, are also extracted. In principle, it is possible by the use of packed countercurrent columns, to turn small differences in extraction behavior into excellent separations as in the case of ion exchange. In practice, however, such methods are not often used for the separation of small quantities of material because of the complexity of the equipment required.

Solvent extraction is particularly useful where substantial quantities of material are involved. For example, several grams of iron or gold can readily be extracted from HCl solution with ether. To achieve the same result by ion exchange would require an inconveniently large column of anion resin. Solvent extraction is used for the separation of uranium and plutonium from fission products in reactor fuel elements. The fuel elements are dissolved in nitric acid, from which uranium in its 6+ oxidation state (the ion UO_2^{++}) and plutonium in its 4+ oxidation state can be extracted by a variety of solvents. One of the most widely used is tributyl phosphate diluted with an inert solvent such as kerosene. The metal ions form neutral molecules containing the nitrate group and the tributyl phosphate molecule.

On a big scale, the extraction can be done in counterflow packed columns and the process is continuous. The plutonium is recovered from the solvent phase by washing the latter with an aqueous phase containing a reducing agent such as Fe^{++}. The Pu^{3+} thus produced is not appreciably soluble in the organic phase. Finally, the uranium can be recovered by washing the organic phase with water.

E. Thin Source Preparation Methods

Following a chemical separation, the final step is usually the preparation of a source for counting or for radiation measurement in some type of spectrometer. Frequently the requirements of the experiment are such that the source must be extremely thin.

Sources prepared by evaporation of aqueous solutions on the surfaces of metal, glass, or plastic plates are often disappointingly thick, even when the deposit of material is almost invisible. All the involatile components of the solution are naturally present, and even if the desired radioactive component is present in trace quantity, it is not easy to avoid contamination with microgram amounts of such common elements as Na, Ca, Fe, Mg, and Si, which dissolve from glassware or float around as specks of dust. Further, very nonuniform deposits are obtained by the evaporation of aqueous solutions, so that even if the total mass of material is quite small, it may all be piled up into a very small area. If metal plates are used, they must clearly be very little attacked by the solution, and for this reason platinum or gold are often chosen. If the source material is itself involatile, the metal source disks should be heated to redness after the evaporation of the solution, to drive off unwanted volatile materials such as water of hydration or ammonium salts, and to burn away organic materials.

Thinner and more uniform deposits may be obtained by adding to the solution a spreading agent which helps to keep the liquid spread uniformly over the surface of the plate during the evaporation. For β-particle sources mounted on thin plastic films (to minimize backscattering), insulin is sometimes used. Obviously, the spreading agent should not add appreciably to the mass of material on the source.

If nonaqueous solutions can be used, much more uniform sources can sometimes be made. For example, the nitrates of several elements, notably Ce, Th, U, Np, and Pu are soluble in amyl acetate, and the solutions spread on clean metal plates much more uniformly than aqueous solutions. A small amount of cellulose acetate is usually added so that it forms a thin adhering layer when the solvent evaporates. Heating to redness in air then burns off the cellulose acetate and converts the metal nitrate to oxide, which adheres tenaciously to the surface of the backing plate. Layers of any desired thickness up to about 1 mg/cm^2 can be built up by repeating the procedure as many times as required.

Almost any element can be evaporated *in vacuo* from a hot tungsten or tantalum filament. Very thin and uniform deposits are obtained by condensation of the evaporating material on to a support, which can even be a thin plastic film. There is inevitably some loss of material in this procedure, since the hot filament tends to emit in all directions. By shaping the filament as shown in Figure 15.3, a fairly well-directed beam of vaporizing material can be obtained.

The solution of the source material must be purified as carefully as possible, and then the desired quantity evaporated to dryness on the surface of the filament. The loaded filament is then placed in the vacuum system and electrically heated to a temperature just below the evaporation temperature of the source material, which must be found in a separate investigation. In this way, many volatile impurities can be eliminated. The source backing plate is then swung into place over the filament, and the temperature of the latter is raised to the minimum required to evaporate the source material in a reasonable time (e.g., one minute).

Excellent thin and uniform deposits can often be produced by electrodeposition. If the source material is a metallic element such as nickel or copper, which readily form adherent deposits, then conventional electroplating methods may be used, although it may not always be possible to deposit 100% of the material present in a solution.

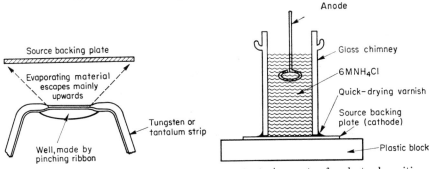

Fig. 15.3. Directional filament for evaporation of small quantities of material

Fig. 15.4. Apparatus for electrodeposition of insoluble hydroxides. The bottom end of the glass chimney is ground flat to ensure a good seal. Rubber bands around the "ears" and the block hold the assembly together

If the source material is one of the many elements with a highly insoluble hydroxide, a different method is available. The material is dissolved in a $6M$ ammonium chloride solution whose pH is about 1. The source backing plate (which must be a noncorroding metal such as platinum or gold) is made the cathode in an electrolysis cell such as that shown in Figure 15.4. With a current density of about 1 amp per cm^2 of cathode surface, the rapid discharge of hydrogen ions to form hydrogen gas at the cathode surface produces a layer of solution depleted in hydrogen ions and therefore of very high hydroxide ion concentration (since $[OH^-] \times [H^+] = K_w = 10^{-14}$). Insoluble hydroxides are therefore precipitated. The violent stirring due to the gas formation brings each part of the solution in turn to the cathode surface layer where the source material is deposited. The strange thing is that, even though the turbulence near the cathode surface is so great, the precipitated hydroxides cling tenaciously to that surface and are not dispersed throughout the solution.

Yields of virtually 100% can often be obtained in only a few minutes.

Before the current is turned off, the electrolyte is made basic by the addition of a few drops of ammonium hydroxide solution. If this step is omitted, the collapse of the basic cathode layer when the current is turned off causes the deposited hydroxides to redissolve immediately in the electrolyte. Finally, the cathode is removed, washed free of ammonium chloride, and heated to redness in air to drive off water, and to convert the hydroxides to oxides. Although this method depends on the precipitation of insoluble hydroxides with no added carrier, it will give extremely high yields even when the quantity of source material is as small as a few atoms.

E. Recoil Techniques

Following a radioactive decay or a nuclear reaction, conservation of linear momentum requires that there shall be a recoiling nucleus whose momentum is equal to the vector sum of the momenta of all the particles

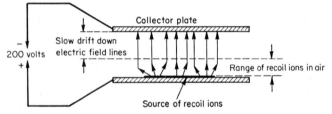

Fig. 15.5. Apparatus for the collection of recoil ions. Distance between the plates is unimportant as long as it exceeds the range of the recoils. If they reach the collector before the end of their range, they will penetrate its surface so that the resulting source will be thick

that were involved in the event. Since the recoiling nucleus is usually much heavier than the emitted particle or particles, its velocity will usually be much lower and its range in matter will be correspondingly short. However, by the methods described above, it is possible to make sources and targets thin enough to permit the escape of nuclei recoiling from α-decay or from nuclear reactions. The ranges and angular distributions of the recoil nuclei can then be studied.

Nuclei recoiling from such events carry with them most of the bound atomic electrons, so that they are actually ions. They can be used in a few cases to prepare extremely thin radioactive sources. For example, the ions of Ra^{224} recoiling from the α-decay of Th^{228} can be allowed to come to rest in air and then attracted towards a negatively charged plate, as shown in Figure 15.5. If the recoil ions are allowed to strike the plate before they have come to rest in air, they will penetrate the plate so that the deposit will not be truly thin.

If thin targets prepared by electrodeposition or vacuum evaporation are bombarded with charged particles as shown in Figure 15.6, the nuclei recoiling in the downbeam direction can be stopped in a thin foil (of gold, for example), and their radioactivity can then be examined, perhaps after chemical separation from the "stopper" foil. There is virtually no loss of the target material, so that the same target can be used repeatedly. However, the very small fraction of the target which is "knocked over" may be troublesome if it is a radioactive material. If the target consists of some very rare isotope, this method may be much preferable to bombardments of the usual type in which the whole target is dissolved to recover the products. In order to obtain a high yield of the nuclear

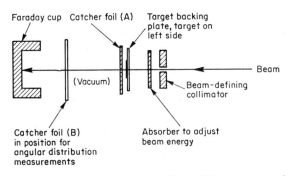

Fig. 15.6. Apparatus for collection of recoil ions from nuclear reactions. For angular distribution measurements, the catcher foil is placed in position B, and is subsequently cut into concentric rings which are analyzed. The catcher foil is placed in position A when the object of the experiment is to collect all the reaction products

reaction products, the target thickness must be less than the range of these products in the target material. If the reaction involves the formation of a compound nucleus, then the average momentum of the recoiling ions is equal to the momentum of the incident particle, and an estimate of the range can be obtained from the range–energy relations given in Chapter 11 F.

Under bombardment with charged particles, targets are often observed to become covered with a yellow or brown stain at the point of impact of the beam. The deposit is believed to be due to the partial decomposition of organic matter by the beam; the organic matter comes from vacuum pump oil, lubricating greases, or rubber gaskets. It can be partially avoided by the use of very clean grease-free vacuum apparatus, and by the use of liquid nitrogen traps between the apparatus and the diffusion pumps. In many nuclear reaction studies, the presence of hydrogen in the deposit causes difficulties, since the beam particles produce large numbers of recoil protons by elastic scattering from these hydrogen atoms. Sometimes, the target is continuously heated electrically to prevent formation of the deposit. The organic deposit may reduce to zero the yield of recoiling nuclear reaction products.

REFERENCES

1. Choppin, G. R., *Experimental Nuclear Chemistry*, Prentice-Hall, Inc., Englewood Cliffs, N. J., 1961.

2. Cook, G. B., and J. F. Duncan, *Modern Radiochemical Practice*, Clarendon Press, Oxford, 1952.

3. Haissinsky, M., *La Chimie Nucléaire et ses Applications*, Masson et Cie., Paris, 1957.

4. Wahl, A. C., and N. A. Bonner, *Radioactivity Applied to Chemistry*, John Wiley & Sons, New York, 1951.

5. Welcher, F. J., *Organic Analytical Reagents*, D. Van Nostrand, New York, 1947 (4 vols.).

6. Nachod, F. C., *Ion Exchange, Theory and Application*, Academic Press, New York, 1949.

7. Nachod, F. C., and J. Schubert (eds.), *Ion Exchange Technology*, Academic Press, New York, 1956.

8. Kunin, R., *Elements of Ion Exchange*, Reinhold Publishing Corp., New York, 1960.

9. Salmon, J. E., and D. K. Hale, *Ion Exchange: A Laboratory Manual*, Butterworths Scientific Publications, London, 1959.

10. Cassidy, H. G., *Fundamentals of Chromatography*, Interscience, New York, 1957.

11. Osborn, G. H., *Synthetic Ion Exchangers*, Chapman and Hall Ltd., London, 1955.

12. Kitchener, J. A., *Ion Exchange Resins*, Methuen and Co. Ltd., London, 1957.

13. Yost, D. M., H. Russell, and C. S. Garner, *The Rare Earth Elements and Their Compounds*, John Wiley & Sons, New York, 1947.

14. Coryell, C. D., *Radiochemical Studies: The Fission Products*, National Nuclear Energy Series, McGraw-Hill Book Co., New York, 1951.

15. Seaborg, G. T., *The Transuranium Elements*, Yale University Press, New Haven, 1958.

16. Katz, J. J., and G. T. Seaborg, *The Chemistry of the Actinide Elements*, Methuen and Co. Ltd., London, 1957.

17. Seaborg, G. T., and J. J. Katz, *The Actinide Elements*, National Nuclear Energy Series, McGraw-Hill Book Co., New York, 1954.

18. Seaborg, G. T., J. J. Katz, and W. M. Manning, *The Transuranium Elements*, National Nuclear Energy Series, McGraw-Hill Book Co., New York, 1949.

19. Graves, A. C., and D. K. Froman, *Miscellaneous Physical and Chemical*

Techniques of the Los Alamos Project, National Nuclear Energy Series, McGraw-Hill Book Co., New York, 1952.

20. Bleuler, E., and G. J. Goldsmith, *Experimental Nucleonics*, Rinehart and Company Inc., New York, 1957.

21. Extermann, R. C. (ed.), *Radioisotopes in Scientific Research: Proceedings of the UNESCO International Conference in Paris*, Pergamon Press, London, 1958 (4 vols.).

22. *Radioactive Materials and Stable Isotopes*, Catalogue Number 4, Atomic Energy Research Establishment, Harwell, England, 1957.

23. *Source Material for Radiochemistry*, National Academy of Sciences–National Research Council, Publication 825 (Nuclear Science Series Report Number 27, revision no. 1). (A useful list of references.)

24. National Research Council Monograph Series on the Radiochemistry of the Elements. (All the elements except H, He, Li and B are covered by monographs either published or in preparation.) Available from Office of Technical Services, Department of Commerce, Washington 25, D. C.

25. Overman, R. T., and H. M. Clark, *Radioisotope Techniques*, McGraw-Hill Book Co., New York, 1960.

26. Morrison, H. G., and H. Freiser, *Solvent Extraction in Analytical Chemistry*, John Wiley & Sons, New York, 1957.

27. Freiser, H., and H. G. Morrison, "Solvent Extraction," *Ann. Revs. Nuclear Sci.*, **9** (1959).

28. Thompson, S. G., and M. L. Muga, Paper P/825 in *Proceedings of Second United Nations International Conference on the Peaceful Uses of Atomic Energy*, United Nations, Geneva, 1958. (Chemical separation techniques for the trans-curium elements.)

PROBLEMS

1. The solubility product of ferric hydroxide is 10^{-36}. Calculate the minimum hydroxide ion concentration which must exist at the cathode surface in an electrolytic cell which gives a 99% yield of carrier-free Fe^{59}, whose initial concentration is 2000 disintegrations per min per ml.

2. (a) Calculate the maximum thickness of a Bi^{209} target which permits the escape of all the At^{211} produced in the reaction $Bi^{209}(\alpha,2n)At^{211}$ with 30 Mev helium ions. Assume that all the At^{211} ions are projected forward in the beam direction (a good assumption in this case).

(b) If the cross section for the reaction is 0.9 barns, how many disintegrations per min of At^{211} would the catcher foil contain at the end of a 2 hr bombardment with 0.2 μamp of $(He^4)^{+2}$ ions?

3. Devise a separation scheme for the purification of Cu^{62} produced by the bombardment of Ni^{60} with 32 Mev helium ions. The Ni^{60}, being a separated isotope, must be recovered in high yield. Consider what radioactive isotopes of other elements might be present, and make sure that the separation scheme will eliminate them. The Ni^{60} deposit is electroplated on a gold foil, and to recover the Cu^{62}, the whole target, including the gold, must be dissolved.

CHAPTER 16

Radiation Safety Precautions

A. Biological Effects of Radiation

Any form of radiation—charged particles, neutrons, or electromagnetic radiation—produces ionization and chemical change in its passage through matter. The human body is not exempt from damage. Intense irradiation of its surface with α- or β-particles (which produce intense local ionization) can cause loss of hair, and skin burns which sometimes heal very slowly. Irradiation with X- or γ-rays, which penetrate more deeply, disrupts cells throughout the body, and can cause as well as cure cancer. The blood-producing cells of the spleen and bone marrow are particularly sensitive, so that exposure to radiation increases the statistical probability of death from leukemia. Genetic mutations are caused by disruption of the chromosomes in the reproductive organs of both sexes.

322

Death can be caused by exposure to large doses of radiation, often as a result of the destruction of the body's infection-resisting mechanisms. Equally large amounts of radiation received over a long period of time are much less serious. It may be that there is a "threshold" rate such that radiation received at a rate below the threshold is virtually harmless, but this is still unsure. It is certainly wiser to assume that all exposure to radiation should be avoided whenever possible. Even a single quantum may cause damage to an ovary or a sperm cell which might later be used in reproduction. Cells which are multiplying rapidly, such as cancer cells or cells in young people who are still growing, are particularly sensitive to radiation damage.

B. Safety Standards

Since it is clearly impossible to avoid completely all exposure to radiation in the modern world, recommended safety standards have been published by an International Commission on Radiological Protection, both for the quantity of radiation external to the body and for the quantities of the various radioactive isotopes which may become incorporated into the body as a result of exposure to contaminated air or water, or as a result of accidental injection.

Before discussing the recommended standards, it is necessary to define the units in which they are expressed. The *roentgen* (r) is that quantity of X- or γ-radiation which will produce, in 0.001293 gm of air, 1 esu of electrical charge of either sign. This quantity of charge equals 2.1×10^9 ion pairs. The roentgen is thus a measure of the amount of ionization produced by X- or γ-rays in air. The milliroentgen (mr) is also frequently used; radiation monitoring counters are often calibrated to read directly in mr per hour.

When 1 r of radiation falls on an absorbing substance, it causes absorption in the medium of an amount of energy which depends on the stopping power of the medium. Assuming 34 ev per ion pair in air, the absorbed energy is 87 ergs per gm of air. The *rad* is defined as that quantity of absorbed radiation of any type which deposits 100 ergs in each gram of material. Since it is a unit which measures the absorbed energy independent of the stopping power of the medium, it is particularly suitable for the study of biological effects. The roentgen, on the other hand, is basically a unit which measures the radiation dose, regardless of the extent to which it is absorbed.

The biological effects of radiation depend not only on the number of rads but also on the type of radiation. In general, particles producing a high *density* of ionization (such as α-particles) are more destructive than the same number of rads of radiation which produces only a low ionization density. The relative biological effectiveness (RBE) has been measured for various types of radiation, with the results shown in Table 16.1. Recoil ions are given there because, in the case of ingestion of α-emitting substances into the body, there will naturally be exposure to the recoil ions as well as to the α-particles themselves.

TABLE 16.1. Relative Biological Effectiveness (RBE) of Various Types of Radiation

Radiation	RBE
β^-, β^+, conversion electrons, X-rays, γ-rays	1
Thermal neutrons	3
Fast neutrons and protons to 10 Mev	10
α-particles	10
Recoil ions	20

The different RBE values are taken into account by the use of a third unit, the *rem*. It is the product of the absorbed dose in rads and the RBE of the absorbed radiation.

For radiation workers, the recommended maximum acceptable exposures are as shown in Table 16.2. Note that the maximum accumulated

TABLE 16.2. Maximum Recommended Doses for Radiation Workers

Organ exposed	Max. accumulated dose, rem	Max. dose in 13 week period, rem
Whole body	$5(N - 18)$ [a]	3
Hands and forearms	—	25 [b]

[a] N = age of individual in years.
[b] Maximum 75 rem per year.

TABLE 16.3. Maximum Permitted Concentrations in Air of Soluble Radioactive Nuclides, Assuming a 40 Hour Working Week

Nuclide	Tissue most affected	Maximum total body content, μc	Maximum concentration in air, μc per cm^3
C^{14}	Fat	300	4×10^{-6}
Na^{24}	Gastrointestinal tract	—	10^{-6}
P^{32}	Bone	6	7×10^{-8}
S^{35}	Testis	90	3×10^{-7}
Co^{60}	Gastrointestinal tract	10	3×10^{-7}
Sr^{90}	Bone	2	3×10^{-7}
I^{131}	Thyroid	0.7	9×10^{-9}
Cs^{137}	All body	30	6×10^{-8}
Ce^{144}	Bone	5	10^{-8}
Pu^{239}	Bone	0.04	2×10^{-12}
Cm^{244}	Bone	0.1	9×10^{-12}

dose is zero for workers up to 18 years of age. This reflects the greater sensitivity of rapidly dividing cells which was mentioned above. For a 60 year old worker, the maximum accumulated dose would be 210 rem. A dose of this magnitude produces very serious effects if received over a short period of time—in fact, doses of about 400 rems received in one flash are likely to be fatal.

Standards have also been set for the maximum concentrations of radioactive nuclides which may be permitted in air or drinking water. Some of these are shown in Table 16.3.

The relative danger of a given nuclide depends on:

(1) The rate of excretion from the body

(2) Its half life

(3) Penetrating power of the radiation

(4) RBE of the radiation

(5) Whether the absorbed substance is concentrated into one organ or dispersed throughout the body

(6) Sensitivity of the organ where concentrated (if concentrated). The problem of arriving at the figures shown in Table 16.3 is therefore quite complex, and it is obvious that the results are only approximate.

C. Safe Working Methods

In experimental work, exposure is most likely to occur in one or both of two ways. First, there may be a more or less intense exposure from a radioactive source or from an accelerator or reactor, and the exposure may involve a substantial part of the body volume. Such exposures are likely to be of comparatively short duration in any well-regulated laboratory. In any case, workers will not be exposed except during working hours. The second form of exposure is caused by ingestion of radioactive materials into the body. This may take place through the lungs, mouth, or directly into the blood stream through open wounds. Many elements, particularly Sr, Pu, Ra, or Ca are selectively deposited into the bone structure where they remain indefinitely. The bone marrow is thereafter exposed for an indefinite period. Immediately after ingestion, special diets and injections of complexing agents can speed up the process of elimination, but once these elements are deposited into the bone structure, there is nothing that can be done.

External exposures can be reduced or avoided by simple precautions. The radiation intensity from a point source falls off as the square of the distance from the source (or faster if there is appreciable absorption of the radiation by the air). The flux at a distance d from a source emitting N particles per second is $F = N/(4\pi d^2)$ particles per cm^2 per sec. Suitable shielding may be erected, following the principles given in Chapter

11. But equally important is the intelligent use of radiation monitoring instruments such as portable Geiger or scintillation counters. Since radiation cannot be detected by any of the human senses, the instinct for safe working can be developed only by the continual use of detectors. Any laboratory which is not adequately supplied with good instruments in good working order is not fit for human habitation.

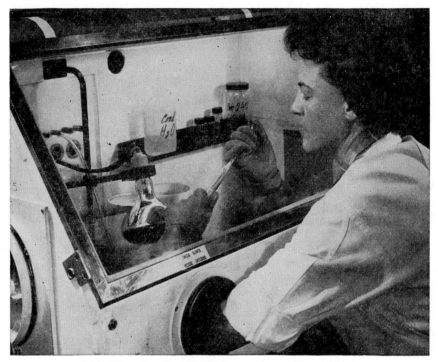

Fig. 16.1. Glove box for chemical operations with α-emitters or small quantities of β-emitters

Ingestion of radioactive materials can occur in chemical operations and in the use of radioactive sources which are not firmly attached to their backing plates or covered. (In any case, such sources are sure to contaminate the counting equipment of the laboratory.) Small amounts of material, especially the less dangerous elements or those with short half lives, can be handled in well-ventilated fume hoods, and the worker's hands can be protected from surface contamination by rubber gloves (which are thick enough to provide protection against α-particles but not against β-particles or γ-rays). If larger amounts of material are to be handled, especially in dry or dusty form, completely sealed glove boxes such as that shown in Figure 16.1 are essential.

The quantity of material which *must* be handled in a glove box is often fixed by local laboratory regulations. In their absence, it is difficult to make definite suggestions because safety depends so much on the skill of the worker and on the exact nature of the operations which are carried out. Again, the use of portable monitoring instruments is essential.

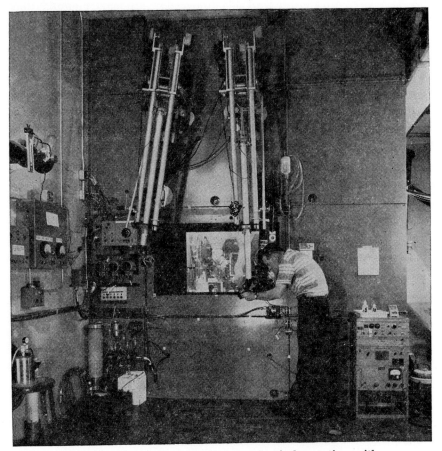

Fig. 16.2. Lead-shielded enclosure for chemical operations with large amounts of α- or β-emitters. The interior of the enclosure is visible through a thick window of high density glass. The vertical rods operate tongs inside the enclosure. Almost all movements of the human hand and wrist can be duplicated by the tongs

By their continual use, the worker can learn how to avoid contamination of working surfaces and thus can improve his personal skill. If an experimenter finds *any detectable contamination* of the bench top or of the outside surfaces of glassware as a result of his work, then he must either improve his skill or, if that is impossible, he must start using a glove box.

Protection of the hands and forearms against radiation capable of penetrating rubber gloves can be improved by the use of local shielding inside a fume hood or glove box. For example, a lead brick drilled with holes can be used as a test-tube rack. In more severe cases, however, it is necessary to use a heavy lead shielding wall and to make manipulations by means of remotely controlled tongs. The operations can be viewed through thick windows of high density glass or by means of periscopes over the top of the shielding wall. Figure 16.2 shows an installation of

Fig. 16.3. Close-up view of shielded enclosure showing the remotely-controlled tongs and equipment for typical chemical operations

this type. It will be obvious from this figure that operations with high levels of radioactive materials require careful planning and the expenditure of rather large amounts of money to provide the special equipment which is essential. Figure 16.3 shows the interior of the enclosure behind the shielding wall. The equipment is designed for making a typical chemical separation.

REFERENCES

1. Lapp, R. E., and H. L. Andrews, *Nuclear Radiation Physics*, Prentice-Hall, Inc., Englewood Cliffs, N. J., 1956.

2. *National Bureau of Standards Handbook 69*, Government Printing Office, Washington, D. C.

3. *Health Physics*, **3,** 1 (1960).

4. Rajewsky, B., *Wissenschaftliche Grundlagen der Strahlenschutzes*, G. Braun Verlag, Karlsruhe, 1957.

5. Braestrup, C. B., and H. O. Wyckoff, *Radiation Protection*, Charles C Thomas, Springfield, Ill., 1958.

6. Spears, F. C., *Radiation and Living Cells*, John Wiley & Sons, New York, 1953.

7. Hollaender, A., *Radiation Biology*, McGraw-Hill Book Co., New York, 1954.

8. Saddington, K., and W. L. Templeton, *Disposal of Radioactive Wastes*, George Newnes Ltd., London, 1958.

9. Hines, J., and G. L. Brownell, *Radiation Dosimetry*, Academic Press, New York, 1956.

10. Faires, R. A., and B. H. Parks, *Radioisotope Laboratory Techniques*, George Newnes Ltd., London, 1958.

11. Whitehouse, W. J., and J. C. Putnam, *Radioactive Isotopes*, Clarendon Press, Oxford, 1953.

12. Stang, L. G., *Hot Laboratory Equipment*, Brookhaven National Laboratory, 1958.

13. Blatz, H. (ed.), *Radiation Hygiene Handbook*, McGraw-Hill Book Co., New York, 1959.

PROBLEMS

1. Calculate the radiation intensity in roentgens per hour due to the γ-rays from a 1 curie Co^{60} source at a distance of 1 meter. Co^{60} decays to the 2.505 Mev level of Ni^{60} which in turn decays to the 1.333 Mev level and then to the ground state. There is no transition between the 2.505 Mev level and the ground state. Use the mass absorption coefficients for Al given in Figure 11.12. They are close to the value for air.

2. Using the mass absorption coefficient obtained from Figure 11.12, calculate the radiation intensity at a distance of 1 meter from a 1 curie Co^{60} source which is surrounded by 1 cm of lead shielding.

3. Calculate the exposure (rems per 13 week period) of bone containing 1 $\mu\mu c$ of Pu^{239} per gm. Assume that all the particles and recoil nuclei are absorbed in the bone.

4. Calculate the thickness of lead required to shield a worker from a 10 curie source emitting 1 quantum of 1 mev γ-radiation per disintegration. The worker is to be at a distance of 10 feet from the source for 1 hour per day, 5 days per week.

5. In disassembling cyclotron targets, a member of the crew is required to remove two small screws. This operation takes 5 minutes. On the average, he opens 20 targets per week. The targets average 0.5 curie of 1 mev γ-rays, and very large quantities of β-radiation. Design a simple piece of equipment to permit this operation to be carried out safely. Make reasonable assumptions about the working distance.

6. The absorption of 48 Mev helium ions in cobalt produces about 4 γ-quanta of average energy 1.5 Mev per helium ion absorbed. The photons are approximately isotropic. Estimate the thickness of lead shielding which must be placed around a 5 mg per cm^2 cobalt target exposed to 10 μamp of helium ions in order to give a radiation level of 5 mr per hour at a distance of 10 feet. Assume a reasonable value for the cobalt total cross section.

7. Confirm that the energy absorbed from 1 roentgen in 1 gm of air is 87 ergs (assuming 34 ev per ion pair).

8. Look up the properties of the members of the decay chain starting with Th^{228}. Discuss the equipment that you would use for safe handling of 1 curie of Th^{228} in simple chemical operations designed to separate from it a sample of Ra^{224}.

APPENDIX I

Useful Physical Constants

Symbol	Quantity	Value
π	Ratio of diameter to circumference of circle	3.1415927
π^2		9.8696044
e	Base of natural logarithms	2.7182818
$\log_e 2$		0.693148
h	Planck's constant	6.62517×10^{-27} erg sec
$\hbar$	$h/2\pi$	1.05443×10^{-27} erg sec
c	Velocity of light *in vacuo*	2.997930×10^{10} cm sec^{-1}
e	Electronic charge	4.80286×10^{-10} esu
m_e	Electron rest mass	$\begin{cases} 9.1083 \times 10^{-28} \text{ gm} \\ 0.510976 \text{ Mev} \end{cases}$
m_p	Proton rest mass	$\begin{cases} 1.67239 \times 10^{-24} \text{ gm} \\ 938.21 \text{ Mev} \end{cases}$
m_n	Neutron rest mass	$\begin{cases} 1.67470 \times 10^{-24} \text{ gm} \\ 939.51 \text{ Mev} \end{cases}$
m_p/m_e	Ratio of proton to electron rest masses	1836.12
N	Avogadro's number (C^{12} mass scale)	6.02294×10^{23} mol^{-1}
F	Faraday's constant (C^{12} mass scale)	9649.12 esu mol^{-1}
k	Boltzmann's constant (R/N)	1.38044×10^{-16} erg deg^{-1}
R	Ideal gas constant (C^{12} mass scale)	8.3144×10^7 erg mol^{-1} deg^{-1}
μ_n	Nuclear magneton $(he/4\pi m_p c)$	5.05038×10^{-24} erg gauss^{-1}
μ_a	Bohr magneton $(he/4\pi m_e c)$	9.2731×10^{-21} erg gauss^{-1}

Conversion Factors

1 Mev	$= 1.6020 \times 10^{-6}$ erg
1 ev	$= 1.6020 \times 10^{-12}$ erg
1 erg	$= 6.242 \times 10^5$ Mev
1 ev per molecule	$= 23{,}045$ cals per mole
1 amu (C^{12} scale)	$= 1.66032 \times 10^{-24}$ gm
1 amu (C^{12} scale)	$= 931.437$ Mev
1 day	$= 86{,}400$ sec
1 year (siderial)	$= 3.15581 \times 10^7$ sec (mean solar)
1 fermi	$= 10^{-13}$ cm
1 barn	$= 10^{-24}$ cm^2
1 curie	$= 3.7 \times 10^{10}$ disintegrations per sec

APPENDIX II

Table of Atomic Mass Excesses[a]

Atomic masses on the scale $C^{12} = 12$. The mass excess is the difference between the atomic mass and the mass number.

Z	A	Symbol	Mass excess ($C^{12} = 0$)					
			Decimal (MeV)	(keV)			$(\mu u)^b$	
0	1	n	8 071.34	±	0.41	8 665.44	±	0.43
1	1	H	7 288.73		0.11	7 825.22		0.08
1	2	D	13 135.36		0.17	14 102.19		0.11
1	3	T	14 949.07		0.26	16 049.40		0.23
2	3	He	14 930.94		0.26	16 029.94		0.23
2	4	He	2 425.11		0.35	2 603.61		0.37
2	5	He	11 453		20	12 296		21
3	5	Li	11 681		37	12 541		40

[a] From F. Everling, L. A. König, J. H. E. Mattauch and A. H. Wapstra, *Nuclear Physics*, **18**, 529 (1960).

[b] $1\mu u = 10^{-6}$ atomic mass units.

Z	A	Symbol	Mass excess ($C^{12} = 0$)				
			(keV)			$(\mu u)^b$	
2	6	He	17 604	$\pm$	17	18 900 $\pm$	18
3	6	Li	14 089.3		1.0	15 126.3	1.0
3	7	Li	14 908.0		1.1	16 005.3	1.1
4	7	Be	15 768.7		1.1	16 929.3	1.2
3	8	Li	20 946.6		1.5	22 488.4	1.6
4	8	Be	4 944.4		0.7	5 308.3	0.8
5	8	B	22 924.4		1.6	24 611.7	1.7
4	9	Be	11 350.3		0.9	12 185.8	0.9
5	9	B	12 420.5		1.8	13 334.7	2.0
4	10	Be	12 607.3		2.1	13 535.3	2.3
5	10	B	12 051.9		0.7	12 938.9	0.7
6	10	C	15 670		60	16 830	60
5	11	B	8 667.14		0.41	9 305.09	0.43
6	11	C	10 649.5		3.1	11 433.4	3.3
5	12	B	13 368.9		1.0	14 352.9	1.0
6	12	C	0		0	0	0
7	12	N	17 600		90	18 900	100
5	13	B	16 560		50	17 780	50
6	13	C	3 124.3		0.7	3 354.3	0.7
7	13	N	5 345.5		1.3	5 738.9	1.4
6	14	C	3 019.67		0.38	3 241.93	0.41
7	14	N	2 863.60		0.16	3 074.38	0.17
8	14	O	8 012		5	8 601	5
6	15	C	9 873.3		1.1	10 600.0	1.2
7	15	N	100.7		0.8	108.1	0.9
8	15	O	2 861.3		1.8	3 071.9	1.9
7	16	N	5 672		6	6 089	6
8	16	O	−4 736.43		0.26	−5 085.06	0.28
7	17	N	7 990		200	8 580	210
8	17	O	−807.2		0.9	−866.6	0.9
9	17	F	1 954.5		2.3	2 098.4	2.4
8	18	O	−782.57		0.32	−840.17	0.34
9	18	F	884.8		4.0	949.9	4.3
10	18	Ne	5 100		200	5 480	210

0.000,000 1 amu

Z	A	Symbol	Mass excess ($C^{12} = 0$)			
			(keV)		(μu)[b]	
8	19	O	3 332.1 $\pm$	4.0	3 577.3 $\pm$	4.3
9	19	F	-1 486.1	0.7	-1 595.4	0.7
10	19	Ne	1 762	5	1 892	5
9	20	F	-13.5	3.8	-14.5	4.0
10	20	Ne	-7 041.3	0.5	-7 559.6	0.5
11	20	Na	8 280	300	8 890	320
9	21	F	-26	25	-28	27
10	21	Ne	-5 729.1	1.6	-6 150.8	1.7
11	21	Na	-2 207	30	-2 370	32
10	22	Ne	-8 024.9	0.6	-8 615.5	0.6
11	22	Na	-5 183.3	4.6	-5 565	5
10	23	Ne	-5 146	5	-5 525	5
11	23	Na	-9 526.2	1.5	-10 227.4	1.6
12	23	Mg	-5 467	10	-5 869	11
10	24	Ne	-5 964	40	-6 403	43
11	24	Na	-8 413.8	2.7	-9 033.1	2.9
12	24	Mg	-13 930.1	1.8	-14 955.4	1.9
13	24	Al	90	300	90	320
11	25	Na	-9 390	200	-10 080	210
12	25	Mg	-13 189.4	1.9	-14 160.3	2.0
13	25	Al	-8 928	6	-9 586	7
12	26	Mg	-16 215.5	2.2	-17 409.1	2.4
13	26	Al	-12 201.5	4.7	-13 100	5
12	27	Mg	-14 581.2	3.7	-15 654.5	3.9
13	27	Al	-17 199.2	2.0	-18 465.1	2.1
14	27	Si	-12 384	11	-13 295	12
12	28	Mg	-15 015	6	-16 120	7
13	28	Al	-16 851.5	3.6	-18 091.9	3.9
14	28	Si	-21 491.0	2.9	-23 072.9	3.1
15	28	P	-7 690	300	-8 260	320
13	29	Al	-18 140	50	-19 470	50
14	29	Si	-21 897.4	3.4	-23 509.2	3.6
15	29	P	-16 937	11	-18 184	11
14	30	Si	-24 440.3	4.0	-26 239.3	4.3
15	30	P	-20 193	10	-21 680	11

Z	A	Symbol	Mass excess ($C^{12} = 0$)			
			(keV)		$(\mu u)^b$	
14	31	Si	$-22\ 961.1$ $\pm$	4.6	$-24\ 651$ $\pm$	5
15	31	P	$-24\ 437.8$	1.5	$-26\ 236.6$	1.5
16	31	S	$-19\ 002$	17	$-20\ 401$	18
14	32	Si	$-24\ 200$	50	$-25\ 980$	50
15	32	P	$-24\ 303.2$	2.2	$-26\ 092.1$	2.4
16	32	S	$-26\ 011.7$	1.0	$-27\ 926.2$	1.1
17	32	Cl	$-13\ 010$	300	$-13\ 970$	320
15	33	P	$-26\ 333.9$	3.4	$-28\ 272.2$	3.7
16	33	S	$-26\ 582.9$	2.8	$-28\ 539.5$	3.0
17	33	Cl	$-21\ 008$	12	$-22\ 554$	13
15	34	P	$-24\ 830$	200	$-26\ 660$	210
16	34	S	$-29\ 932.4$	2.9	$-32\ 135.5$	3.1
17	34	Cl	$-24\ 512$	30	$-26\ 317$	32
16	35	S	$-28\ 842.9$	2.6	$-30\ 965.8$	2.8
17	35	Cl	$-29\ 010.2$	2.6	$-31\ 145.5$	2.8
18	35	A	$-23\ 030$	40	$-24\ 725$	43
16	36	S	$-30\ 653$	9	$-32\ 909$	9
17	36	Cl	$-29\ 516$	5	$-31\ 688$	6
18	36	A	$-30\ 227.0$	3.2	$-32\ 451.9$	3.4
16	37	S	$-26\ 980$	90	$-28\ 960$	100
17	37	Cl	$-31\ 765.9$	2.1	$-34\ 104.1$	2.2
18	37	A	$-30\ 949.9$	2.5	$-33\ 228.0$	2.7
19	37	K	$-24\ 830$	100	$-26\ 660$	110
16	38	S	$-26\ 800$	150	$-28\ 780$	160
17	38	Cl	$-29\ 804$	8	$-31\ 998$	9
18	38	A	$-34\ 719.9$	3.2	$-37\ 275.5$	3.4
19	38	K	$-28\ 791$	11	$-30\ 910$	11
17	39	Cl	$-29\ 803$	21	$-31\ 997$	23
18	39	A	$-33\ 233$	6	$-35\ 679$	6
19	39	K	$-33\ 798.3$	2.8	$-36\ 286.0$	3.0
20	39	Ca	$-27\ 188$	40	$-29\ 190$	43
17	40	Cl	$-27\ 500$	500	$-29\ 600$	500
18	40	A	$-35\ 037.3$	0.8	$-37\ 616.2$	0.8
19	40	K	$-33\ 524.5$	3.3	$-35\ 992.1$	3.6
20	40	Ca	$-34\ 846.0$	3.5	$-37\ 410.8$	3.7
21	40	Sc	$-20\ 950$	400	$-22\ 490$	430

Z	A	Symbol	Mass excess ($C^{12} = 0$)				
			M	(keV)		(μu)[b]	
18	41	A	$-33\ 058$	$\pm$	11	$-35\ 492$	$\pm$	12
19	41	K	$-35\ 548.3$		4.3	$-38\ 164.9$		4.6
20	41	Ca	$-35\ 135$		8	$-37\ 721$		9
21	41	Sc	$-29\ 185$		41	$-31\ 333$		44
19	42	K	$-35\ 006$		20	$-37\ 583$		22
20	42	Ca	$-38\ 535.9$		4.2	$-41\ 372.3$		4.4
21	42	Sc	$-32\ 600$		600	$-35\ 000$		600
19	43	K	$-36\ 577$		11	$-39\ 269$		12
20	43	Ca	$-38\ 394.0$		4.5	$-41\ 220.0$		4.8
21	43	Sc	$-36\ 174$		11	$-38\ 837$		12
19	44	K	$-35\ 360$		200	$-37\ 960$		210
20	44	Ca	$-41\ 458.7$		4.5	$-44\ 510.3$		4.8
21	44	Sc	$-37\ 811$		7	$-40\ 594$		7
22	44	Ti	$-37\ 656$		12	$-40\ 427$		13
20	45	Ca	$-40\ 807.0$		4.3	$-43\ 810.6$		4.6
21	45	Sc	$-41\ 058.9$		4.0	$-44\ 081.1$		4.2
22	45	Ti	$-39\ 001$		6	$-41\ 871$		6
20	46	Ca	$-43\ 136$		10	$-46\ 311$		10
21	46	Sc	$-41\ 754$		5	$-44\ 827$		6
22	46	Ti	$-44\ 119.2$		3.5	$-47\ 366.6$		3.7
23	46	V	$-36\ 820$		400	$-39\ 530$		430
20	47	Ca	$-42\ 370$		21	$-45\ 488$		23
21	47	Sc	$-44\ 335$		8	$-47\ 598$		8
22	47	Ti	$-44\ 935$		7	$-48\ 242$		8
23	47	V	$-42\ 023$		12	$-45\ 116$		13
20	48	Ca	$-44\ 226$		14	$-47\ 481$		15
21	48	Sc	$-44\ 494$		10	$-47\ 769$		10
22	48	Ti	$-48\ 483.6$		3.4	$-52\ 052.2$		3.6
23	48	V	$-44\ 467$		6	$-47\ 740$		6
24	48	Cr	$-43\ 070$		200	$-46\ 240$		210
20	49	Ca	$-41\ 298$		15	$-44\ 338$		16
21	49	Sc	$-46\ 490$		90	$-49\ 910$		100
22	49	Ti	$-48\ 559.1$		3.3	$-52\ 133.4$		3.5
23	49	V	$-47\ 948$		6	$-51\ 477$		6
24	49	Cr	$-45\ 388$		11	$-48\ 729$		12
21	50	Sc	$-45\ 100$		500	$-48\ 400$		500
22	50	Ti	$-51\ 425.7$		4.5	$-55\ 210.9$		4.8
23	50	V	$-49\ 213.0$		3.7	$-52\ 835.4$		4.0
24	50	Cr	$-50\ 250.6$		4.2	$-53\ 949.3$		4.5
25	50	Mn	$-42\ 600$		500	$-45\ 700$		500

Z	A	Symbol	Mass excess ($C^{12} = 0$)			
			(keV)		$(\mu u)^b$	
22	51	Ti	$-49\ 716$ ±	20	$-53\ 376$ ±	22
23	51	V	$-52\ 181.3$	3.9	$-56\ 022.1$	4.2
24	51	Cr	$-51\ 428.7$	4.1	$-55\ 214.1$	4.5
25	51	Mn	$-48\ 250$	50	$-51\ 800$	50
23	52	V	$-51\ 414$	7	$-55\ 198$	8
24	52	Cr	$-55\ 407.9$	3.3	$-59\ 486.3$	3.6
25	52	Mn	$-50\ 705$	9	$-54\ 437$	9
26	52	Fe	$-48\ 322$	17	$-51\ 879$	19
23	53	V	$-52\ 750$	50	$-56\ 630$	50
24	53	Cr	$-55\ 280.0$	3.4	$-59\ 348.9$	3.7
25	53	Mn	$-54\ 683$	9	$-58\ 707$	9
26	53	Fe	$-50\ 691$	40	$-54\ 422$	43
24	54	Cr	$-56\ 930.3$	4.5	$-61\ 120.6$	4.8
25	54	Mn	$-55\ 551$	6	$-59\ 640$	7
26	54	Fe	$-56\ 239$	6	$-60\ 379$	6
27	54	Co	$-47\ 400$	500	$-50\ 900$	500
24	55	Cr	$-54\ 880$	140	$-58\ 920$	150
25	55	Mn	$-57\ 699.4$	3.8	$-61\ 946.4$	4.1
26	55	Fe	$-57\ 467.7$	4.2	$-61\ 697.6$	4.6
27	55	Co	$-54\ 008$	11	$-57\ 983$	12
25	56	Mn	$-56\ 898$	5	$-61\ 086$	6
26	56	Fe	$-60\ 607$	5	$-65\ 068$	6
27	56	Co	$-56\ 007$	16	$-60\ 130$	17
25	57	Mn	$-57\ 480$	300	$-61\ 710$	320
26	57	Fe	$-60\ 177$	6	$-64\ 606$	6
27	57	Co	$-59\ 607$	31	$-63\ 994$	33
28	57	Ni	$-56\ 372$	34	$-60\ 521$	37
26	58	Fe	$-62\ 153$	7	$-66\ 728$	7
27	58	Co	$-59\ 841$	14	$-64\ 246$	15
28	58	Ni	$-60\ 225$	6	$-64\ 658$	6
29	58	Cu	$-51\ 710$	70	$-55\ 510$	80
26	59	Fe	$-60\ 667$	6	$-65\ 133$	7
27	59	Co	$-62\ 230.4$	4.3	$-66\ 810.9$	4.6
28	59	Ni	$-61\ 154.6$	4.8	$-65\ 656$	5
29	59	Cu	$-56\ 356$	21	$-60\ 504$	22
27	60	Co	$-61\ 656$	5	$-66\ 194$	6
28	60	Ni	$-64\ 472$	5	$-69\ 217$	6
29	60	Cu	$-58\ 325$	40	$-62\ 618$	43

Z	A	Symbol	Mass excess ($C^{12} = 0$)			
			(keV)		$(\mu u)^b$	
27	61	Co	$-62\ 934$	$\pm\ \ \ 40$	$-67\ 566$	$\pm\ \ \ 43$
28	61	Ni	$-64\ 224$	8	$-68\ 951$	9
29	61	Cu	$-61\ 993$	10	$-66\ 556$	10
30	61	Zn	$-56\ 190$	300	$-60\ 330$	320
27	62	Co	$-61\ 522$	40	$-66\ 051$	43
28	62	Ni	$-66\ 742$	6	$-71\ 655$	7
29	62	Cu	$-62\ 812$	12	$-67\ 436$	13
30	62	Zn	$-61\ 122$	14	$-65\ 621$	16
28	63	Ni	$-65\ 512$	5	$-70\ 334$	6
29	63	Cu	$-65\ 579$	5	$-70\ 406$	6
30	63	Zn	$-62\ 213$	7	$-66\ 792$	7
28	64	Ni	$-67\ 102$	6	$-72\ 041$	6
29	64	Cu	$-65\ 424$	5	$-70\ 239$	6
30	64	Zn	$-65\ 997$	5	$-70\ 855$	5
31	64	Ga	$-58\ 980$	150	$-63\ 320$	160
28	65	Ni	$-65\ 160$	200	$-69\ 960$	210
29	65	Cu	$-67\ 263$	6	$-72\ 214$	6
30	65	Zn	$-65\ 915$	6	$-70\ 766$	6
31	65	Ga	$-62\ 656$	16	$-67\ 267$	17
28	66	Ni	$-66\ 052$	31	$-70\ 914$	33
29	66	Cu	$-66\ 252$	9	$-71\ 129$	9
30	66	Zn	$-68\ 882$	9	$-73\ 952$	10
31	66	Ga	$-63\ 712$	31	$-68\ 401$	34
29	67	Cu	$-67\ 284$	13	$-72\ 237$	14
30	67	Zn	$-67\ 856$	10	$-72\ 851$	11
31	67	Ga	$-66\ 858$	11	$-71\ 779$	12
32	67	Ge	$-62\ 460$	100	$-67\ 060$	110
30	68	Zn	$-69\ 984$	9	$-75\ 135$	9
31	68	Ga	$-67\ 066$	10	$-72\ 003$	11
32	68	Ge	$-66\ 400$	600	$-71\ 300$	600
30	69	Zn	$-68\ 318$	27	$-73\ 347$	29
31	69	Ga	$-69\ 223$	26	$-74\ 318$	28
32	69	Ge	$-66\ 986$	28	$-71\ 917$	30
33	69	As	$-63\ 090$	300	$-67\ 730$	320
30	70	Zn	$-69\ 534$	15	$-74\ 652$	16
31	70	Ga	$-68\ 882$	16	$-73\ 952$	17
32	70	Ge	$-70\ 532$	19	$-75\ 723$	20
33	70	As	$-63\ 990$	100	$-68\ 700$	110

Z	A	Symbol	Mass excess ($C^{12} = 0$)			
			(keV)		$(\mu u)^b$	
30	71	Zn	−67 100	± 210	−72 030	± 220
31	71	Ga	−70 005	47	−75 160	50
32	71	Ge	−69 772	47	−74 910	50
33	71	As	−67 763	47	−72 750	50
34	71	Se	−63 360	300	−68 030	330
30	72	Zn	−67 300	210	−72 260	220
31	72	Ga	−68 902	48	−73 970	50
32	72	Ge	−72 890	48	−78 260	50
33	72	As	−68 530	60	−73 570	60
31	73	Ga	−69 840	80	−74 980	80
32	73	Ge	−71 390	70	−76 640	70
33	73	As	−71 020	70	−76 240	80
34	73	Se	−68 270	70	−73 290	80
31	74	Ga	−67 790	210	−72 780	220
32	74	Ge	−73 440	50	−78 850	60
33	74	As	−70 880	50	−76 090	50
34	74	Se	−72 230	50	−77 550	60
32	75	Ge	−71 870	50	−77 160	60
33	75	As	−73 045	48	−78 420	50
34	75	Se	−72 179	48	−77 490	50
35	75	Br	−69 460	50	−74 570	60
32	76	Ge	−73 250	90	−78 640	90
33	76	As	−72 264	45	−77 583	48
34	76	Se	−75 233	45	−80 771	48
35	76	Br	−70 643	46	−75 843	49
32	77	Ge	−71 140	70	−76 380	70
33	77	As	−73 893	45	−79 332	49
34	77	Se	−74 577	44	−80 066	48
35	77	Br	−73 212	44	−78 601	48
36	77	Kr	−70 332	49	−75 510	50
32	78	Ge	−71 990	150	−77 290	160
33	78	As	−72 890	110	−78 250	120
34	78	Se	−76 986	44	−82 652	48
35	78	Br	−73 520	80	−78 930	80
36	78	Kr	−74 172.2	4.9	−79 632	5
33	79	As	−73 590	100	−79 010	110
34	79	Se	−75 893	19	−81 479	20
35	79	Br	−76 054	18	−81 652	19
36	79	Kr	−74 432	19	−79 911	20

Z	A	Symbol	Mass excess ($C^{12} = 0$)				
			(keV)			(μu)[b]	
33	80	As	−71 760	± 200	−77 050	±	220
34	80	Se	−77 764	16	−83 488		17
35	80	Br	−75 875	15	−81 459		16
36	80	Kr	−77 880	12	−83 612		13
37	80	Rb	−72 800	500	−78 100		500
34	81	Se	−76 510	60	−82 140		60
35	81	Br	−77 920	35	−83 656		37
36	81	Kr	−77 680	90	−83 390		100
37	81	Rb	−75 440	100	−80 990		100
34	82	Se	−77 630	70	−83 340		70
35	82	Br	−77 494	7	−83 198		8
36	82	Kr	−80 586	7	−86 517		8
37	82	Rb	−76 416	31	−82 041		33
34	83	Se	−75 530	90	−81 090		100
35	83	Br	−78 982	21	−84 795		23
36	83	Kr	−79 982	7	−85 869		8
35	84	Br	−77 730	50	−83 450		50
36	84	Kr	−82 428.6	4.9	−88 496		5
37	84	Rb	−79 776	7	−85 648		7
38	84	Sr	−80 685	11	−86 624		11
35	85	Br	−78 760	110	−84 560		120
36	85	Kr	−81 560	50	−87 570		60
37	85	Rb	−82 240	50	−88 290		60
38	85	Sr	−81 130	60	−87 100		60
36	86	Kr	−83 255	7	−89 383		8
37	86	Rb	−82 750	80	−88 840		90
38	86	Sr	−84 520	80	−90 740		80
39	86	Y	−78 510	90	−84 290		100
35	87	Br	−72 690	400	−78 040		430
36	87	Kr	−80 689	49	−86 630		50
37	87	Rb	−84 590	80	−90 820		80
38	87	Sr	−84 870	80	−91 110		80
39	87	Y	−83 180	210	−89 300		230
40	87	Zr	−79 670	220	−85 530		230
36	88	Kr	−79 920	230	−85 800		240
37	88	Rb	−82 720	100	−88 810		110
38	88	Sr	−87 920	80	−94 390		90
39	88	Y	−84 470	80	−90 690		90

Z	A	Symbol	Mass excess ($C^{12} = 0$)				
			(keV)			$(\mu u)^b$	
37	89	Rb	$-82\ 700$	$\pm$ 100	$-88\ 780$	$\pm$ 110
38	89	Sr	$-86\ 620$	90	$-92\ 990$	90
39	89	Y	$-88\ 090$	90	$-94\ 570$	90
40	89	Zr	$-85\ 240$	90	$-91\ 520$	90
41	89	Nb	$-81\ 360$	130	$-87\ 350$	140
38	90	Sr	$-86\ 330$	90	$-92\ 680$	90
39	90	Y	$-86\ 860$	90	$-93\ 260$	90
40	90	Zr	$-89\ 120$	90	$-95\ 680$	90
41	90	Nb	$-83\ 000$	90	$-89\ 110$	100
42	90	Mo	$-80\ 460$	140	$-86\ 390$	150
38	91	Sr	$-84\ 040$	100	$-90\ 220$	100
39	91	Y	$-86\ 710$	100	$-93\ 090$	100
40	91	Zr	$-88\ 260$	100	$-94\ 750$	100
41	91	Nb	$-86\ 660$	140	$-93\ 040$	150
42	91	Mo	$-82\ 220$	140	$-88\ 270$	150
43	91	Tc	$-79\ 680$	170	$-85\ 540$	180
38	92	Sr	$-83\ 350$	120	$-89\ 480$	130
39	92	Y	$-85\ 270$	110	$-91\ 540$	120
40	92	Zr	$-88\ 870$	100	$-95\ 410$	110
41	92	Nb	$-86\ 790$	110	$-93\ 180$	120
42	92	Mo	$-87\ 280$	120	$-93\ 710$	130
43	92	Tc	$-80\ 900$	600	$-86\ 800$	700
39	93	Y	$-84\ 590$	100	$-90\ 810$	110
40	93	Zr	$-87\ 480$	100	$-93\ 920$	110
41	93	Nb	$-87\ 540$	100	$-93\ 980$	110
42	93	Mo	$-87\ 060$	110	$-93\ 470$	120
43	93	Tc	$-83\ 900$	110	$-90\ 070$	120
39	94	Y	$-82\ 430$	390	$-88\ 490$	420
40	94	Zr	$-87\ 430$	330	$-93\ 860$	360
41	94	Nb	$-86\ 660$	110	$-93\ 040$	110
42	94	Mo	$-88\ 730$	120	$-95\ 260$	130
43	94	Tc	$-84\ 410$	120	$-90\ 620$	130
40	95	Zr	$-85\ 770$	330	$-92\ 080$	360
41	95	Nb	$-86\ 890$	330	$-93\ 280$	360
42	95	Mo	$-87\ 820$	330	$-94\ 280$	360
43	95	Tc	$-86\ 160$	330	$-92\ 500$	360
44	95	Ru	$-83\ 960$	350	$-90\ 140$	370
40	96	Zr	$-85\ 500$	800	$-91\ 800$	800
41	96	Nb	$-85\ 780$	330	$-92\ 090$	360
42	96	Mo	$-88\ 900$	330	$-95\ 450$	360
43	96	Tc	$-85\ 930$	450	$-92\ 250$	480
44	96	Ru	$-86\ 100$	600	$-92\ 400$	700

Z	A	Symbol	Mass excess ($C^{12} = 0$)			
			(keV)		$(\mu u)^b$	
40	97	Zr	−83 200	± 370	−89 320	± 400
41	97	Nb	−85 860	370	−92 180	400
42	97	Mo	−87 790	370	−94 250	400
42	98	Mo	−88 010	380	−94 490	410
43	98	Tc	−86 300	800	−92 700	800
44	98	Ru	−88 000	700	−94 500	800
45	98	Rh	−83 800	800	−90 000	800
42	99	Mo	−85 810	460	−92 130	490
43	99	Tc	−87 190	460	−93 610	490
44	99	Ru	−87 480	460	−93 920	490
45	99	Rh	−85 380	460	−91 670	490
46	99	Pd	−81 600	500	−87 600	500
42	100	Mo	−86 090	450	−92 430	490
43	102	Tc	−85 580	350	−91 880	380
44	102	Ru	−89 680	180	−96 280	200
45	102	Rh	−87 410	180	−93 850	200
46	102	Pd	−88 540	180	−95 060	190
44	103	Ru	−87 920	180	−94 390	200
45	103	Rh	−88 670	180	−95 200	200
46	103	Pd	−88 110	190	−94 590	200
44	104	Ru	−88 000	370	−94 470	400
45	104	Rh	−87 390	180	−93 820	200
46	104	Pd	−89 830	190	−96 440	200
47	104	Ag	−85 550	190	−91 850	200
44	105	Ru	−86 350	250	−92 710	270
45	105	Rh	−88 260	250	−94 750	270
46	105	Pd	−88 820	250	−95 360	270
47	105	Ag	−86 800	500	−93 200	600
44	106	Ru	−86 600	110	−92 970	120
45	106	Rh	−86 630	110	−93 010	120
46	106	Pd	−90 160	110	−96 800	120
47	106	Ag	−87 190	110	−93 610	120
48	106	Cd	−87 600	350	−94 050	370
45	107	Rh	−86 980	120	−93 380	120
46	107	Pd	−88 480	110	−94 990	110
47	107	Ag	−88 510	110	−95 030	110
48	107	Cd	−87 070	110	−93 480	110

Z	A	Symbol	Mass excess ($C^{12} = 0$)			
			(keV)		$(\mu u)^b$	
46	108	Pd	$-89\ 490$	$\pm$ 110	$-96\ 080$	$\pm$ 120
47	108	Ag	$-87\ 650$	100	$-94\ 110$	110
48	108	Cd	$-89\ 420$	110	$-96\ 000$	120
49	108	In	$-84\ 320$	150	$-90\ 530$	160
46	109	Pd	$-87\ 650$	110	$-94\ 100$	110
47	109	Ag	$-88\ 760$	110	$-95\ 300$	110
48	109	Cd	$-88\ 610$	110	$-95\ 130$	110
49	109	In	$-86\ 590$	110	$-92\ 960$	110
46	110	Pd	$-88\ 950$	300	$-95\ 500$	320
47	110	Ag	$-87\ 510$	110	$-93\ 950$	110
48	110	Cd	$-90\ 380$	110	$-97\ 030$	110
49	110	In	$-86\ 420$	110	$-92\ 780$	120
46	111	Pd	$-86\ 030$	180	$-92\ 360$	190
47	111	Ag	$-88\ 230$	180	$-94\ 720$	190
48	111	Cd	$-89\ 280$	170	$-95\ 850$	190
49	111	In	$-88\ 040$	190	$-94\ 520$	210
50	111	Sn	$-85\ 520$	190	$-91\ 820$	210
46	112	Pd	$-86\ 160$	110	$-92\ 510$	120
47	112	Ag	$-86\ 460$	110	$-92\ 830$	110
48	112	Cd	$-90\ 500$	100	$-97\ 160$	110
49	112	In	$-87\ 890$	100	$-94\ 360$	110
50	112	Sn	$-88\ 540$	110	$-95\ 060$	110
47	113	Ag	$-86\ 850$	100	$-93\ 240$	110
48	113	Cd	$-88\ 850$	90	$-95\ 390$	100
49	113	In	$-89\ 160$	90	$-95\ 720$	100
50	113	Sn	$-88\ 470$	90	$-94\ 990$	100
47	114	Ag	$-85\ 220$	410	$-91\ 500$	440
48	114	Cd	$-89\ 820$	90	$-96\ 430$	100
49	114	In	$-88\ 400$	90	$-94\ 910$	100
50	114	Sn	$-90\ 390$	100	$-97\ 040$	100
47	115	Ag	$-85\ 010$	320	$-91\ 260$	340
48	115	Cd	$-87\ 910$	100	$-94\ 380$	100
49	115	In	$-89\ 360$	100	$-95\ 930$	100
50	115	Sn	$-89\ 860$	100	$-96\ 470$	110
48	116	Cd	$-88\ 480$	300	$-94\ 990$	320
49	116	In	$-87\ 890$	170	$-94\ 360$	190
50	116	Sn	$-91\ 180$	180	$-97\ 890$	190
51	116	Sb	$-86\ 480$	350	$-92\ 840$	370

Z	A	Symbol	Mass excess ($C^{12} = 0$)			
			(keV)		$(\mu u)^b$	
48	117	Cd	−86 280	± 350	−92 640	± 370
49	117	In	−88 820	170	−95 360	190
50	117	Sn	−90 290	170	−96 940	190
51	117	Sb	−88 470	180	−94 990	190
50	118	Sn	−91 470	180	−98 210	190
50	119	Sn	−89 990	180	−96 610	200
51	119	Sb	−89 410	190	−95 990	200
50	120	Sn	−91 160	130	−97 870	140
51	120	Sb	−88 430	130	−94 940	140
52	120	Te	−88 940	370	−95 490	400
53	120	I	−83 940	420	−90 120	450
50	121	Sn	−89 260	130	−95 830	140
51	121	Sb	−89 650	130	−96 250	140
50	122	Sn	−89 970	130	−96 590	140
51	122	Sb	−88 380	120	−94 880	130
52	122	Te	−90 350	120	−97 000	130
53	122	I	−86 210	130	−92 550	140
50	123	Sn	−87 860	130	−94 330	140
51	123	Sb	−89 280	130	−95 850	140
52	123	Te	−89 250	120	−95 820	130
50	124	Sn	−88 260	120	−94 760	130
51	124	Sb	−87 660	120	−94 110	130
52	124	Te	−90 580	120	−97 240	130
53	124	I	−87 390	130	−93 820	130
54	124	Xe	−87 440	150	−93 880	160
50	125	Sn	−85 930	120	−92 250	130
51	125	Sb	−88 270	120	−94 770	130
52	125	Te	−89 030	120	−95 580	130
53	125	I	−88 880	120	−95 420	130
52	126	Te	−90 125	34	−96 758	37
53	126	I	−88 010	29	−94 488	31
54	126	Xe	−89 261	29	−95 831	32
55	126	Cs	−84 460	400	−90 680	430
51	127	Sb	−86 800	50	−93 190	60
52	127	Te	−88 401	23	−94 908	25
53	127	I	−89 090	22	−95 648	23
54	127	Xe	−88 390	350	−94 900	380
55	127	Cs	−86 310	350	−92 660	380

Z	A	Symbol	Mass excess ($C^{12} = 0$)			
			(keV)		$(\mu u)^b$	
52	128	Te	$-88\ 760$	$\pm$ 130	$-95\ 290$	$\pm$ 140
53	128	I	$-87\ 725$	12	$-94\ 182$	13
54	128	Xe	$-89\ 849$	9	$-96\ 462$	10
55	128	Cs	$-85\ 850$	100	$-92\ 170$	110
52	129	Te	$-87\ 019$	11	$-93\ 424$	12
53	129	I	$-88\ 499$	10	$-95\ 013$	11
54	129	Xe	$-88\ 688$	9	$-95\ 216$	10
52	130	Te	$-86\ 910$	130	$-93\ 300$	140
53	130	I	$-86\ 918$	31	$-93\ 315$	33
54	130	Xe	$-89\ 875$	9	$-96\ 490$	9
55	130	Cs	$-86\ 884$	22	$-93\ 279$	23
56	130	Ba	$-87\ 326$	22	$-93\ 753$	24
52	131	Te	$-85\ 156$	21	$-91\ 424$	23
53	131	I	$-87\ 436$	7	$-93\ 872$	8
54	131	Xe	$-88\ 406$	7	$-94\ 913$	7
55	131	Cs	$-88\ 051$	9	$-94\ 532$	10
52	132	Te	$-85\ 192$	43	$-91\ 463$	46
53	132	I	$-85\ 697$	41	$-92\ 005$	44
54	132	Xe	$-89\ 267$	7	$-95\ 838$	8
55	132	Cs	$-87\ 450$	140	$-93\ 890$	150
56	132	Ba	$-88\ 370$	300	$-94\ 880$	320
53	133	I	$-86\ 080$	150	$-92\ 410$	160
54	133	Xe	$-87\ 980$	140	$-94\ 450$	150
55	133	Cs	$-88\ 400$	140	$-94\ 910$	150
56	133	Ba	$-87\ 910$	140	$-94\ 390$	150
54	134	Xe	$-88\ 116$	7	$-94\ 602$	8
55	134	Cs	$-87\ 070$	140	$-93\ 480$	150
56	134	Ba	$-89\ 130$	140	$-95\ 690$	150
57	134	La	$-85\ 430$	240	$-91\ 710$	260
54	135	Xe	$-86\ 580$	250	$-92\ 960$	270
55	135	Cs	$-87\ 740$	250	$-94\ 200$	270
56	135	Ba	$-87\ 950$	250	$-94\ 430$	260
53	136	I	$-79\ 420$	100	$-85\ 260$	110
54	136	Xe	$-86\ 418$	10	$-92\ 779$	10
55	136	Cs	$-86\ 510$	130	$-92\ 870$	140
56	136	Ba	$-89\ 090$	130	$-95\ 640$	140
57	136	La	$-86\ 090$	240	$-92\ 420$	250
58	136	Ce	$-86\ 550$	490	$-92\ 900$	500

Z	A	Symbol	Mass excess ($C^{12} = 0$)			
			(keV)		(μu)[b]	
55	137	Cs	-86 790	$\pm$ 120	-93 180	$\pm$ 130
56	137	Ba	-87 960	120	-94 440	130
55	138	Cs	-83 640	90	-89 800	100
56	138	Ba	-88 470	70	-94 990	80
57	138	La	-86 800	80	-93 190	80
58	138	Ce	-87 810	80	-94 280	80
55	139	Cs	-80 820	210	-86 770	230
56	139	Ba	-85 120	70	-91 390	80
57	139	La	-87 500	70	-93 940	80
58	139	Ce	-87 230	70	-93 650	80
59	139	Pr	-85 230	120	-91 510	130
56	140	Ba	-83 400	50	-89 540	60
57	140	La	-84 450	50	-90 670	60
58	140	Ce	-88 223	47	-94 720	50
59	140	Pr	-84 964	46	-91 218	49
57	141	La	-83 250	50	-89 380	60
58	141	Ce	-85 681	44	-91 987	47
59	141	Pr	-86 261	43	-92 610	46
60	141	Nd	-84 461	44	-90 678	48
58	142	Ce	-84 730	70	-90 960	80
59	142	Pr	-84 025	44	-90 210	47
60	142	Nd	-86 179	44	-92 522	47
58	143	Ce	-81 805	49	-87 830	50
59	143	Pr	-83 246	48	-89 370	50
60	143	Nd	-84 180	48	-90 380	50
61	143	Pm	-83 080	160	-89 200	170
62	143	Sm	-79 580	250	-85 440	270
58	144	Ce	-80 630	50	-86 570	50
59	144	Pr	-80 942	49	-86 900	50
60	144	Nd	-83 922	48	-90 100	50
62	144	Sm	-82 290	220	-88 350	240
58	145	Ce	-78 010	170	-83 760	190
59	145	Pr	-80 010	140	-85 900	150
60	145	Nd	-81 820	140	-87 840	150
61	145	Pm	-81 680	140	-87 690	150
62	145	Sm	-81 030	140	-87 000	150
58	146	Ce	-76 130	260	-81 730	280
59	146	Pr	-77 130	240	-82 800	260
60	146	Nd	-81 330	140	-87 310	150
61	146	Pm	-80 380	120	-86 300	130
62	146	Sm	-81 130	70	-87 100	70

Z	A	Symbol	Mass excess ($C^{12} = 0$)				
			(keV)			$(\mu u)^b$	
60	147	Nd	$-78\ 400$	$\pm$	50	$-84\ 170$	$\pm$	50
61	147	Pm	$-79\ 302$		49	$-85\ 140$		50
62	147	Sm	$-79\ 527$		49	$-85\ 380$		50
63	147	Eu	$-77\ 700$		190	$-83\ 410$		200
60	148	Nd	$-77\ 800$		150	$-83\ 520$		160
62	148	Sm	$-79\ 580$		120	$-85\ 440$		130
64	148	Gd	$-76\ 620$		240	$-82\ 260$		260
60	149	Nd	$-74\ 670$		140	$-80\ 170$		150
61	149	Pm	$-76\ 310$		120	$-81\ 930$		130
62	149	Sm	$-77\ 370$		120	$-83\ 070$		130
64	149	Gd	$-75\ 520$		210	$-81\ 080$		220
60	150	Nd	$-73\ 850$		140	$-79\ 290$		150
61	150	Pm	$-73\ 500$		420	$-78\ 910$		450
62	150	Sm	$-77\ 300$		120	$-82\ 990$		130
63	150	Eu	$-74\ 880$		150	$-80\ 390$		160
64	150	Gd	$-75\ 950$		150	$-81\ 540$		160
60	151	Nd	$-70\ 590$		220	$-75\ 780$		240
61	151	Pm	$-72\ 990$		190	$-78\ 360$		210
62	151	Sm	$-74\ 790$		170	$-80\ 290$		180
63	151	Eu	$-74\ 860$		170	$-80\ 370$		180
65	151	Tb	$-71\ 740$		210	$-77\ 020$		230
62	152	Sm	$-75\ 130$		310	$-80\ 650$		330
63	152	Eu	$-73\ 270$		310	$-78\ 660$		330
64	152	Gd	$-75\ 080$		310	$-80\ 600$		330
66	152	Dy	$-70\ 430$		260	$-75\ 620$		270
62	153	Sm	$-73\ 040$		330	$-78\ 420$		350
63	153	Eu	$-73\ 850$		330	$-79\ 280$		350
64	153	Gd	$-73\ 640$		330	$-79\ 060$		350
66	153	Dy	$-69\ 520$		210	$-74\ 630$		230
62	154	Sm	$-72\ 960$		280	$-78\ 330$		300
63	154	Eu	$-72\ 330$		260	$-77\ 650$		280
64	154	Gd	$-74\ 300$		260	$-79\ 770$		280
66	154	Dy	$-70\ 060$		150	$-75\ 220$		160
62	155	Sm	$-70\ 630$		250	$-75\ 830$		270
63	155	Eu	$-72\ 400$		240	$-77\ 730$		260
64	155	Gd	$-72\ 640$		240	$-77\ 990$		260
63	156	Eu	$-69\ 890$		250	$-75\ 040$		270
64	156	Gd	$-72\ 430$		240	$-77\ 760$		260

Z	A	Symbol	Mass excess ($C^{12} = 0$)			
			(keV)		$(\mu u)^b$	
63	157	Eu	−69 050	± 270	−74 140	± 290
64	157	Gd	−70 750	250	−75 960	270
64	158	Gd	−70 610	250	−75 810	270
65	158	Tb	−70 400	1 000	−75 600	1 100
64	159	Gd	−69 600	1 000	−74 700	1 100
65	159	Tb	−70 500	1 000	−75 700	1 100
66	159	Dy	−70 100	1 000	−75 300	1 100
64	160	Gd	−67 720	490	−72 700	500
65	160	Tb	−68 900	900	−74 000	1 000
66	160	Dy	−70 800	900	−76 000	1 000
64	161	Gd	−66 500	900	−71 400	1 000
65	161	Tb	−68 500	900	−73 600	1 000
66	161	Dy	−69 100	900	−74 200	1 000
66	162	Dy	−69 200	900	−74 300	1 000
66	163	Dy	−67 400	900	−72 400	1 000
67	163	Ho	−65 900	800	−70 700	900
66	164	Dy	−67 000	900	−71 900	1 000
67	164	Ho	−65 600	600	−70 400	700
68	164	Er	−66 500	600	−71 400	700
66	165	Dy	−64 400	600	−69 100	700
67	165	Ho	−65 600	600	−70 400	700
66	166	Dy	−63 400	600	−68 100	600
67	166	Ho	−63 900	600	−68 600	600
68	166	Er	−65 700	600	−70 600	600
69	166	Tm	−62 600	700	−67 300	700
67	167	Ho	−63 200	600	−67 900	600
68	167	Er	−64 200	600	−68 900	600
68	168	Er	−63 900	600	−68 600	600
68	170	Er	−60 500	2 000	−64 900	2 100
71	176	Lu	−54 550	430	−58 560	460
72	176	Hf	−55 570	430	−59 660	460
70	177	Yb	−52 220	430	−56 060	460
71	177	Lu	−53 600	430	−57 550	460
72	177	Hf	−54 100	430	−58 080	460
73	177	Ta	−52 950	430	−56 840	460

Z	A	Symbol	Mass excess ($C^{12} = 0$)				
			(keV)			$(\mu u)^b$	
72	178	Hf	−53 570	± 410	−57 510	±	440
72	179	Hf	−51 770	410	−55 580		440
72	180	Hf	−51 120	400	−54 880		430
73	180	Ta	−50 560	360	−54 280		380
74	180	W	−51 260	360	−55 030		380
72	181	Hf	−49 110	350	−52 720		380
73	181	Ta	−50 130	350	−53 820		380
74	181	W	−49 930	360	−53 610		380
73	182	Ta	−48 130	350	−51 670		380
74	182	W	−49 860	350	−53 530		380
72	183	Hf	−44 710	410	−48 000		440
73	183	Ta	−46 910	350	−50 360		380
74	183	W	−47 980	350	−51 510		380
74	184	W	−47 360	360	−50 850		390
73	185	Ta	−44 400	1 500	−47 600		1 600
74	185	W	−46 100	1 500	−49 500		1 600
75	185	Re	−46 500	1 500	−49 900		1 600
76	185	Os	−45 500	1 500	−48 900		1 600
74	186	W	−45 300	1 500	−48 600		1 600
75	186	Re	−42 770	330	−45 920		350
76	186	Os	−43 840	330	−47 060		350
74	187	W	−40 620	320	−43 610		340
75	187	Re	−41 940	320	−45 020		340
76	187	Os	−41 940	320	−45 030		340
75	188	Re	−39 810	280	−42 740		300
76	188	Os	−41 930	280	−45 020		300
77	188	Ir	−38 930	350	−41 790		370
78	188	Pt	−38 410	350	−41 230		380
79	188	Au	−33 230	360	−35 670		390
76	189	Os	−39 850	310	−42 780		330
76	190	Os	−39 660	340	−42 580		360
78	190	Pt	−38 030	380	−40 830		410
76	191	Os	−37 040	270	−39 770		290
77	191	Ir	−37 350	270	−40 100		290

Z	A	Symbol	Mass excess (C^{12} = 0)			
			(keV)		$(\mu u)^b$	
76	192	Os	−36 780 ± 320		−39 490 ± 340	
77	192	Ir	−35 370	270	−37 970	290
78	192	Pt	−36 820	270	−39 530	290
79	192	Au	−33 580	270	−36 050	290
76	193	Os	−33 950	270	−36 450	290
77	193	Ir	−35 080	270	−37 660	290
78	193	Pt	−35 030	270	−37 610	290
77	194	Ir	−32 760	220	−35 170	240
78	194	Pt	−34 990	220	−37 570	240
79	194	Au	−32 430	220	−34 810	240
78	195	Pt	−33 100	220	−35 540	240
79	195	Au	−32 830	220	−35 250	240
78	196	Pt	−32 950	220	−35 380	240
79	196	Au	−31 159	19	−33 453	21
80	196	Hg	−31 838	17	−34 181	18
78	197	Pt	−30 405	18	−32 643	20
79	197	Au	−31 155	15	−33 448	16
78	198	Pt	−30 240	280	−32 470	310
79	198	Au	−29 581	14	−31 758	15
80	198	Hg	−30 953	14	−33 231	15
78	199	Pt	−27 330	100	−29 340	110
79	199	Au	−29 112	20	−31 255	21
80	199	Hg	−29 567	19	−31 744	20
79	200	Au	−27 190	100	−29 190	110
80	200	Hg	−29 486	13	−31 656	14
81	200	Tl	−27 036	16	−29 026	17
79	201	Au	−26 150	100	−28 070	110
80	201	Hg	−27 650	17	−29 685	18
81	201	Tl	−27 240	60	−29 240	70
80	202	Hg	−27 356	21	−29 370	23
81	202	Tl	−25 960	200	−27 870	220
82	202	Pb	−25 910	200	−27 810	220
80	203	Hg	−25 286	37	−27 147	40
81	203	Tl	−25 772	37	−27 669	40
82	203	Pb	−24 775	47	−26 600	50
83	203	Bi	−21 580	70	−23 170	70

Z	A	Symbol	Mass excess (C^{12} = 0)				
			(keV)			(μu)^b	
80	204	Hg	−24 700	±	18	−26 518	±	19
81	204	Tl	−24 320		22	−26 110		24
82	204	Pb	−25 085		22	−26 931		24
83	204	Bi	−20 800		500	−22 300		500
80	205	Hg	−22 140		100	−23 770		110
81	205	Tl	−23 787		25	−25 538		27
82	205	Pb	−23 737		37	−25 484		40
83	205	Bi	−21 090		50	−22 640		50
81	206	Tl	−22 280		15	−23 920		16
82	206	Pb	−23 790		11	−25 541		12
83	206	Bi	−20 190		150	−21 680		160
84	206	Po	−18 160		200	−19 500		220
81	207	Tl	−21 008		14	−22 554		15
82	207	Pb	−22 450		11	−24 102		12
83	207	Bi	−20 050		42	−21 526		45
84	207	Po	−17 144		42	−18 406		45
85	207	At	−13 300		70	−14 280		80
81	208	Tl	−16 760		13	−17 994		14
82	208	Pb	−21 755		11	−23 356		12
83	208	Bi	−18 879		27	−20 269		29
84	208	Po	−17 451		23	−18 736		25
85	208	At	−12 600		500	−13 500		500
81	209	Tl	−13 697		42	−14 705		44
82	209	Pb	−17 610		23	−18 906		25
83	209	Bi	−18 240		25	−19 583		27
84	209	Po	−16 340		38	−17 543		41
85	209	At	−12 910		50	−13 860		50
81	210	Tl	−9 313		32	−9 998		35
82	210	Pb	−14 738		13	−15 823		14
83	210	Bi	−14 801		13	−15 890		14
84	210	Po	−15 959		11	−17 134		12
85	210	At	−12 140		150	−13 030		160
86	210	Em	−9 580		200	−10 280		220
82	211	Pb	−10 429		36	−11 197		39
83	211	Bi	−11 835		14	−12 706		15
84	211	Po	−12 436		19	−13 351		20
85	211	At	−11 647		42	−12 504		45
86	211	Em	−8 756		42	−9 400		45

Z	A	Symbol	Mass excess ($C^{12} = 0$)			
			(keV)		(μu)[b]	
82	212	Pb	$-7\ 548$ $\pm$	14	$-8\ 104$ $\pm$	16
83	212	Bi	$-8\ 130$	13	$-8\ 729$	14
84	212	Po	$-10\ 377$	11	$-11\ 141$	12
85	212	At				
86	212	Em	$-8\ 638$	24	$-9\ 274$	26
87	212	Fr	$-3\ 600$	500	$-3\ 900$	500
83	213	Bi	$-5\ 282$	29	$-5\ 671$	31
84	213	Po	$-6\ 672$	27	$-7\ 163$	29
85	213	At	$-6\ 440$	200	$-6\ 910$	220
82	214	Pb	-220	60	-240	60
83	214	Bi	$-1\ 273$	33	$-1\ 366$	35
84	214	Po	$-4\ 479$	13	$-4\ 808$	14
85	214	At	$-3\ 420$	50	$-3\ 670$	60
83	215	Bi	$1\ 770$	120	$1\ 900$	130
84	215	Po	-495	38	-531	41
85	215	At	$-1\ 250$	25	$-1\ 342$	26
86	215	Em	$-1\ 240$	100	$-1\ 330$	110
84	216	Po	$1\ 786$	15	$1\ 917$	16
85	216	At	$2\ 240$	33	$2\ 405$	35
86	216	Em	218	32	234	34
85	217	At	$4\ 328$	31	$4\ 647$	33
86	217	Em	$3\ 648$	41	$3\ 917$	44
87	217	Fr	$4\ 450$	280	$4\ 780$	310
84	218	Po	$8\ 320$	60	$8\ 930$	60
85	218	At	$7\ 968$	33	$8\ 554$	36
86	218	Em	$5\ 209$	16	$5\ 592$	18
87	218	Fr	$7\ 010$	70	$7\ 520$	80
85	219	At	$10\ 580$	110	$11\ 360$	120
86	219	Em	$8\ 870$	38	$9\ 523$	41
87	219	Fr	$8\ 615$	32	$9\ 249$	34
88	219	Ra	$9\ 340$	140	$10\ 030$	150
86	220	Em	$10\ 615$	15	$11\ 396$	16
87	220	Fr	$11\ 485$	44	$12\ 330$	48
88	220	Ra	$10\ 220$	38	$10\ 972$	41
87	221	Fr	$13\ 204$	32	$14\ 176$	35
88	221	Ra	$12\ 910$	50	$13\ 860$	50
89	221	Ac	$14\ 620$	300	$15\ 690$	320

Z	A	Symbol	Mass excess ($C^{12} = 0$)					
			(keV)			$(\mu u)^b$		
86	222	Em	16 320	±	60	17 530	±	60
87	222	Fr						
88	222	Ra	14 312		19	15 365		21
89	222	Ac	16 530		90	17 750		90
87	223	Fr	18 444		38	19 802		42
88	223	Ra	17 292		37	18 565		41
89	223	Ac	17 808		37	19 119		40
90	223	Th	19 460		170	20 890		170
88	224	Ra	18 830		15	20 216		16
89	224	Ac	20 200		50	21 690		60
90	224	Th	19 913		42	21 379		46
88	225	Ra	21 906		34	23 518		37
89	225	Ac	21 556		33	23 143		35
90	225	Th	22 030		60	23 660		60
88	226	Ra	23 620		60	25 360		60
89	226	Ac	24 380		100	26 180		110
90	226	Th	23 184		22	24 890		23
91	226	Pa	25 890		100	27 800		110
88	227	Ra	27 217		43	29 220		47
89	227	Ac	25 907		39	27 814		41
90	227	Th	25 864		39	27 768		41
91	227	Pa	26 815		42	28 789		46
92	227	U	28 800		200	30 920		220
88	228	Ra	29 087		39	31 228		42
89	228	Ac	29 032		39	31 169		42
90	228	Th	26 778		15	28 749		16
91	228	Pa	28 830		60	30 950		60
92	228	U	29 134		44	31 278		47
90	229	Th	29 461		37	31 629		40
91	229	Pa	29 761		44	31 952		48
92	229	U	31 000		60	33 280		70
90	230	Th	30 820		60	33 080		60
91	230	Pa	32 010		22	34 366		24
92	230	U	31 600		22	33 926		24
90	231	Th	33 858		39	36 350		42
91	231	Pa	33 472		39	35 936		42
92	231	U	33 840		60	36 330		60
93	231	Np	35 640		70	38 260		70

Z	A	Symbol	Mass excess ($C^{12} = 0$)				
			(keV)			$(\mu u)^b$	
90	232	Th	35 591	±	38	38 211 ±	42
91	232	Pa	35 869		25	38 509	27
92	232	U	34 619		15	37 167	17
93	232	Np					
94	232	Pu	38 260		70	41 080	70
90	233	Th	38 588		39	41 428	42
91	233	Pa	37 358		38	40 108	40
92	233	U	36 790		38	39 498	40
93	233	Np	37 820		70	40 600	70
94	233	Pu	39 840		70	42 770	70
90	234	Th	40 590		80	43 570	80
91	234	Pa	40 400		80	43 370	80
92	234	U	38 100		60	40 900	60
93	234	Np	39 900		120	42 830	130
94	234	Pu	40 330		50	43 290	60
91	235	Pa	42 320		110	45 440	120
92	235	U	40 921		41	43 933	43
93	235	Np	41 048		42	44 069	44
94	235	Pu	42 220		70	45 330	70
92	236	U	42 598		38	45 733	40
93	236	Np	43 428		18	46 625	19
94	236	Pu	42 913		16	46 072	17
92	237	U	45 250		38	48 581	41
93	237	Np	44 737		38	48 030	41
94	237	Pu	44 967		42	48 277	46
95	237	Am	46 370		80	49 780	90
92	238	U	47 280		80	50 760	80
93	238	Np	47 430		60	50 930	70
94	238	Pu	46 130		60	49 520	70
95	238	Am					
96	238	Cm	49 380		60	53 010	70
92	239	U	50 590		60	54 320	60
93	239	Np	49 309		42	52 938	45
94	239	Pu	48 585		41	52 161	44
95	239	Am	49 340		50	52 970	60
92	240	U	52 680		70	56 560	80
93	240	Np	52 320		70	56 180	80
94	240	Pu	50 274		37	53 974	40
95	240	Am					
96	240	Cm	51 698		34	55 503	37

Z	A	Symbol	Mass excess ($C^{12} = 0$)			
			(keV)		$(\mu u)^b$	
93	241	Np	54 450 ±	110	58 460 ±	110
94	241	Pu	52 823	38	56 711	41
95	241	Am	52 802	38	56 689	41
96	241	Cm	53 570	70	57 510	70
94	242	Pu	54 690	80	58 710	80
95	242	Am	55 400	60	59 480	70
96	242	Cm	54 770	60	58 800	70
94	243	Pu	57 740	50	61 990	60
95	243	Am	57 174	42	61 382	46
96	243	Cm	57 169	41	61 377	44
97	243	Bk	58 600	70	62 920	80
95	244	Am	60 100	110	64 520	110
96	244	Cm	58 596	38	62 910	40
97	244	Bk				
98	244	Cf	61 413	40	65 933	43
95	245	Am	61 860	100	66 420	110
96	245	Cm	60 950	100	65 430	100
97	245	Bk	61 700	50	66 240	60
98	245	Cf	63 230	70	67 890	70
94	246	Pu	65 420	100	70 230	110
95	246	Am	65 040	90	69 830	100
96	246	Cm	62 750	80	67 370	90
97	246	Bk				
98	246	Cf	64 060	60	68 780	70
97	247	Bk	65 370	70	70 180	70
98	248	Cf	67 391	48	72 350	50
97	249	Bk	69 790	100	74 930	100
98	249	Cf	69 670	100	74 800	100
99	249	Es	70 990	70	76 220	80
97	250	Bk	73 110	130	78 490	140
98	250	Cf	71 310	80	76 550	90
99	250	Es				
100	250	Fm	74 040	80	79 480	80
99	251	Es	74 380	80	79 850	90
100	252	Fm	76 980	50	82 650	60
99	253	Es	78 960	100	84 780	100
99	254	Es	82 070	130	88 110	140
100	254	Fm	81 040	80	87 000	90

APPENDIX III

Some Values of Nuclear Spins

Some Values of Nuclear Spins.

Nuclide	Spin	Nuclide	Spin	Nuclide	Spin	Nuclide	Spin
H^1	$\frac{1}{2}$	O^{17}	$\frac{5}{2}$	S^{35}	$\frac{3}{2}$	Ca^{43}	$\frac{7}{2}$
H^2	1	F^{19}	$\frac{1}{2}$	Cl^{35}	$\frac{3}{2}$	Sc^{45}	$\frac{7}{2}$
H^3	$\frac{1}{2}$	Ne^{21}	$\frac{3}{2}$	Cl^{36}	2	Sc^{46m}	7
He^3	$\frac{1}{2}$	Na^{22}	3	Cl^{37}	$\frac{3}{2}$	Sc^{46}	4
Li^6	1	Na^{23}	$\frac{3}{2}$	A^{39}	$\frac{7}{2}$	Ti^{47}	$\frac{5}{2}$
Li^7	$\frac{3}{2}$	Na^{24}	4	A^{41}	$\frac{7}{2}$	Ti^{49}	$\frac{7}{2}$
Be^9	$\frac{3}{2}$	Mg^{25}	$\frac{5}{2}$	K^{39}	$\frac{3}{2}$	V^{48}	4
B^{10}	3	Al^{27}	$\frac{5}{2}$	K^{40}	1	V^{49}	$\frac{7}{2}$
B^{11}	$\frac{3}{2}$	Si^{29}	$\frac{1}{2}$	K^{41}	$\frac{3}{2}$	V^{50}	6
C^{13}	$\frac{1}{2}$	P^{31}	$\frac{1}{2}$	K^{42}	2	V^{51}	$\frac{7}{2}$
N^{14}	1	P^{32}	1	Ca^{39}	$\frac{3}{2}$	Cr^{49}	$\frac{5}{2}$
N^{15}	$\frac{1}{2}$	S^{33}	$\frac{3}{2}$	Ca^{41}	$\frac{7}{2}$	Cr^{51}	$\frac{7}{2}$

Nuclide	Spin	Nuclide	Spin	Nuclide	Spin	Nuclide	Spin
Cr^{53}	$\frac{3}{2}$	As^{74}	2	Nb^{91}	$\frac{9}{2}$	In^{116m}	5
Cr^{55}	$\frac{3}{2}$	As^{75}	$\frac{3}{2}$	Nb^{93}	$\frac{9}{2}$	In^{116}	1
Mn^{52m}	2	As^{76}	2	Nb^{95m}	$\frac{1}{2}$	Sn^{115}	$\frac{1}{2}$
Mn^{52}	6	As^{77}	$\frac{3}{2}$	Nb^{95}	$\frac{9}{2}$	Sn^{117}	$\frac{1}{2}$
Mn^{53}	$\frac{7}{2}$	Se^{73}	$\frac{9}{2}$	Mo^{91}	$\frac{9}{2}$	Sn^{119}	$\frac{1}{2}$
Mn^{55}	$\frac{5}{2}$	Se^{75}	$\frac{5}{2}$	Mo^{93}	$\frac{5}{2}$	Sb^{121}	$\frac{5}{2}$
Mn^{56}	3	Se^{77}	$\frac{1}{2}$	Mo^{95}	$\frac{5}{2}$	Sb^{122}	2
Fe^{55}	$\frac{3}{2}$	Se^{79}	$\frac{7}{2}$	Mo^{97}	$\frac{5}{2}$	Sb^{123}	$\frac{7}{2}$
Fe^{57}	$\frac{1}{2}$	Se^{81m}	$\frac{7}{2}$	Tc^{95m}	$\frac{1}{2}$	Sb^{124}	3
Fe^{59}	$\frac{3}{2}$	Se^{81}	$\frac{1}{2}$	Tc^{95}	$\frac{9}{2}$	Te^{123}	$\frac{1}{2}$
Co^{56}	4	Br^{79}	$\frac{3}{2}$	Tc^{97}	$\frac{9}{2}$	Te^{125m}	$\frac{11}{2}$
Co^{57}	$\frac{7}{2}$	Br^{80}	1	Tc^{99}	$\frac{9}{2}$	Te^{125}	$\frac{1}{2}$
Co^{59}	$\frac{7}{2}$	Br^{81}	$\frac{3}{2}$	Tc^{101}	$\frac{9}{2}$	Te^{127m}	$\frac{11}{2}$
Co^{60m}	2	Br^{82}	5	Ru^{99}	$\frac{5}{2}$	Te^{127}	$\frac{3}{2}$
Co^{60}	5	Kr^{79}	$\frac{1}{2}$	Ru^{101}	$\frac{5}{2}$	Te^{129m}	$\frac{11}{2}$
Ni^{57}	$\frac{3}{2}$	Kr^{81}	$\frac{7}{2}$	Ru^{103}	$\frac{5}{2}$	Te^{129}	$\frac{3}{2}$
Ni^{59}	$\frac{3}{2}$	Kr^{83}	$\frac{9}{2}$	Rh^{103}	$\frac{1}{2}$	Te^{131m}	$\frac{11}{2}$
Ni^{61}	$\frac{3}{2}$	Kr^{85}	$\frac{9}{2}$	Rh^{104}	1	Te^{131}	$\frac{3}{2}$
Ni^{65}	$\frac{5}{2}$	Rb^{81m}	$\frac{9}{2}$	Rh^{105}	$\frac{7}{2}$	I^{123}	$\frac{5}{2}$
Cu^{60}	2	Rb^{81}	$\frac{3}{2}$	Rh^{106}	1	I^{124}	2
Cu^{61}	$\frac{3}{2}$	Rb^{82m}	5	Pd^{105}	$\frac{5}{2}$	I^{125}	$\frac{5}{2}$
Cu^{63}	$\frac{3}{2}$	Rb^{83}	$\frac{5}{2}$	Ag^{104}	2	I^{126}	2
Cu^{64}	1	Rb^{84}	2	Ag^{105}	$\frac{1}{2}$	I^{127}	$\frac{5}{2}$
Cu^{65}	$\frac{3}{2}$	Rb^{85}	$\frac{5}{2}$	Ag^{106}	1	I^{128}	1
Zn^{65}	$\frac{5}{2}$	Rb^{86}	2	Ag^{107}	$\frac{1}{2}$	I^{129}	$\frac{7}{2}$
Zn^{67}	$\frac{5}{2}$	Rb^{87}	$\frac{3}{2}$	Ag^{108}	1	I^{131}	$\frac{7}{2}$
Zn^{69m}	$\frac{9}{2}$	Sr^{85}	$\frac{9}{2}$	Ag^{109}	$\frac{1}{2}$	Xe^{129}	$\frac{1}{2}$
Zn^{69}	$\frac{1}{2}$	Sr^{87}	$\frac{9}{2}$	Ag^{110m}	6	Xe^{131}	$\frac{3}{2}$
Zn^{71m}	$\frac{9}{2}$	Sr^{89}	$\frac{5}{2}$	Ag^{111}	$\frac{1}{2}$	Xe^{133m}	$\frac{11}{2}$
Zn^{71}	$\frac{1}{2}$	Sr^{91}	$\frac{5}{2}$	Cd^{111}	$\frac{1}{2}$	Xe^{133}	$\frac{3}{2}$
Ga^{66}	0	Y^{87}	$\frac{1}{2}$	Cd^{113}	$\frac{1}{2}$	Cs^{129}	$\frac{1}{2}$
Ga^{67}	$\frac{3}{2}$	Y^{88}	4	Cd^{115m}	$\frac{11}{2}$	Cs^{130}	1
Ga^{68}	1	Y^{89}	$\frac{1}{2}$	Cd^{115}	$\frac{1}{2}$	Cs^{131}	$\frac{5}{2}$
Ga^{69}	$\frac{3}{2}$	Y^{90}	2	In^{111}	$\frac{9}{2}$	Cs^{132}	2
Ga^{71}	$\frac{3}{2}$	Y^{91m}	$\frac{9}{2}$	In^{112}	1	Cs^{133}	$\frac{7}{2}$
Ga^{72}	3	Y^{91}	$\frac{1}{2}$	In^{113m}	$\frac{1}{2}$	Cs^{134m}	8
Ge^{73}	$\frac{9}{2}$	Zr^{89}	$\frac{9}{2}$	In^{113}	$\frac{9}{2}$	Cs^{134}	4
Ge^{75}	$\frac{1}{2}$	Zr^{91}	$\frac{5}{2}$	In^{114m}	5	Cs^{135}	$\frac{7}{2}$
Ge^{77}	$\frac{7}{2}$	Zr^{93}	$\frac{5}{2}$	In^{114}	1	Cs^{137}	$\frac{7}{2}$
As^{73}	$\frac{3}{2}$	Zr^{95}	$\frac{5}{2}$	In^{115}	$\frac{9}{2}$	Ba^{133}	$\frac{1}{2}$

Nuclide	Spin	Nuclide	Spin	Nuclide	Spin	Nuclide	Spin
Ba^{135m}	$\frac{11}{2}$	Ho^{166}	0	Os^{183m}	$\frac{1}{2}$	Pb^{207m}	$\frac{13}{2}$
Ba^{135}	$\frac{3}{2}$	Ho^{167}	$\frac{7}{2}$	Os^{183}	$\frac{9}{2}$	Pb^{207}	$\frac{1}{2}$
Ba^{137}	$\frac{3}{2}$	Er^{163}	$\frac{5}{2}$	Os^{185}	$\frac{1}{2}$	Bi^{201}	$\frac{9}{2}$
La^{137}	$\frac{7}{2}$	Er^{165}	$\frac{5}{2}$	Os^{187}	$\frac{1}{2}$	Bi^{204}	6
La^{138}	5	Er^{167m}	$\frac{1}{2}$	Os^{189}	$\frac{3}{2}$	Bi^{206}	6
La^{139}	$\frac{7}{2}$	Er^{167}	$\frac{7}{2}$	Os^{191}	$\frac{9}{2}$	Bi^{207}	$\frac{9}{2}$
La^{140}	4	Er^{169}	$\frac{1}{2}$	Ir^{191}	$\frac{3}{2}$	Bi^{209}	$\frac{9}{2}$
Ce^{137m}	$\frac{11}{2}$	Er^{171}	$\frac{5}{2}$	Ir^{193}	$\frac{3}{2}$	Bi^{210}	1
Ce^{137}	$\frac{3}{2}$	Tm^{167}	$\frac{1}{2}$	Pt^{195}	$\frac{1}{2}$	Bi^{212}	1
Ce^{139m}	$\frac{11}{2}$	Tm^{169}	$\frac{1}{2}$	Pt^{197}	$\frac{5}{2}$	Po^{209}	$\frac{1}{2}$
Ce^{139}	$\frac{3}{2}$	Tm^{170}	1	Au^{191}	$\frac{3}{2}$	Ac^{227}	$\frac{3}{2}$
Ce^{141}	$\frac{7}{2}$	Tm^{171}	$\frac{1}{2}$	Au^{192}	1	Th^{229}	$\frac{5}{2}$
Pr^{141}	$\frac{5}{2}$	Yb^{169}	$\frac{7}{2}$	Au^{193}	$\frac{3}{2}$	Th^{231}	$\frac{5}{2}$
Pr^{143}	$\frac{5}{2}$	Yb^{171}	$\frac{1}{2}$	Au^{194}	1	Pa^{227}	$\frac{5}{2}$
Pr^{144}	0	Yb^{173}	$\frac{5}{2}$	Au^{195m}	$\frac{11}{2}$	Pa^{229}	$\frac{5}{2}$
Nd^{143}	$\frac{7}{2}$	Yb^{177}	$\frac{9}{2}$	Au^{195}	$\frac{3}{2}$	Pa^{230}	2
Nd^{145}	$\frac{7}{2}$	Lu^{172}	4	Au^{197}	$\frac{3}{2}$	Pa^{231}	$\frac{3}{2}$
Nd^{147}	$\frac{5}{2}$	Lu^{173}	$\frac{7}{2}$	Au^{199}	$\frac{3}{2}$	Pa^{233}	$\frac{3}{2}$
Sm^{147}	$\frac{7}{2}$	Lu^{174}	1	Hg^{195}	$\frac{3}{2}$	U^{231}	$\frac{5}{2}$
Sm^{149}	$\frac{7}{2}$	Lu^{175}	$\frac{7}{2}$	Hg^{197}	$\frac{1}{2}$	U^{233}	$\frac{5}{2}$
Eu^{151}	$\frac{5}{2}$	Lu^{176}	6	Hg^{199}	$\frac{1}{2}$	U^{235}	$\frac{7}{2}$
Eu^{152}	3	Lu^{177}	$\frac{7}{2}$	Hg^{201}	$\frac{3}{2}$	Np^{235}	$\frac{5}{2}$
Eu^{153}	$\frac{5}{2}$	Hf^{173}	$\frac{1}{2}$	Tl^{197}	$\frac{1}{2}$	Np^{236}	1
Eu^{154}	3	Hf^{175}	$\frac{5}{2}$	Tl^{198m}	7	Np^{237}	$\frac{5}{2}$
Eu^{155}	$\frac{5}{2}$	Hf^{177}	$\frac{7}{2}$	Tl^{198}	2	Np^{238}	2
Gd^{155}	$\frac{3}{2}$	Hf^{179}	$\frac{9}{2}$	Tl^{199}	$\frac{1}{2}$	Np^{239}	$\frac{5}{2}$
Gd^{157}	$\frac{3}{2}$	Hf^{181}	$\frac{1}{2}$	Tl^{200}	2	Pu^{239}	$\frac{1}{2}$
Gd^{159}	$\frac{3}{2}$	Ta^{173}	$\frac{7}{2}$	Tl^{201}	$\frac{1}{2}$	Pu^{241}	$\frac{5}{2}$
Tb^{151}	$\frac{3}{2}$	Ta^{177}	$\frac{7}{2}$	Tl^{203}	$\frac{1}{2}$	Am^{241}	$\frac{5}{2}$
Tb^{153}	$\frac{3}{2}$	Ta^{179}	$\frac{7}{2}$	Tl^{204}	2	Am^{242m}	5
Tb^{155}	$\frac{3}{2}$	Ta^{181}	$\frac{7}{2}$	Tl^{205}	$\frac{1}{2}$	Am^{242}	1
Tb^{157}	$\frac{3}{2}$	Ta^{183}	$\frac{7}{2}$	Tl^{208}	5	Am^{243}	$\frac{5}{2}$
Tb^{159}	$\frac{3}{2}$	W^{179}	$\frac{7}{2}$	Tl^{209}	$\frac{1}{2}$	Cm^{241}	$\frac{1}{2}$
Tb^{161}	$\frac{3}{2}$	W^{181}	$\frac{9}{2}$	Pb^{197m}	$\frac{13}{2}$	Cm^{243}	$\frac{5}{2}$
Dy^{159}	$\frac{3}{2}$	W^{183}	$\frac{1}{2}$	Pb^{197}	$\frac{5}{2}$	Bk^{245}	$\frac{3}{2}$
Dy^{161}	$\frac{5}{2}$	W^{185}	$\frac{3}{2}$	Pb^{199m}	$\frac{13}{2}$	Bk^{249}	$\frac{7}{2}$
Dy^{163}	$\frac{5}{2}$	Re^{181}	$\frac{5}{2}$	Pb^{199}	$\frac{5}{2}$	Cf^{249}	$\frac{9}{2}$
Dy^{165}	$\frac{7}{2}$	Re^{183}	$\frac{5}{2}$	Pb^{202m}	9	E^{253}	$\frac{7}{2}$
Ho^{163}	$\frac{7}{2}$	Re^{185}	$\frac{5}{2}$	Pb^{203m}	$\frac{13}{2}$		
Ho^{165}	$\frac{7}{2}$	Re^{187}	$\frac{5}{2}$	Pb^{203}	$\frac{5}{2}$		

Index